WILLIAM BLAKE

IN THE COLLECTION OF THE NATIONAL GALLERY OF VICTORIA

Portrait of Blake (cat. **44 a**), frontispiece to Blair's *Grave*, 1808

WILLIAM BLAKE
IN THE COLLECTION OF THE NATIONAL GALLERY OF VICTORIA

Martin Butlin and Ted Gott

With an Introduction by
Irena Zdanowicz

NATIONAL GALLERY OF VICTORIA

The Robert Raynor Publications
in Prints and Drawings
Number Three

Published by the National Gallery of Victoria
180 St Kilda Road, Melbourne, Victoria, 1989

National Library of Australia Cataloguing-in-Publication entry

National Gallery of Victoria.
William Blake in the collection of the National Gallery of Victoria.

Bibliography.
Includes index.
ISBN 0 7241 0138 1.
ISBN 0 7241 0139 X (pbk).

1. Blake, William, 1757–1827. 2. National Gallery of Victoria. I. Butlin, Martin 1929– . II. Gott, Ted, 1960– . III. Blake, William, 1757–1827. IV. Title. (Series : Robert Raynor publications in prints and drawings; no. 3).

760'.092'4

Editor: Angela Gundert
Design: Tactix Design Pty Ltd
Typesetting: Typographical Services
Printing: Owen King Printers
Photography: Helen Skuse

ISBN 0 7241 0138 1.
ISBN 0 7241 0139 X (pbk).

Cover Illustration:
William Blake, *Antaeus Setting Down Dante and Virgil in the Last Circle of Hell* 1824–27. Pen and water-colour, 52.6 x 37.4 cm.
Felton Bequest, 1920 1012/3

William Blake, *Unyoked Heifers Loitering Homeward, Low*
Wood-engraving and bistre wash
3.3 x 7.7 cm OS 29

Other books in the Robert Raynor Publications in Prints and Drawings series are:

Sonia Dean, *Master Drawings from the Collection of the National Gallery of Victoria* (Number One), NGV, Melbourne, 1986.

John Gregory and Irena Zdanowicz, *Rembrandt in the Collections of the National Gallery of Victoria* (Number Two), NGV, Melbourne, 1988.

Contents

Director's Preface

The National Gallery of Victoria's collection of water-colours, prints and books by William Blake is one of the chief jewels of the Department of Prints and Drawings. The popularity of Blake's art with the people of Melbourne, and throughout Australia, is evidenced by the large crowds which attend every display of the unique Dante water-colours. The return to figuration in contemporary art of the 1980s has brought an even greater audience to Blake's symbolic vision and draughtsmanly genius. The influence of Melbourne's Blake collection on local artists is, in fact, much deeper than is generally recognized.

It is indeed a pleasure that we are now able to present the National Gallery of Victoria's Blakes to a wider public than ever before, with the first complete publication of the Melbourne collection. This publication has been made possible through the great generosity of Mr Robert Raynor who, through The Art Foundation of Victoria, has endowed the special programme of Robert Raynor Publications in Prints and Drawings. It is more than fitting that our Blake water-colours and prints are always exhibited in the Robert Raynor Gallery, a space for the display of works on paper with which Mr Raynor's name will forever be associated.

This publication also stands as a tribute to the beneficence of the Felton Bequest, which acquired such a magnificent series of Blakes at the John Linnell sale in 1918. The Felton Bequest continues to strengthen its relationship to the National Gallery of Victoria's Blake holdings, with the two most recent additions to this collection—the *Songs of Innocence* and *Night Thoughts*—again having been acquired for the Gallery by the Bequest.

The assistance of The Ian Potter Foundation, the British Council and McPherson's Limited for their generous contributions to sponsorship of the publication, scholarly analysis and exhibition of the Melbourne Blakes in 1989, is also gratefully acknowledged.

Kenneth Hood
Acting Director

Acknowledgements

William Blake in the Collection of the National Gallery of Victoria builds on a generation of Blake study in the Department of Prints and Drawings of the National Gallery of Victoria. The authors would like to acknowledge the foundation research of Dr Ursula Hoff and Nicholas Draffin on the Melbourne collection. They are also indebted to the vast tableau of preceding Blake scholarship, and in particular to those whose published works are mentioned in the notes and select bibliography. Professor Gerald E. Bentley Jr most generously read the final draft of Ted Gott's and Irena Zdanowicz's essays, and supportively discussed textual issues with them. Professors David Bindman and Robert N. Essick also assisted Ted Gott greatly with advice in the early stages of the manuscript.

Martin Butlin gratefully acknowledges the kind assistance of the British Council and The Ian Potter Foundation for sponsoring his visits to Australia to work with the collection at first hand. He offers a special note of thanks to Nicholas Draffin who provided information about the dimensions and the inscriptions on the backs of the Dante drawings long before he was able to check them for himself.

Irena Zdanowicz wishes to warmly thank Gerard Hayes, an understanding and invaluable research companion, and also the following: Mr Robert Davies, Pontesbury, for information on Robert Ross; Krzysztof Z. Cieszkowski, Curator E, Library, Tate Gallery, London, for making available the manuscript of his unpublished article on the dispersal of the Dante water-colours and for his remarks on the introduction; Sonia Dean, Principal Curator of Western Art, National Gallery of Victoria, and Dr Peter Otto, Department of English, University of Melbourne, for their active interest and support of this publication; and Michael Watson, National Gallery of Victoria; Joyce McGrath, State Library of Victoria, Melbourne; and Muff Read, The Mitchell Library, Sydney, for their attentiveness to enquiries. Special thanks are also due to Mr James Mollison, Canberra, and Dr Gerard Vaughan, Oxford University, for their inestimable assistance at a crucial stage during the publication of this book.

Ted Gott is indebted to the many curators and museum researchers who have generously assisted him with studying their Blake collections, often at short notice. Particular thanks are owed to: David Becker, Fogg Art Museum, Harvard University; Anselmo Carini, Art Institute of Chicago; Margaret Grasselli, National Gallery of Art, Washington, DC; Craig Hartley, Fitzwilliam Museum, Cambridge; Patrick Noon, Yale Center for British Art, New Haven; Eleanor Garvey, Houghton Library, Harvard University; Stephen Coppel, Australian National Gallery, Canberra; and Ann Forsdyke, Andrew Clary, Francis Carey and Antony Griffiths, British Museum, London. He is also extremely grateful for the research support and bibliographical assistance provided by Russell Maylone, Special Collections Librarian, Northwestern University Library, Evanston, Illinois; and Michael Watson, Librarian, National Gallery of Victoria. A special debt is owed to Robert Gott, Richard Linden and Helen Murnane for attentive proofreading. Ted Gott's research in the United States was made possible by a Harkness Fellowship from the Commonwealth Fund of New York, and was partly completed during a year as visiting scholar with the Department of Art History, Northwestern University. Research in London was undertaken while on a Harold Wright scholarship at the Department of Prints and Drawings of the British Museum.

For their assistance with the present manuscript the authors thank Angela Gundert for her careful and thoughtful editing, Judy Shelverton for her superb typing of the manuscripts, and Daphne Hewlett for her meticulous attention to the typing of departmental correspondence. Gerard Hayes worked closely with the authors to compile the thorough indexes.

For their unstinting help in preparing the Melbourne Blakes for exhibition, the authors are grateful to Garth McLean, mount-cutting and framing; Anne Cotter-Ross, paper conservation; Philip Jago, catalogue production; Jennie Maloney, photography co-ordination; Christine Lewis, graphic design; Gordon Morrison and Anne Rowland, registration; Peter Chaloupka and Gervais Battour, frame-making; David Legg, Robert Cirelli, Tony Wright and John Darby, installation and picture-hanging; and Russell Magee, Richard Glover and Adam Worrell, exhibition design.

The authors wish to thank Jill Keyte, Executive Director of the National Gallery of Victoria Business Council, and the Business Council itself, for their assistance throughout this project. And they acknowledge the generous sponsorship of McPherson's Limited in mounting the exhibition.

Mr Robert Raynor, on whose patronage the Robert Raynor Publications in Prints and Drawings series depends, and The Ian Potter Foundation, have generously assisted with additional grants which have enabled us, at short notice, to publish and reproduce in colour the Gallery's most recent Blake acquisition, the illustrations to Young's *Night Thoughts*.

This book is respectfully dedicated to the memory of Alfred Felton (1831–1904) and Robert Ross (1869–1918).

For permission to reproduce illustrations acknowledgement is gratefully made to the following: The Beinecke Rare Books and Manuscript Library, Yale University (fig. 21); The British Museum, London (figs 8, 15, 17); The City of Manchester Art Galleries (fig. 1); Robert N. Essick (figs 10, 18, 20); The Fitzwilliam Museum, Cambridge (figs 13, 14, 16); The Fogg Art Museum, Harvard University (fig. 4); The Henry E. Huntington Library and Art Gallery, San Marino, California (figs 3, 6); The Mitchell Library, Sydney (fig. 9); The Museum of Fine Arts, Boston (figs 2, 5); The National Gallery of Art, Washington, DC (figs 11, 22); and The Tate Gallery, London (fig. 7).

Martin Butlin

Ted Gott

Irena Zdanowicz

Chronology

1757
William Blake born in Soho, London, 28 November, the son of a hosier.

1767–68
Enters Henry Pars's drawing school in the Strand, aged ten. Blake's favourite brother Robert probably born 1767.

1771
Apprenticed for seven years to James Basire (1730–1802), Lincoln's Inn Fields, as an engraver.

1772–79
Blake probably lives with James Basire, training as a reproductive engraver. Draws monuments in Westminster Abbey.

1779
Admitted to the Royal Academy Schools as an engraver; probably ceases formal attendance after several months. Thomas Stothard (1755–1834) and John Flaxman (1756–1826) are fellow students.

1780
Exhibits *Death of Earl Goodwin* at the Royal Academy. Witnesses the Lord George Gordon 'No Popery' riots. Employed as commercial engraver for the publisher Joseph Johnson.

1782
Marries Catherine Butcher (or Boucher, b. 1762). Patronized by the fashionable salon of Harriet Mathew.

1783
Publication of Blake's *Poetical Sketches* financed by the Reverend and Mrs Mathew, and John Flaxman. Commercial engraving after Stothard.

1784
Blake's father dies. Opens a short-lived print shop with a fellow apprentice of Basire, James Parker (1750–1805). Probably writes the satirical *Island in the Moon*.

1787
Robert Blake dies in Blake's arms.

1789
Publishes *Songs of Innocence* and *The Book of Thel*. Probably writes *Tiriel*.

1791
The French Revolution printed for Joseph Johnson; never published. Blake's illustrations to Mary Wollstonecraft's *Original Stories from Real Life* published by Johnson.

1792–93
Executes engravings for John Gabriel Stedman's *Narrative, of a Five Years' Expedition, Against the Revolted Negroes of Surinam* (not published until 1796).

1793
Publishes the illuminated books *Visions of the Daughters of Albion*, *For Children: The Gates of Paradise* and *America*.

1794
Publishes *Songs of Experience*, *The First Book of Urizen* and *Europe*.

1794–95
Commissioned by his friend George Cumberland (1754–1848) to engrave eight plates for Cumberland's *Thoughts on Outline* (published 1796).

1795
Publishes more illuminated books: *The Book of Los*, *The Song of Los* and *The Book of Ahania*.

1796–97
Engraves his own designs for Richard Edwards's edition of Young's *Night Thoughts*. Forty-three of these plates published in 1797.

1799
First documented commissions from Thomas Butts, a series of designs from the Bible.

1800
Moves with Mrs Blake to the coast at Felpham, Sussex, under the patronage of William Hayley (1745–1820). Paints heads of the poets for Hayley's library (1800–03).

1802
Engraves his own compositions to illustrate Hayley's *Designs to a Series of Ballads*.

1803
Violent confrontation with the soldier John Scolfield at Felpham. Blake charged with sedition. In September the Blakes return to live in London.

1804
Acquitted on sedition charge 11 January. Begins etching plates for the last great poems *Milton* and *Jerusalem*.

1805
Engraves five more of his own compositions for the second edition of William Hayley's *Ballads*. Commissioned by Robert Hartley Cromek (1770–1812) to provide illustrations for Blair's *Grave*. But commission to engrave the designs soon transferred to Luigi Schiavonetti.

1807
Thomas Phillips's portrait of Blake exhibited at the Royal Academy.

1808
Blair's *Grave* published.

1809–10
Blake exhibits his own paintings at his brother's house, 28 Broad Street, London. Attracts little attention.

1810
Publishes engraving after his painting of *Chaucer's Canterbury Pilgrims*.

1814
George Cumberland finds Blake 'still poor still Dirty'.

1815
Cumberland's two sons find William and Catherine Blake 'durtyer than ever'. Blake engraves eighteen plates of pottery outlines for Wedgwood's catalogue.

1815–19
Engraves plates for Rees's *Cyclopedia*. Executes stipple engravings for Flaxman's *Hesiod*.

1818
Meets John Linnell (1792–1882), his last great patron.

1819
Begins to draw Visionary Heads for John Varley.

1821
The Blakes move to a small lodging in Fountain Court, Strand. Wood-engravings published in Thornton's *Virgil*. Sells his print collection to Colnaghi's.

1822
Royal Academy votes 25 pounds for Blake, 'an able Designer & Engraver laboring under great distress'.

1823–26
Engraves twenty-two designs for *The Book of Job*, commissioned by John Linnell.

1826–27
Engraves seven of 102 water-colour designs to Dante's *Divine Comedy*, undertaken for John Linnell.

1827
William Blake dies at Fountain Court, 12 August.

Introduction: The Melbourne Blakes—Their Acquisition and Critical Fortunes in Australia

Irena Zdanowicz
Senior Curator of Prints and Drawings, National Gallery of Victoria

The year 1918, which marked the end of the First World War, is notable in the annals of the National Gallery of Victoria for the acquisition of a group of Blake's drawings and prints from the Linnell collection. The institution had been founded fifty-seven years earlier and, since it was unable to rely on existing private collections formed by scholars or royalty, its collections had to be built from scratch. For this it depended to a great extent on the energy, wisdom and vision of its founders and on the generosity of Melbourne's citizens, qualities which, fortunately, were not lacking in the colony of Victoria. Gifts were made as early as the 1860s and, unremarkable though most of them may have been, they were important gestures and established a precedent and a climate for greater things.[1]

However, no one could have been prepared for the extraordinary beneficence of the Felton Bequest, a fiscal gift that came, without warning, as a windfall in 1904.[2] In that year Alfred Felton (b. 1831), a prosperous citizen of Melbourne who had made his fortune in the pharmaceutical business, died. He was a modest collector, never married, lived unostentatiously, and on his death bequeathed a net sum of £383 163 to form an investment fund. The income was to be held in trust and allocated, in perpetuity, in equal division between charitable purposes and the purchase of works of art for the National Gallery of Victoria. This gift was responsible for transforming the Gallery's collections. A Felton adviser was appointed in London whose responsibilities were to recommend acquisitions, thereby ensuring that the National Gallery of Victoria retained a presence in the very centre of the art market. The adviser's recommendations had to be vetted jointly in Melbourne by the Felton Bequests' Committee as well as the trustees of the National Gallery of Victoria and, as might be expected from the number of participants in the process, there were clashes of opinion and decisions were rarely straightforward. Nevertheless, much was achieved in these early years of the Bequest, with the acquisition of the Linnell Blakes remaining a highlight in the history of the Felton Bequest and the collections of the Gallery. The Melbourne Dante illustrations are, to a significant extent, responsible for the international reputation enjoyed by an institution which is physically far removed from the major museum collections of Europe and the United States.

Since this book is the first of the Gallery's publications to provide a complete descriptive catalogue of Melbourne's Blake holdings, it is appropriate to retell the history of the collection and to bring it up to date. The key events of this history are the appointment of Robert Ross as London adviser to the Felton Bequests' Committee, and the celebrated sale of the Linnell collection at Christie's on Friday, 15 March 1918, especially lot 148, the illustrations to the *Divine Comedy*.

In 1916, after the resignations of Sir Sidney Colvin and Frank Gibson from their posts as joint advisers to the Felton Bequest, the trustees of the National Gallery of Victoria appointed one of their own number, Professor Baldwin Spencer, to go to London in search of a suitable replacement.[3] Spencer fulfilled his brief conscientiously, obtaining advice from established contacts, interviewing candidates and canvassing opinions from a range of respected professional sources. He returned to Melbourne in March 1917, filed a detailed account of his mission and, armed with a number of important references supporting his choice, recommended Robert Ross to the position of London adviser to the Felton Bequest. Ross's candidacy was strongly supported by a number of the leading figures in the museum profession in London, including Charles Aitken, then keeper of the Tate Gallery and about to be named its first director. What emerges strongly from Spencer's report is that his consultations in London were not restricted to the search for a new adviser, but also touched on fundamental issues and problems concerning the responsibilities and the demands of the post. Spencer repeated the opinion that emerged from his discussions in London:

> Though mistakes may now and then be made, the best results will be obtained by trusting the adviser, and giving him as free a hand as is possible under the terms of the Bequest, within, of course, limits imposed by the amount of money available, or which it is thought advisable to spend at any particular time, and . . .by prescribing the period of which, or the artists of whom, it is desired to secure examples . . .The opinion was courteously but strongly expressed, that his [Robert Ross's] recommendations should be accepted as sufficient proof of the art excellence and suitability for the Gallery of any works thus suggested for purchase, and should, under the conditions above mentioned, be followed as closely as possible.[4]

Ross was offered and duly accepted the post of adviser for the purchase of works of art for the Felton Bequests' Committee in March 1917.[5] His appointment was widely and favourably reported in the Melbourne press. The newspaper accounts were based on Baldwin Spencer's earlier confidential report to the trustees and reiterated Ross's eminent suitability for the job: he was an acknowledged expert in art matters and a man of broad knowledge; he had held trusted public posts in England where he had been an adviser to the Inland Revenue; he had worked as an adviser for the Johannesburg Gallery; he had also been a director of the Carfax Gallery and was thus familiar with the commercial side of the art market; and he was willing to visit Melbourne.[6] Biographical résumés were published and Ross's friendship with Oscar Wilde was noted, the *Bulletin* reporting that 'Ross stuck to Oscar when to be a friend of his was to be a target for every mud-slinger in England, then in the throes of one of its moral spasms'.[7] His talents were further rewarded in England with his selection to the Board of Trustees of the Tate Gallery (then also called the National Gallery of British Art).[8]

Ross had hoped to leave for Melbourne in late May but was prevented from doing so by wartime conditions. Dismayed and relieved at the same time, he wrote to the Felton trustees stating his belief in the importance of meeting them in person and suggesting that little would be lost by suspending regular operations. He qualified this prudently by saying that Melbourne would be alerted should anything exceptional become available.

On 8 March 1918 Ross despatched a cable informing the Felton trustees that such an extraordinary opportunity had indeed arisen:

> Christies sale fifteenth March Linnells famous collection Blakes see Gilchrists life volume two page twentytwo and following last possible public sale Blakes keen competition high prices expected if Blakes wanted Ross strongly recommends various purchases cable general instructions up to fivethousand guineas.[9]

Ross could hardly have exaggerated the importance of the Linnell collection. On 14 March, the day before the sale, the trustees of the Gallery and the Felton Bequest agreed to empower him to bid up to 5000 guineas.[10]

John Linnell (1792–1882), a landscape painter, had been Blake's solicitous friend and the most important patron of his late years. His intercessions on Blake's behalf were many and, difficult as Blake's final years were, they were constantly eased by Linnell's acts of kindness and practical encouragement. It was he who obtained for Blake the commission to illustrate Thornton's *Virgil*, and who commissioned and published *The Book of Job*, and it was at Linnell's suggestion that in 1824 Blake embarked on the illustrations to the *Divine Comedy*. Linnell introduced Blake to John Varley, for whom the curious Visionary Heads were drawn, used his influence to gain Blake a small gratuity from the Royal Academy, and was instrumental in commissioning for himself, and finding other sales for, the illuminated books.

Linnell kept in constant touch with Blake and his wife Catherine at their final lodgings in Fountain Court, Strand. It was here that Blake, often severely ill and bedridden, worked on the drawings for the *Divine Comedy*, and it was from here that he wrote to George Cumberland on 12 April 1827: 'I have been very near the Gates of Death & have returned very weak & an Old Man feeble & tottering, but not in Spirit and Life, not in The Real Man The Imagination which Liveth for Ever. In that I am stronger & stronger as this Foolish Body decays'.[11] He died a few months later, on 12 August, still working on the folio of Dante illustrations. These were claimed by John Linnell and joined a remarkable array of drawings, prints and books which remained in the Linnell family collection until 1918.

It was not until 1893 that a selection of the Dante designs was exhibited at the Royal Academy and not until 1913 that a further display was organized for the Tate Gallery.[12] That year Charles Aitken, keeper of the Tate Gallery, and Laurence Binyon, keeper of prints and drawings at the British Museum, approached Herbert Linnell, John Linnell's grandson, enquiring about the family's collection, but nothing eventuated from these approaches.[13] Later, in 1918, Aitken was also unsuccessful in trying to persuade Herbert Linnell and Christie's to sell the Dante illustrations individually. There was thus a real danger that the Dante drawings—the most important item in the Linnell sale—could leave Britain *en bloc*. Since at that time it appeared impossible for any British institution to buy them outright, it was decided that an endeavour should be made to keep them in the Empire. In this way British collections could be assured of obtaining a selection of the Dante designs. Efforts were therefore initiated to form a consortium to bid at the sale.

In 1918 the Tate Gallery was in a particularly difficult position regarding funds and Charles Aitken had not only hurriedly to raise subscriptions but also to canvass opinions to prevent fruitless and inflationary counter-bidding. In his view the Dante drawings could be expected to fetch £6000 (of which the Tate had already had £4700 promised) and Aitken thought it possible that 'Melbourne or one or two rich benefactors may put up the rest'.[14] In the light of these circumstances Melbourne was splendidly placed, not only because of the funds available through the Felton Bequest but also because it could rely on the advice and judgement of Robert Ross.

Ross was on the board of the Tate Gallery, as well as on the Executive Committee of the National Art-Collections Fund (NACF), the organization under whose auspices the dispersal of the Dante illustrations was eventually to take place and who agreed to act as banker for the occasion. Other members of the NACF committee included Laurence Binyon, Charles Aitken and Charles Ricketts, with whom Ross had a warm and long-standing friendship.[15] Aitken and Ricketts were among the chief organizers of the bid for lot 148 and its subsequent dispersal. Ross was highly regarded professionally and had the advantage of personal acquaintance with all those interested in the Linnell sale. These connections would presumably have smoothed any negotiations.

Moreover Ross had long harboured a serious interest in Blake's work. In 1904 and 1906, while still a director of the Carfax Gallery, he had organized important exhibitions devoted to Blake, and in 1906 he published an article on him in the *Burlington Magazine*.[16] In his 1909 review of recent Blake literature, Ross prophetically made known his attitude to the dispersal of Blake's art outside England when he surmised that 'no one would have resented more than he [Blake] the attempts of any national Art-Collections Fund to stay the tide of his Prophetic Books ebbing to America'.[17]

When it came to the auction itself, bidding for the Dante drawings was made through Martin, a deputy of the NACF, starting at 2000 guineas and reaching the sum of £7665.[18] The other items acquired for Melbourne were: lot 152, *The Creation of Eve* (420 gns); lot 153, *Satan Watching the Endearments of Adam and Eve* (330 gns); lot 158, *The Three Despondent Persons* (70 gns); lot 177, the so-called *Unpublished Design from the 'Europe'* . . . engraved and coloured by Blake (90 gns); lot 178, a *Design for a Prophetic Book* (90 gns); and lot 182, a set of the *Illustrations of the Book of Job* (52 gns).

After the sale the allocation of drawings was made according to a procedure carefully worked out by Charles Aitken, the distribution being supervised by Laurence Binyon, and Charles Ricketts and Charles Holmes of the National Gallery, London. The account of the proceedings, including the enclosure describing the complicated system of selection, which Ross sent to the National Gallery of Victoria, is dated 30 June 1918. It is one of the key documents of the dispersal and is therefore published here in its entirety for the first time. It was addressed to the secretary of the Public Library, Museums, and the National Gallery of Victoria:

> Dear Sir,
>
> In a letter of September 21st, 1917, the Chairman of the Felton Bequests Committee instructed me that letters of general advice should be addressed to you. I beg therefore to enclose you [*sic*] a report in regard to the purchase of the William Blake's at the Linnell Sale on Friday, March 15th. I trust it will be fairly clear.
>
> You will have heard from Messrs. St. Barbe, Sladen & Wing that the negotiations by which I was able to purchase certain items in the Sale, were the subject of long and numerous discussions with the Directors of the Tate Gallery and the British Museum before I cabled to Melbourne, through the solicitors, asking for instructions and the exercise of my private judgment according to circumstances. I am satisfied with the result, and only hope that the purchase will satisfy the Trustees of the Felton Bequest and the National Gallery; and that the drawings which I was able to secure will arouse in Melbourne as much interest and appreciation as they did in London. With the competition it would have been impossible to have obtained any of the Dante series at any reasonable price, and it would have been almost impossible, without unlimited money, to have obtained, except by arrangement, any of the other finer items in the sale. By 'arrangement', I mean an understanding with competitors that I would not bid against them for certain items if they did not bid against me for others. In the case of the Dante set, as you know already, I agreed to pool my bid along with the Tate Gallery, British Museum, Birmingham, Oxford and the Collectors, Mr. Ricketts and Mr. Shannon (whose collection is destined for Cambridge University). Shortly after the sale Messrs. Christie received a telegram from America, fortunately delayed in transition, instructing them to purchase the entire Dante set at any price. I mention this circumstance because I am well aware that Blake's art does not appeal to everyone, and that the acquisition of so many examples might be open to criticism from those to whom his peculiar genius makes no appeal. Mr. Levy, for example, to whom I showed the drawings a few days ago, did not like them, I fear, at all, though he was most kind about the matter. And I want to record my thanks for the great confidence which the Trustees have reposed in my judgment, for without that confidence and the freedom of the instructions I received by cable I would have been quite unable to secure any examples of Blake worth speaking about; nor would the English Galleries have been able to secure for the country any of the Dante set on which they were particularly keen. The action of the Melbourne Trustees is deeply appreciated by the Trustees and Directors of the English Galleries, and I think I can say that it will lead in the future to great benefits so far as the Melbourne Gallery is concerned, a precedent of mutual goodwill and understanding having been established.
>
> The division of the Dante series took a considerable time, and No. 1 of my enclosures explains the principle on which we worked; this has been drawn up by Mr. Charles Aitken, Director of the Tate Gallery. You will know already that we secured thirty-six in all, and I may add as a matter of interest that there were only six of the drawings allotted to the other Galleries, which I should have liked for Melbourne; two of these were secured by the Tate, two by the British Museum, one by Birmingham and one by Oxford. You will, of course, let me know if Mr. Aitken's description of the transaction is not quite clear.
>
> My second enclosure is a catalogue of the items in the Dante series and the other Blake items secured by us in the Linnell Sale. In the margin are references so that they may be identified in Rossetti's catalogue or elsewhere in Gilchrist's 'Life of Blake'.
>
> I have received a great many applications, chiefly verbal, for permission to have the Melbourne Blakes, as they may now be called, photographed and reproduced. The most important application comes from Mr. Emery Walker, who has been entrusted by the Tate, British and other Galleries to reproduce a portfolio of the entire Dante set before it is finally dispersed. I shall be glad for instructions on this point. It appears to be rather a pity that Melbourne should stand out, as if the Melbourne items are omitted, of course, the value of the portfolio to students would be very much reduced. Mr. Levy seemed to think there might be an objection, and that objection I must notify to you though I do not see any

myself. There is no copyright in the drawings, it is merely a matter of courtesy; and students in Australia as well as in Europe and America would benefit by having the whole series in one volume. The other applications are from the Editors of the 'Burlington Magazine' and the 'Studio' to reproduce in reduced form one or two of our Dante set and the five other items purchased by us in the Linnell sale. Here again I should be in favour of acquiescence, but it is a matter so entirely for the Trustees that I won't urge the point.

Yours faithfully,

[signed] Robert Ross

1st Enclosure

MR. CHARLES AITKEN'S NOTE ON THE DIVISION OF THE BLAKES

Purchase of 102 Illustrations to DANTE by WILLIAM BLAKE at the Linnell Sale at Christie's, March 15th 1918.

The price was £7665. Ninety of the 102 drawings were completed. Twelve were so slight and in pencil as to be of little value. The ninety finished drawings were divided into three categories:—

30 'A' Drawings
30 'B' Drawings
30 'C' Drawings

To work a plan out in round figures it was assumed that £7500 was subscribed as follows in £250 shares there being thirty such shares for the ninety drawings:—

Melbourne	£3000	(12 shares)
Tate Gallery	£3000	(12 shares)
British Museum	500	(2 shares)
Birmingham	500	(2 shares)
Oxford	250	(1 share)
Mr. Ricketts & Mr. Shannon	250	(1 share)
	£7500	

It was decided to allot on the principle of one £250 share entitling to selection of 1 'A' drawing, 1 'B' and 1 'C'. Melbourne, therefore, having 12 £250 shares received 12 'A', 12 'B' and 12 'C' drawings, 36 in all, as the Tate also: the British Museum and Birmingham 6 each, and Oxford, and Ricketts and Shannon 3 each.

The twelve slight drawings were taken over by the Tate for the balance (£7665 - £7500) £165. They are not worth even this sum probably and none of the other galleries wished to take them.

Melbourne had the first choice and in picking a careful plan was worked out and adopted with the approval of all galleries concerned, to secure fairness proportionate to the size of the subscription.

30 'A' Drawings

Melbourne	*Tate*	*British Museum*
1st Fifteen		
1st choice	2nd	3rd
7th		
8th	9th	
11th	10th	
12th	13th	
15th	14th	

Birmingham	*Oxford*	*Ricketts*
4th	5th	6th (counted as a Tate selection)

Melbourne	*Tate*	*British Museum*
2nd Fifteen		
16th	17th	19th
21st	20th	
22nd	23rd	
25th	24th	
26th	27th	*Birmingham*
29th	28th	
	30th	18th
12 in all	12 in all	

And so on with the 'B' and 'C' Drawings.

This system adopted to prevent small sharers getting all their picks too high up.

A slight concession made to them in letting them have their *first* pick in turn.[19]

Charles Ricketts's opinion of Ross's conduct in this dispersal is contained in an undated letter written to Charles Aitken:

> I agree with you Ross behaved splendidly, he secured a sound average without undue claims upon that which should be here. I only regret the Giant [*Antaeus*, cat. 27] which I think is one of the five best. So all is well and we are all to be congratulated. I think the series will prove most popular in the best sense with the visitors to the Tate, it would have been a scandal and a disaster had the set left the country.[20]

Bernard Hall, then director of the National Gallery of Victoria, could see no objection to the drawings being reproduced and this contributed to their delay in reaching Australia. However, in addition to this Ross argued strongly for withholding immediate shipment because of the continued risk of ocean transport due to enemy activity and because all competent packers (by which, he explained, he meant the Italians and the French) were engaged in the war effort and 'the art of scientific packing is unknown to the English'.[21]

News of the Gallery's purchases at the Linnell sale reached the Melbourne newspapers quickly. On 18 March the *Argus*, a respected daily, carried an accurate and favourable report under the heading 'Rare Drawings Purchased'.[22] A few days later the *Australasian* commented that they should make an interesting addition to the National Gallery of Victoria.[23] There was some grumbling about the amount of money spent on works of art in time of war, but the argument in this case was mixed with trivializing observations about the nudity of Eve in the Milton designs and could not be taken seriously.[24] Meanwhile Ross was preparing to leave London to make his important journey of acquaintance to Melbourne. However it was not to be; Robert Ross died suddenly of natural causes on the eve of his departure on 5 October 1918.[25] The works of art which he had recommended to the Felton Bequest were listed in the reports of his death with the explanation that they were being stored in basements in London until after the war.[26]

An announcement of their despatch from London preceded the arrival of the set,[27] and the drawings legally remained the property of the Felton Bequests' Committee until they arrived in Melbourne and were formally handed over to the Gallery. Though bought for Melbourne in 1918, Gallery records thus list their date of acquisition and accession as 1920. Blake's set of 102 illustrations to the *Divine Comedy* is now divided among the following institutions: National Gallery of Victoria (36), The Fogg Art Museum, Harvard University, Cambridge, Massachusetts (23), Tate Gallery, London (20), British Museum, London (13), City Museum and Art Gallery, Birmingham (6), Ashmolean Museum, Oxford (3), Royal Institution of Cornwall, Truro (1).

The decision in 1918 to acquire drawings by Blake—this 'unusual artist, so little known in Melbourne'[28]—has always been considered a surprising one. Certainly the extreme hostility which greeted their initial showing seems to support the view. When the drawings and prints were first exhibited they were vituperatively dismissed by the critics of the major newspapers. Alexander Colquhoun (1862–1941), painter and critic, writing in the *Herald* on 10 August 1920, criticized the 'glaring absurdities' in anatomical description and discounted Blake claiming there was nothing artistic in him to justify the expenditure of £4000. It is pertinent to note here that later, from 1936 to 1941, Colquhoun served on the Board of Trustees of the National Gallery of Victoria.

The *Argus* critic was no kinder:

> Apart from their literary merit, which may or may not be great, many of his pictures, considered artistically, are grotesque in the extreme, and in some cases repulsive in treatment. Neither good drawing nor design is apparent, though a certain knowledge of the human figure is shown in the best examples, which are, however, somewhat marred by an unnatural contortion of attitude, and over-emphasis of anatomy. Thirty pictures by the artist are on view, and the price paid was £4000, which seems to be very much in excess of their value. One or two examples would have been welcome as showing the manner of work done, but no justification can surely be shown for the purchase of so many artistically inferior pictures, which will no doubt before long find their way to the cellars.[29]

A reference in the *Leader* was more reasonable and appreciative in tone, but warned that the Blake display:

> should not be viewed by sensitive children, and parents who go there would be well advised to see the collection for themselves before taking any child there . . . For students of the evolution of the idea of the condition of evil-doers in the next world, it is most highly instructive and interesting, but one needs a course of Dante and Dore before being able to look at them quite dispassionately.[30]

Robert Ross's letter cited above demonstrates that he was prepared for some difference of opinion about the merits of Blake's art but, as it turned out, he was spared the venomous response of Melbourne's critics. Judging from Baldwin Spencer's private letter to Frank Rinder (Ross's successor as adviser to the Felton Bequest), dated 11 October 1918, the trustees, having publicly put their confidence in their man in London at the Linnell sale, privately held certain reservations. The issue was not so much Blake's art itself, as a clear preference for paintings over prints and drawings:

> You can imagine [wrote Spencer] that, in a young country like this, where art works at once good of their kind and likely to interest the ordinary art-loving public are far to seek, Blake in large quantities and 5,000 gs. for Whistler's lithographs [never acquired] were somewhat severe tests which the Trustees stood manfully . . . As you can understand, it is one thing to collect for an old established Gallery which already possesses masterpieces on its walls and can afford to put Blakes and Whistlers in portfolios where they can be enjoyed by the connoisseur, and quite another thing to collect for a young Gallery which is very anxious, naturally, to have a certain number of first class paintings on its walls to justify its existence in the eyes of the public.

This, Spencer hastened to add prophetically, was not an objection to Ross's recommendations, 'because I feel quite sure that if not now, in years to come, they will be regarded by Australians as a great acquisition to the Gallery, but now and again one must give a "sop to Cerberus" provided that, in this case, the "sop" be artistically good'.[31]

It is, of course, impossible to know exactly what the 'ordinary art-loving public' in Melbourne knew about Blake but evidence recently collated strongly suggests that the educated public in Australia was certainly aware of his literary and artistic work and the growing literature on it. There is, moreover, a long series of direct and indirect connections linking

Blake and Australia since the earliest years of the colony established at Port Jackson. It has been suggested that as early as 1777 Blake may have been responsible for some of the engravings after William Hodges which were produced at James Basire's workshop for the publication of Cook's voyages.[32] However the first widely accepted connection appears to be that provided by his engraving of *A Family of New South Wales* for Captain John Hunter's *Historical Journal of the Transactions at Port Jackson and Norfolk Island*, 1793 (cat. 40).

The arrival in Tasmania in 1837 of Thomas Griffiths Wainewright (1794–1847), writer and artist transported for forgery and later suspected of multiple murder, provides a different personal link. Wainewright and Blake knew each other and, according to Samuel Palmer, Blake admired his painting. Wainewright owned several of Blake's works, including one of the most beautiful copies of the *Songs of Innocence and of Experience*, he was full of praise for the illustrations to Dante,[33] and it is also possible that he introduced Blake to Henry Cary,[34] the translator of the version of the *Divine Comedy* which Blake consulted.

In 1848 Samuel Calvert (1828–1913), the son of Edward Calvert, one of 'The Ancients'—the group of young artists for whom Blake was a model of inspiration in his last years—arrived in Adelaide to join his elder brothers John and William who had emigrated in 1843. In 1852 he moved to Melbourne where he worked as a wood-engraver. In 1893, while briefly living in England, he published memoirs of his father[35] and returned to Melbourne the following year. In 1904 or 1905 he left Melbourne for good.[36] In 1904 Samuel Calvert made a gift of four drawings by George Strafford to the Department of Prints and Drawings at the British Museum[37] and this fact establishes another link in the Blake chain. Strafford (b. India 1820; arr. Vic. *c.* 1850, d. Melbourne 1886) worked as an engraver for the *Illustrated Australian Magazine* and for Samuel Calvert. He went insane and was eventually confined to the lunatic asylum at Yarra Bend in Melbourne.[38] It was Strafford's madness that in 1872 provoked a substantial reference to Blake in the Melbourne *Argus*. This is particularly interesting since it assumes a growing knowledge of the artist, chiefly as the result of the publication of A. C. Swinburne's *William Blake: A Critical Essay* (1868):

> Those persons who are familiar with the works of William Blake—and since the publication of Mr. Swinburne's rhapsody upon him the number of such persons has doubtless increased—will be glad to learn that Melbourne lately possessed an artist whose drawings may claim to rival that weird fancy which is the characteristic of the author of the poems and sketches which so fascinated Mr. Swinburne. The talent of each artist took its rise in a similar condition of the brain, and has ended in a similar catastrophe. The composer of the *Tiger* and the *Grave*, the seer of visions, the dreamer of dreams, was twice in a lunatic asylum, and died insane [both statements false]. His compeer, Mr. Strafford, who suffered from hallucinations similar to those which afflicted Blake, is now, and has been for some years, an inmate of Yarra Bend.[39]

'Mr. Swinburne's rhapsody' was itself the subject of a lengthy review in the *Argus* in June 1868, only months after the book was first published in London. The reviewer, while discounting much of the later part of Blake's literary work, was convinced of his genius: sufficiently so to be highly critical of Swinburne's book for revealing more of the author than of his subject.[40] When in 1869 an impression of Blake's *Canterbury Pilgrims* was exhibited at the Art Museum in Melbourne, in a loan exhibition of Art Treasures, it was singled out by the *Argus* critic on 12 May as one of the gems of the engraving collection and 'a work full of force and meaning'.

This brief outline, sketchy though it is, shows that Blake, and some of the myths surrounding him, were perhaps better known in Melbourne than has been assumed. However, it seems to have made little difference. When in 1924, five years after the Linnell sale, Frank Rinder promptly informed the trustees that the Macgeorge collection of Blake's illuminated books was to be sold at Sotheby's,[41] there was a terse reply by cable: 'no action'.[42] The trustees had obviously had their fill of Blake and, instead, were searching for 'sops for Cerberus'. And so Melbourne missed the opportunity of bidding for copies of *Thel*, *Songs of Innocence*, *Songs of Experience*, *The Marriage of Heaven and Hell*, *America*, *Visions of the Daughters of Albion*, *Europe*, and *The First Book of Urizen*, a number of which the Felton Bequest would certainly have been able to purchase. These books are now in the collections of the Pierpont Morgan Library, the Library of Congress, The Paul Mellon Collection, and the British Museum. The National Gallery of Victoria would have to wait over sixty years for a renewed opportunity of acquiring one of Blake's illuminated books.

During the 1920s, with the approaching centenary of Blake's death, several articles devoted to his art appeared in the Australian press. The publication of Laurence Binyon's *The Drawings and Engravings of William Blake* (1922) prompted Lionel Lindsay (1874–1961) to write an article, 'William Blake, The Artist', for the journal *Art in Australia*[43] in which he stated his preference for Blake's poetry and ideas over his art. Lindsay liked the woodcuts to Thornton's *Virgil* best and considered him disappointing as a colourist. Blake's art derived from art and, great though his imagination was, he paid insufficient attention to that observation of nature which—according to Lindsay—characterizes the work of the greatest artists; Blake's was an entirely metaphysical art. Lionel Lindsay does not mention Melbourne's newly acquired drawings and prints.

Throughout the 1920s newspaper opinion about Blake and the collection of the National Gallery of Victoria was polarized. On the one hand there were the reports which fed on the initial hostility of the critics, questioning 'the wisdom of purchasing the eccentric drawings of Blake'.[44] The *Bulletin* referred to that 'set of watercolour freaks . . . supposed to illustrate Dante's "Inferno", but really illustrating only the pretentious eccentricity of Blake',[45] while the Melbourne *Sun* was of the opinion that 'if we put them [the Blake drawings] in a window in Collins Street they would be laughed at. It's the name that is bought, not the art'.[46] These prejudiced reports were far more common than any informed expressions of opinion or fact.

But in the 1920s, with the growth of interest in theosophy and in the heroic archetypes of classical mythology, the time was also ripe for a sympathetic reappraisal. The outstanding example of this attitude was Napier Waller (1893–1972), painter, mosaicist, designer of stained glass and printmaker, and a trustee of the National Gallery of Victoria from 1944 to 1946. Waller was a particular admirer of Blake's art and his own work incorporated motifs directly derived from Blake.[47] In May 1926 he gave a public address, in the first series of newly instituted guide lectures at the Gallery. The lecture was given in front of the 'excellent collection of Blake's pictures, and the building was packed with art enthusiasts'.[48] Fortunately, what appears to be a complete transcription of the talk was published in the *Illustrated Tasmanian Mail* (9 June 1926, pp. 25–6). Waller chose not to give an account of Blake's life but referred his audience to the information available in Gilchrist, Swinburne and Yeats, as well as to Geoffrey Keynes's Nonesuch edition of the complete writings. He talked instead about the nature of Blake's art, giving an interpretation of its literary and symbolic character, explaining relief etching and countering the accusation of madness with Blake's own response to his accusers: 'If these men are sane, I prefer to be mad'. He noted that 'in this institution will be found a volume devoted to Blake's genius by one of the most splendid ornaments of modern culture, yet in this gallery you may overhear loud whispered ridicule' and he ended his analysis and appreciation of Blake's art by observing that:

> his work is charged with a great earnestness, a rare seriousness that we observe chiefly in children. We find ourselves looking through a different plane, in which is being enacted some mighty heroic drama . . . His work is a kind of sympathetic magic. It has a power of invocation, but only according to our sense of faith. From William Blake we take only what we have the ability to bring.

According to Waller, many of the Dante designs: 'which we are very fortunate in possessing . . . are but the groundplans compared with Blake's intensity of finish. The addition of one of his tempera panels to this collection would be an easier introduction to the public'. Until his death in 1972 Waller would recollect the general hostility with which the Blakes were greeted in their early years in Melbourne.[49]

With the Felton Bequests' Committee's purchase of a Samuel Palmer water-colour in 1927, and the simultaneous gift of another, the *Argus* was able to link the rediscovery of Palmer's art with the Blake centenary, and this time did not miss the opportunity of referring to the Dante designs in Melbourne.[50] But even in the context of the growing Blake literature, the Dante illustrations came in for some harsh censure. In 1929 the Melbourne *Advocate*, a Catholic weekly, printed an article entitled 'William Blake—Poet and Painter' which was of the opinion that: 'There is a curious duality and correspondency between Blake the painter and Blake the poet. His best work in painting is very good indeed. But his worst work—and the National Gallery of Victoria has some hideous examples of it—was very bad'.[51]

The journalist and critic Basil Burdett (1897–1942), reviewing the history of the Felton Bequest in 1934, wrote of Robert Ross that his 'monument in the Melbourne Gallery is the large collection of drawings illustrating Dante and other subjects, by William Blake, which, in the opinion of some connoisseurs, is one of the major glories of the Felton Bequest'.[52] That same year a display of the works prompted the following response from the *Argus* critic:

> The engravings are remarkable for finely drawn lines; 'free drawing', perhaps expresses the quality of his technique in a better way. The drawings are in charcoal and water-colour and depict scenes from Dante's 'Inferno', 'Purgatory', and 'Paradise'. Some are gruesome enough to persuade any hardened sinner to tread the straight and narrow path for evermore. The work is of great historic interest from an art point of view, and expresses the mind of a man possessed of an extraordinary imagination . . . Based on present-day standards, the works are full of crudities as regards drawing and composition. Yet a principal figure in some instances is delightfully rendered. Many of these drawings are mere sketches, however, graphic expressions of this curious imagination.

The review ended with this advice: 'There are at least two points of view from which drawings and prints may be considered—the collector's and the artist's. These on view are rarities, so, when viewing them, the collector's attitude is, perhaps, the better'.[53]

During the 1940s press accounts reflect a distinct shift of attitude. Not only are the writers more accurately informed about Blake's life and art, and its place in British art, but they seem suddenly to show an awareness of the importance of the stature of the acquisition and of certain precise details surrounding it. This reorientation is vividly demonstrated in an admission contained in Leon Gellert's review of the book *Masterpieces of the National Gallery of Victoria*, published in 1949.[54] Gellert (1892–1977), writer, critic and an editor of *Art in Australia*, confessed that:

> Thirty-odd years ago I would probably have regarded them [the Melbourne Dante illustrations] as the work of an inspired amateur who had little control of form. To-day they seem full of impassioned thought unencumbered by the rules and regulations that preside over mortal flesh. They have all the startling clarity of the intense visionary.[55]

Gellert here is presumably recollecting the criticisms voiced by Lionel Lindsay in his 1923 article in *Art in Australia*, a magazine which Gellert joined as editor in the very year that the article was published.

In giving notice of a display of the works in the Gallery in November 1940, the *Argus* commented that 'few Felton Bequest acquisitions have reflected more credit on the purchasing committee'.[56] Basil Burdett, writing in the *Herald*, devoted his entire column to Blake and the Melbourne drawings, describing the shift from Blake's early lyricism to the later mystic mood and calling him a man 'divinely appointed to illustrate Dante'.[57] The *Sun* welcomed the exhibition, writing that it had been far too long since the last display and judging Blake to be: 'the world's first modern artist 150 years before his time. These are works which everyone can enjoy, and which should attract wide attention among the public'.[58]

The reasons for this apparently sudden change of heart lie not only in a maturing of attitudes, the presence of better informed critics and a discovery of the contemporary relevance of Blake's art, but also in the appointment in 1940 of Daryl Lindsay (1889–1976) first as keeper of prints (1940–41) and then as director of the National Gallery of Victoria (1942–56). Furthermore, in 1943 Lindsay appointed Ursula Hoff to succeed him as keeper of prints. In her account of the Felton Bequest Dr Hoff has drawn attention to Daryl Lindsay's efforts to educate the public through annotated exhibitions, writing, and 'articulate verbal pleading'.[59] In 1941 the drawings were lent to the state galleries of Adelaide and New South Wales. While in Sydney they received an enthusiastic welcome from Frank Medworth (1892–1947), artist and teacher, who wrote:

> The value of such an exhibition as this in Sydney will be borne out in increased discussion of the meaning of art symbols, and in the first-hand study of those principles which dictate the highest form of pictorial expression. That lust for information which is typical of the average human should be satisfied here . . . Artists, students, and general visitors to the galleries will all extract a measure of enjoyment from the works displayed. The enthusiastic modernist will find precedent for the dream-like unreality he seeks in surrealism.[60]

When the journalist Clive Turnbull reported a Blake display in 1945 he clearly had access to the Gallery's documentation of the Linnell sale since he quoted from Robert Ross's letter of report. 'It is upon a few things such as these [the Blakes]', wrote Turnbull, 'that the claim of the gallery to international distinction rests'. He referred to Ross as 'the editor of Wilde and a conspicuous member of a notorious circle . . . a curious representative of the staid trustees' and ended by observing that 'we have the Blakes, even, perhaps, if they are rather more than we deserved'.[61] George Bell (1878–1966), artist and the most influential teacher of modernist principles in Melbourne, applauded Daryl Lindsay's policy of repeated showings of the Blake collection and stated that 'the total adequacy as illustration, the power of design, the richness of colour all combining to express nobility and immensity, leave us speechless and profoundly moved'.[62] This, however, did not apply to the critics of the *Age* [63] and the *Bulletin*,[64] who remained unmoved, the former accusing Blake of diminishing whatever he touched, the latter wondering how Blake ever got his reputation as an artist.

In the context of the 1940s one further notable event must be recorded: the founding of the Herald Chair of Fine Arts at the University of Melbourne which established the first department of its kind in Australia.[65] It was funded by Sir Keith Murdoch with the support and encouragement of Daryl Lindsay. The first professor was Joseph Burke, a specialist in eighteenth-century English art who encouraged the use of the Gallery's collection in teaching, and conducted seminars on the subject of Blake. His article 'The Eidetic and the Borrowed Image: An Interpretation of Blake's Theory and Practice of Art', first published in 1964,[66] is evidence of the fundamentally changed nature of the critical and scholarly framework. Three years earlier, to mark the centenary of the founding of the Gallery, Ursula Hoff had published a fully illustrated booklet on the Dante illustrations with an essay on their historical context and quoting the relevant passages from Cary's translation of the *Divine Comedy*.[67]

Since the relocation of the Gallery to its current premises in 1968, the Blake collection has been put on public display every two or three years, either as a complete group of works, or in the context of Blake's contemporaries and followers. It is one of the most frequently viewed parts of the collection in the Print Room. As the references to international exhibitions in the catalogue which follows attest, the illustrations to Dante as well as Milton have been included in all of the major recent Blake exhibitions, beginning with that organized in West Germany in 1975. Apart from the acquisition of several prints (including two sets of restrikes of the engravings to Dante) the collection has, until recently, been a largely static one. However in 1988, sixty-four years after bypassing the opportunity presented by the dispersal of the Macgeorge illuminated books, the Felton Bequest once more augmented the Blake collection in an important way. Copy X of the *Songs of Innocence* (cat. 39) was bought in London with the recommendation of the adviser, John Ingamells. Then, within the space of less than a year, due to decisive and swift action (and when this catalogue was already in press) a rare, hand-coloured copy of Blake's illustrations to Young's *Night Thoughts* (cat. 51) was purchased at auction, also in London. Thus the Melbourne collection, which to date has consisted chiefly of the brilliant work of Blake's last years, can now represent his early work with notable examples.

Since they both have a bearing on early collections of Blake in Australia, these recent additions are also important for a further historical reason. The acquisition of the *Songs* is a reminder that in the nineteenth century a copy of the *Songs of Innocence and of Experience* (Copy J) had been in an Australian collection, presumably that of Augustus Henry Tulk (1810–73).[68] Tulk, who arrived in Melbourne in 1854, had been the erudite and hard-working first chief librarian (appointed 1856) of the Public Library in Melbourne and an important figure in the establishment of the first public Art Museum. The provenance of the *Night Thoughts* takes us even further back, to the arrival in Sydney in 1837 of William à Beckett (1806 -69), solicitor-general of New South Wales, then first chief justice of Victoria, and a forebear of the Boyd family of Australian artists.[69] At some stage this copy of the *Night Thoughts* appears to have passed to Alfred Felton himself,[70] from whose collection it is said to have been purchased by Robert Carl Sticht (1856–1922).[71]

Notes

1 The major accounts of the Gallery's history are: Leonard Cox, *The National Gallery of Victoria 1861–1968: A Search for a Collection*, National Gallery of Victoria, Melbourne, 1970, and Ann Galbally, *The Collections of the National Gallery of Victoria*, Oxford University Press, Melbourne, 1987.

2 The two principal accounts of the Felton Bequest are: Daryl Lindsay, *The Felton Bequest: An Historical Record 1904–1959*, Oxford University Press, Melbourne, 1963, and Ursula Hoff, *The Felton Bequest*, National Gallery of Victoria, Melbourne, 1983.

3 The period of Colvin's and Gibson's joint advisership is discussed in Cox, *The National Gallery of Victoria*, ch. 7, pp. 71–80; an account of Professor Baldwin Spencer's search for a replacement is to be found in ch. 8, esp. pp. 81–4.

4 W. Baldwin Spencer to the President of the Trustees of the Public Library, National Gallery and Museums of Victoria, March 1917. Copy held in the correspondence files of the National Gallery of Victoria (hereafter cited as NGV).

5 Ross's letter of acceptance is dated 22 March 1917 (NGV).

6 See Hoff, *The Felton Bequest*, p. 36 for a concise résumé of Ross's public appointments and relevant literature.

7 *Bulletin*, 12 April 1917.

8 Ross informed the Felton Bequests' London solicitors of this invitation in a letter dated 24 March 1917 (NGV). He argued that this circumstance would not cause any conflict of interest but, on the contrary, could result in considerable advantages for Melbourne.

9 NGV.

10 Noted in the *Rough Minute Book: Works of Art Submitted to the Felton Bequest, 1905—12.10.1934*, under 14 March 1918 (NGV).

11 G. Keynes (ed.), *Blake, Complete Writings*, Oxford University Press, Oxford, 1969, p. 878.

12 Those drawings now in Melbourne which were included in the 1893 and 1913 exhibitions are annotated accordingly in the catalogue entries which follow.

13 For information concerning the details of the Tate Gallery's involvement in the dispersal of the Linnell sale I am indebted to Krzysztof Z. Cieszkowski's forthcoming account of the events, which he kindly made available in manuscript form titled: 'They murmuring divide; while the wind sleeps beneath, and the numbers are counted in silence'—the dispersal of the Illustrations to Dante's 'Divine Comedy'.

14 Aitken to Miss Alice Carthew, quoted in Cieszkowski, forthcoming.

15 Charles Ricketts's are among the most spirited letters to Robert Ross in the anthology of letters to him edited by Margery Ross, *Robert Ross: Friend of Friends*, Jonathan Cape, London, 1952.

16 Robert Ross, 'The Place of William Blake in English Art', *Burlington Magazine*, vol. IX, 1906, pp. 150–67.

17 Robert Ross, 'A Recent Criticism of Blake', *Burlington Magazine*, vol. XVI, 1909, p. 84.

18 Quoted in Cieszkowski, forthcoming.

19 NGV.

20 Ricketts to Aitken (undated), quoted in Cieszkowski, forthcoming.

21 Ross to E. Armstrong, 17 September 1918 (NGV).

22 *Argus*, 18 March 1918.

23 *Australasian*, 23 March 1918.

24 *Truth*, 20 April 1918.

25 Obituary, *The Times*, 7 October 1918.

26 *Herald*, 8 October 1918.

27 *Leader*, 3 April 1920.

28 Referred to thus in Cox, *The National Gallery of Victoria*, p. 84.

29 *Argus*, 11 August 1920.

30 *Leader*, 4 September 1920.

31 Spencer to Rinder, 11 October 1918 (extract in NGV).

32 This possibility is argued persuasively in Rüdiger Joppien & Bernard Smith, *The Art of Captain Cook's Voyages*, Oxford University Press, Melbourne, 1985, vol. 2, p. 110.

33 Wainewright's connections with Blake are noted in G. E. Bentley Jr, *Blake Records*, Clarendon Press, Oxford, 1969. For an account of Wainewright's Australian years see Robert Crossland, *Wainewright in Tasmania*, Oxford University Press, Melbourne, 1954.

34 This is suggested in M. Wilson, *The Life of William Blake*, Oxford University Press, London, 1971, p. 360.

35 [S. Calvert], *A Memoir of Edward Calvert Artist*, Sampson Low, Marston & Co. Ltd, London, 1893. A copy of this book is held in the Department of Prints and Drawings, edn 142/350, Felton Bequest 1977, inv. no. P.109/1976.

36 For a biographical account of Samuel Calvert see the entry by Thomas A. Darragh in Joan Kerr (ed.), *Dictionary of Australian Artists—Working Paper I: Painters, Photographers and Engravers 1770–1870, A–H*, Power Institute of Fine Arts, University of Sydney, Sydney, 1984, pp. 124–6.

37 Laurence Binyon, *Catalogue of the Drawings of British Artists and Artists of Foreign Origin Working in Great Britain, Preserved in the Department of Prints and Drawings in the British Museum*, British Museum, London, 1907, vol. IV, p. 162.

38 Alan McCulloch, *Artists of the Australian Gold Rush*, Lansdowne Editions, Melbourne, 1977, p. 25; Alan McCulloch, *Encyclopedia of Australian Art*, Hutchinson, Melbourne, 1984, p. 1155.

39 *Argus*, 14 February 1872. I am indebted to Gerard Hayes for drawing my attention to this article and to the *Argus* review of Swinburne's book on Blake.

40 *Argus*, 2 June 1868.

41 Rinder to E. La Touche Armstrong, 20 March 1924 (NGV).

42 Copy of cable dated 17 June 1924 (NGV). This rejection is also noted in Cox, *The National Gallery of Victoria*, p. 99.

43 Lionel Lindsay, 'William Blake, The Artist', *Art in Australia*, May 1923, n.p.
44 *Herald*, 20 June 1922.
45 *Bulletin*, 30 February 1922.
46 *Sun*, 14 August 1923.
47 Nicholas Draffin, *The Art of Napier Waller*, Sun Books, Melbourne, 1978, p. 4.
48 *Argus*, 22 May 1926.
49 I am grateful to my colleague Terence Lane, trustee of the Napier Waller Estate, for this communication.
50 *Argus*, 7 May 1927.
51 *Advocate*, 31 January 1929.
52 Basil Burdett, *The Felton Bequests—An Historical Record 1904–1933*, Felton Bequests Committee, Melbourne, 1934, p. 15.
53 *Argus*, 2 June 1934.
54 Ursula Hoff (ed.), *Masterpieces of the National Gallery of Victoria*, F. W. Cheshire, Melbourne, 1949. This includes Dr Hoff's essay, 'William Blake's Illustrations to Dante's Divine Comedy', pp. 91–7.
55 *Sydney Morning Herald*, 10 September 1949.
56 *Argus*, 12 October 1940.
57 *Herald*, 9 November 1940.
58 *Sun*, 13 November 1940.
59 Hoff, *The Felton Bequest*, p. 12.
60 *Sydney Morning Herald*, 10 September 1949.
61 *Herald*, 17 February 1945.
62 *Sun*, 20 February 1945.
63 *Age*, 19 February 1945.
64 *Bulletin*, 7 March 1945.
65 See Ursula Hoff, 'Observations on Art History in Melbourne 1946–1964', *Australian Journal of Art*, vol. 3, 1983, pp. 5–9.
66 The essay first appeared in Franz Philipp & June Stewart (eds), *In Honour of Daryl Lindsay: Essays and Studies*, Oxford University Press, Melbourne, 1964, pp. 110–27.
67 U. Hoff, *William Blake's Illustrations to Dante's Divine Comedy*, National Gallery of Victoria, Melbourne, 1961.
68 I am indebted to Roger Butler who alerted me to this fact. The provenance of Copy J is given in G. E. Bentley Jr, *Blake Books*, Clarendon Press, Oxford, 1977, p. 417. For Tulk see the entry in G. Serle & R. Ward (eds), *Australian Dictionary of Biography*, Melbourne University Press, Melbourne, vol. 6, p. 308, and Cox, *The National Gallery of Victoria*.
69 For William à Beckett see the entry in D. Pike (ed.), *Australian Dictionary of Biography*, Melbourne University Press, Melbourne, vol. 3, p. 10; E. G. Coppel, 'The First Chief Justice of Victoria', *Australian Law Journal*, vol. 27, 1953, pp. 209–22; and U. Hoff, *The Art of Arthur Boyd*, Andre Deutsch, London, 1986, p. 35.
70 It is known that after Alfred Felton's death his library was auctioned in Melbourne by Gemmell and Tuckett on 5 and 6 May 1904. However, I have been unable to trace a copy of the sale catalogue.
71 For R. C. Sticht see the entry in P. Serle (ed.), *Dictionary of Australian Biography*, Angus & Robertson, Sydney, 1949, vol. 2, p. 364, and Geoffrey Blainey, *The Peaks of Lyell*, Melbourne University Press, Melbourne, 1959. In 1923 the National Gallery of Victoria acquired, through the Felton Bequest, Sticht's large collection of prints and drawings.

Innocence Regained: Blake's Late Illustrations to Milton and Dante

Martin Butlin
Former Keeper, Historic British Collection, Tate Gallery, London

The acquisition in 1988 by the National Gallery of Victoria of an early copy of William Blake's *Songs of Innocence* (cat. 39 a–n) established an important starting point for a collection already rich in his late water-colours. The collection now spans Blake's whole career as a mature artist. At first sight the similarities between the pages from *Songs of Innocence* and the majority of the late illustrations to Dante's *Divine Comedy* suggest that there was little development in either style or technique during Blake's career. In both, relatively thin washes of delicate colour are applied over an outline, printed in the case of the *Songs of Innocence*, roughly drawn in pencil in the case of the illustrations to Dante. Between 1790, the approximate date at which this particular copy of the *Songs of Innocence* was coloured,[1] and the years 1824–27, during which Blake worked on his unfinished series of illustrations to Dante, nothing seems to have changed, though the more finished of the Dante illustrations show a richness of treatment that is not anticipated in the copy of *Songs of Innocence*. Similarly, the two late illustrations to Milton's *Paradise Lost*, executed in 1822, share the rich texture and colour of the more finished of the Dante illustrations but again in general style show, at first sight, little change from the basically two-dimensional, linear style of over thirty years earlier.

The Dante water-colours, and the pages of the illuminated book *Songs of Innocence* coloured in water-colour, exemplify the two ends of Blake's career, and are marked by a general lightness of tone and optimism of content. The illustrations to Milton, however, in their imagery if not in their treatment, represent an intermediate period, the first decade of the nineteenth century, in which Blake began to paint whole series of illustrations to Milton. The middle years of Blake's career are also represented in some of the engravings and colour-prints in the collection.

In the case of most artists it is too facile to see direct links between the circumstances of the artist's life and the style and content of his or her works. Rembrandt did not need to have experienced bankruptcy to paint the tragic self-portrait in Vienna[2] nor, on a different level, can the elongation of El Greco's figures, or Turner's late style, be explained away as the result of optical troubles.[3] But Blake, the poet and painter, is one of the rare cases in which one can trace a close correlation between life and art. This is helped by the circumstance of his being an artist as much in words as in the visual arts; the progress of his life being expressed as much in verbal terms as in the more difficult to interpret pictorial realm.

Given this correlation one can trace a development in Blake's art from innocence, to innocence regained by way of experience. The late works do echo the early ones, but underlying the similarities there has been a complete transformation. The apparent innocence of Blake's illustrations to Milton and Dante is modified by a critical sense based on experience.

The replacement of innocence by experience was set out by Blake most clearly when he added his *Songs of Experience* to his *Songs of Innocence* to produce the joint publication *Songs of Innocence and of Experience*. The *Songs of Innocence* had first been issued in 1789; the joint publication appeared in 1794.[4] During this period Blake had experienced political disillusionment as the hopes aroused by the French Revolution disappeared with the blood-letting of the Terror, and as the radical group of writers and publishers in London of which he was a member had been driven underground, to flight or into silence by the growing repression of Pitt's government in reaction against events in France.[5] At the same time Blake's own economic prospects had worsened. His book *The French Revolution*, set up in ordinary type in 1791 for general publication, had been halted before any copies for general sale were printed,[6] and his own particular form of 'illuminated printing', of which the *Songs of Innocence* is the first fully accomplished example, could, through its very nature in being coloured by hand, only achieve a very small number of sales. Even as a commercial engraver after other people's designs, Blake was, as a result of his conservative technique, finding it difficult to achieve a market. Thus, by the mid-1790s, both his poetry and the illustrations with which he accompanied it had been completely transformed, from the innocence and optimism of the *Songs of Innocence* to the pessimism borne of experience of the *Songs of Experience*.

In another of his books of 1794, *The First Book of Urizen* (the only book of Urizen to be issued),[7] the change is even more marked. This can be seen in the independent copy of plate 21 from *Urizen* in the National Gallery of Victoria (cat. 43) with its depiction of the way in which the mutual love of a family has been distorted by the father's jealousy, creating an image of self-destructive anguish. In other illustrations to *Urizen* the anguish, as conveyed both in the illustrations and in the text to which they relate, is much more extreme.

The interaction of content and technique transfigured Blake's style in the years between 1789 and 1794.[8] Not only did the illustrations in the books become much more dominant, filling ever more of the page and sometimes even occupying whole pages, but Blake's technique in colouring them was altered. In the first copies of the *Songs of Innocence* and other books of the early 1790s he produced both text and

1–2 Milton's *Paradise Lost* 1822
1 *Satan Watching the Endearments of Adam and Eve*

2 *The Creation of Eve*

the outlines of his illustrations by a form of engraving known as relief etching; printing the text and outlines from his plate, he then coloured the illustrations with thin washes of water-colour. However, in the publications of 1794, and even in copies of earlier books that he finished for sale in that year, he replaced this technique with a form of colour-printing in which, instead of colouring the illustrations by hand, he applied thick pigments to the plates from which he had printed the outlines and then took impressions; this resulted in a much richer, heavier form of colouring appropriate to the more sombre, denser imagery of his writings. Some of these illustrations were then issued as separate designs, for instance the National Gallery of Victoria's plate 21 of *Urizen*, and in 1795 Blake produced the magnificent series of twelve large colour-printed designs, including *Elohim and Adam*, *Nebuchadnezzar* and *The House of Death*, a subject taken from Milton's *Paradise Lost*.[9]

The mid-1790s mark the depths of Blake's personal despair and also the most extreme violence of his visual imagery. The lessons of this period, however, remained with him for the rest of his life. The power and imaginative content of the 1795 colour-prints reappear, in only slightly modified form, in such tempera paintings of *c.* 1799–1800 as *Moses Indignant at the Golden Calf* and in such water-colours of *c.* 1800–05, also of biblical subjects, as *Moses at the Burning Bush*, *Ezekiel's Wheels* and *The Great Red Dragon and the Beast from the Sea*.[10] The same qualities are found in the tempera paintings of *The Spiritual Form of Pitt Guiding Behemoth*, exhibited in Blake's exhibition in 1809, and *The Ghost of a Flea* of *c.* 1819–20[11] and, as will be seen later, are characteristic of a number of the illustrations to Dante of Blake's last years.

However, in the opening years of the nineteenth century a number of things contributed to a renewed faith and optimism. Blake's move to Felpham, at the instigation of a new patron, William Hayley, led to a fresh appreciation of the beauties of nature, as was reflected in the poem he included in a letter to Thomas Butts[12] (the main, and most sympathetic patron of these years[13]), and in passages in Blake's new poem *Milton* which drew its inspiration from these years.[14] More important was a renewed belief in the tenets of Christianity, again reflected in *Milton*. Blake himself dramatized the new vision that inspired him on his arrival at Felpham in the illustration showing *Blakes Cottage at Felpham* on plate 36 of *Milton*[15] and in the rays of light that illuminate the same cottage in his water-colour *Landscape Near Felpham* in the Tate Gallery.[16] During these years his water-colours also show a return to the greater clarity of outline and less broken areas of colour of his earlier, neo-classical origins, a process reinforced by a visit in October 1804 to the Truchsessian Gallery, a collection of pictures which, though largely copies, introduced him to the lucidity and directness of fifteenth-century painting.[17]

It was the return to Christianity that was most significant. Blake was a non-conformist by background, with inclinations towards the tenets of Swedenborg, and never fully lost his Christian faith even in the 1790s. He had, however, in the middle of that decade adopted the heretical view that the God of the Old Testament was distinct from Christ, and a negative force. The creation of man was a stage in man's Fall and for a time even salvation through Christ had seemed beyond reach. The return to a more orthodox form of Christianity in the early years of the nineteenth century is reflected not only in *Milton* but also in the reworkings Blake made in his unfinished manuscript *Vala* or *The Four Zoas*, which was probably begun in 1796 and finally abandoned in 1807.[18] It must also have been reinforced by the commission he received from Thomas Butts to make illustrations of the Bible, first of all in tempera and then in water-colour.[19] As well as the forceful works already mentioned, a new sweetness and delicacy of treatment can be seen in temperas such as *Bathsheba at the Bath* and *The Nativity*,[20] and in such water-colours as *Jacob's Dream* and *The Woman Taken in Adultery*.[21]

The return to a more neo-classical style mentioned above demonstrates an important fact about Blake's style. Far from expressing himself in a personal idiom based entirely upon inspiration as sometimes used to be thought, Blake, like most other artists, had his roots in the art of his time. Trained as an engraver, he expanded his style in other media largely by following the predominant tenet of his most advanced contemporaries—neo-classicism. This manifested itself in two main forms. The first was a severe, highly disciplined style going back by way of Poussin and Raphael to antique reliefs, which had been advanced by Gavin Hamilton and Benjamin West in Rome and introduced to England through their exhibits at the Royal Academy. In Blake this style is revealed in the series of early illustrations to subjects from English history, small water-colours painted in about 1779 and elaborated in a more accomplished group of water-colours of about 1793.[22] There was also a more decorative, softer form of neo-classicism found particularly in the book illustrations of such artists as John Flaxman and Thomas Stothard, both friends of Blake. This style was exhibited in Blake's *Songs of Innocence* and his illustrations to Mary Wollstonecraft's *Original Stories* of about 1791,[23] and persists in the late illustrations to Thornton's *Virgil* (cat. 48 a–n).[24]

In the more extreme works of the mid-1790s Blake seems to have broken away from his neo-classical origins but there is still an insistence on relatively clear, simply understood images, and a certain two-dimensionality that betrays his neo-classical origins. By the time of the biblical water-colours of the early years of the nineteenth century, in such examples as *The Woman Taken in Adultery*,[25] this element is back in full force, though with the grace and accomplishment of the swaying forms it is now in a completely personal manner.

It is in this period of Blake's career that the compositions of the two illustrations to Milton in the National Gallery of Victoria (cat. 1–2) originated.[26] Although most of the works of this time were done for Thomas Butts, who paid Blake a regular stipend in return for illustrations first to the Bible and later, when this main series was apparently completed, more specifically to *The Book of Job*, Blake's series of illustrations to Milton began with a commission from

3–38 **Dante's *Divine Comedy*** **1824–27**
3 *Dante Running from the Three Beasts*

another patron, the Reverend Joseph Thomas.[27] This came about in 1801 through Blake's friend John Flaxman and was for illustrations to *Comus*; much later, in about 1815, Blake was to do a second set for Butts.

In 1807 came Blake's first set of twelve illustrations to *Paradise Lost*, also for Thomas, though Blake had painted an independent water-colour of *Satan Watching the Endearments of Adam and Eve* the year before, possibly for Butts. Blake had derived two subjects from *Paradise Lost* in the heroic years of the 1790s, both being given a much more personal treatment. The first was the frontispiece to his book *Europe*,[28] which transforms Milton's description of how God, in the person of the Son,

> . . . took the golden compasses, prepared
> In God's eternal store, to circumscribe
> This universe, and all created things.

Blake, however, far from showing the Son, showed the Creator in the form of God the Father, changed into the likeness of Blake's own character—developed in his writings—the unenlightened Urizen, a witness that at this stage in Blake's career he saw the Creation as a negative, materialistic act. The second subject that Blake took from *Paradise Lost* at this time was that of the large colour-print of 1795 showing *The House of Death*, an equally negative depiction.[29] The water-colour illustrations of 1807, however, are much more direct illustrations of Milton's text, rather than the utilization of subjects from that text to illustrate Blake's own philosophy. Blake again painted a second series of twelve illustrations for Butts, but only a year later, in 1808, and it is compositions from this series that formed the basis for the works painted in 1822, of which two are at Melbourne.

Blake painted one further series of Milton illustrations for Thomas: those for *On the Morning of Christ's Nativity* in 1809. Again there was a second series for Butts, painted in about 1815. After this Thomas's commissions of Miltonic subjects seem to have come to an end, although Blake did contribute, with water-colours of 1806 and 1809, to his extra-illustrated copy of a second folio edition of Shakespeare.[30] Blake continued, however, to paint illustrations to Milton. A series of twelve designs for *L'Allegro* and *Il Penseroso*, on paper watermarked 1816 and probably painted between then and 1820, also belonged to Butts, while a second series of twelve illustrations to *Paradise Regained*, on similarly watermarked paper and also dating from the same period, were done for Blake's most important patron in his later years, the young artist John Linnell.

John Linnell (1792–1882) seems to have been introduced to Blake by George Cumberland's son George in June 1818 and it was through Linnell that Blake got to know John Varley (1778–1842)—for whom he painted his notorious Visionary Heads—and three younger artists, members of a group who dubbed themselves 'The Ancients': Samuel Palmer (1805–81), George Richmond (1809–96) and Edward Calvert (1799–1883).[31] Like Butts, Linnell seems to have paid Blake regular sums of money in return for most of his output in his late years, up to Blake's death in 1827.

The first important group of works commissioned by Linnell was the second series of illustrations to *The Book of Job*, for which he borrowed the set earlier painted for Butts and traced them as the basis for Blake's new versions; part of the arrangement was that Blake was to engrave the subjects for more general distribution.[32] The next year, while Blake was still working on the *Job* illustrations, he also did the three extant versions of compositions from his earlier *Paradise Lost* series. These were recorded by Linnell in his journal as 'copies from [Blake's] drawings', again lent for the purpose by Butts. At about the same time he must have borrowed Butts's water-colour of *The Parable of the Wise and Foolish Virgins* of about 1805, again for Blake to make a new version.[33] Linnell's last main commission was the unfinished series of illustrations to Dante (cat. 3–38). He also owned a number of earlier works, including the separate designs from *Urizen* and *Jerusalem* in the National Gallery of Victoria (cat. 43, 47), and the series of illustrations to Milton's *Paradise Regained*, now in the Fitzwilliam Museum, Cambridge.[34] Linnell was also instrumental in obtaining Blake's commission to do illustrations for the schoolboy edition of *Virgil* edited by Linnell's doctor, Robert John Thornton (cat. 48 a–n).

These works seem to have followed what may have been a second period of crisis in Blake's life but a period about which, unlike the 1790s, very little is known. Between 1805 and 1810 Blake had two further important chances to achieve public recognition. In 1805 he was commissioned to design and then to engrave illustrations to Robert Blair's *The Grave*,[35] a popular piece of verse moralizing about death that had already passed through a number of editions. In the event Blake's trial white-line etching proved to be too unorthodox and vigorous for his publisher Robert Hartley Cromek, and the more lucrative part of the commission, the execution of the engravings, was given to the fashionable Italian Luigi Schiavonetti. Paradoxically, *The Grave* was nevertheless the means by which most people apart from Blake's close friends came to know his work.

Blake's other appeal to a more general public was in the one-man exhibition he put on in his brother's house in 28 Broad Street.[36] This opened in May 1809 and was due to close at the end of September of the same year. In fact it was still open well into 1810 but not, alas, as the result of any great public interest. Although some of the works belonged to Thomas Butts it is unlikely that any were bought as the result of the exhibition; only one, hostile, review has been traced. The exhibition was particularly designed as a demonstration of Blake's personal technique of painting in tempera, 'Being the Ancient Method of Fresco Painting restored' as the title of Blake's own catalogue to his exhibition has it. These 'frescoes' included the famous *Canterbury Pilgrims*, *The Spiritual Form of Nelson Guiding Leviathan* and *The Spiritual Form of Pitt Guiding Behemoth*, and a version of *Satan Calling up his Legions*, another illustration to *Paradise Lost*.[37] In all there were nine temperas and seven water-colours. The temperas represent the culmination of Blake's experiments with the special glue-based medium that he had first used for colour-printing in the mid-1790s. Despite his

4 *The Vestibule of Hell and the Souls Mustering to Cross the Acheron*

claims for their superiority over oil painting and the attacks from 'blurring demons' that destroyed their clarity of form, most of the tempera paintings up to and including those in Blake's exhibition have, when they survived at all, suffered considerable darkening and losses of paint. Later, for his tempera paintings of the 1820s which include a version of one of the Dante illustrations, *Count Ugolino and his Sons in Prison* of *c.* 1826,[38] he completely altered his method and achieved much more satisfactory results.

The technical shift seen in the late temperas is paralleled by changes in the technique of at least Blake's most finished water-colours of his later years. These final achievements, however, follow a period of relative obscurity that stretches from 1810 until about 1818. Although there are isolated accounts of Blake's activities during these years there are very few works that can be attributed to them. In 1812 Blake contributed three of the temperas that he had shown in 1809 to an exhibition of the Associated Painters in Water Colour,[39] together with isolated pages from the illuminated book that formed his chief occupation over these years—*Jerusalem the Emanation of the Giant Albion*. This, although dated 1804 on the title-page, was not completed until 1820 at the earliest.[40] Blake's book *Milton*, also dated 1804 on the title-page, appears to have occupied him up to about 1815,[41] and some of his water-colour illustrations to Milton's poems, as we have seen, also date from these 'missing' years, but compared to the high numbers of works in the rest of Blake's career the output for this period is relatively small. It has indeed been suggested that Blake went mad and was even incarcerated but this has been discounted.[42] The mystery remains, and some form of spiritual or artistic crisis may be the explanation. Certainly the works of Blake's late years, associated with the patronage of John Linnell rather than that of Thomas Butts (although the latter did continue to purchase works from Blake, such as the engravings to *The Book of Job*, up to Blake's death[43]) do on close inspection demonstrate a distinct style representing the synthesis of Blake's artistic development.

This late style shows a richness in technique and colour unparalleled in Blake's earlier works. This is, of course, most apparent in the finished works such as the two illustrations to Milton (cat. 1–2) and certain of the Dante illustrations (cat. 3, 4, 5, 8, 12, 23, 24, 27), although even the tinted washes that distinguish works in progress show a range and fullness of colour beyond that of Blake's earlier water-colours. In part the technique seems to have been more painstaking, with a lot of stippled work with the point of the brush in the finished water-colours and, as has already been noted, a more successful form of painting in tempera that entailed the careful laying in of a white ground and a meticulous application of paint akin to that of the late finished water-colours. At the same time Blake's figures became more three-dimensional, though still within an overall two-dimensionality based on his neo-classical models. Blake greatly admired the works of Michelangelo although he only knew these from engravings. Perhaps luckily for the survival of his own personal style, a plan early in his career to send him to Rome never came to fruition.[44] It is Michelangelo's figure style that lies behind such powerful images as Blake's *Nebuchadnezzar*, but it is in his late works, such as the Dante illustration of *Antaeus Setting Down Dante and Virgil in the Last Circle of Hell* (cat. 27), that Blake is at his closest to his model; indeed, there is some feeling of Michelangelo's finished presentation drawings in both the general forms and the actual treatment of such figures.

A similar strengthening of the three-dimensional modelling of the figures, though less extreme, is found when one compares the Melbourne illustrations to *Paradise Lost* with their models in the series painted for Thomas Butts.[45] There is also, in these late works, a greater sensual quality, though this is of course partly dependent on the nature of the subject-matter. This new quality is first seen as a dominant feature in the illustrations to Milton's *L'Allegro* and *Il Penseroso* of *c.* 1816–20[46] but is also found in the late Milton illustrations and in a number of the illustrations to Dante, particularly those depicting *Purgatorio* and *Paradiso*. The most outstanding example among the Dante illustrations is perhaps *Beatrice Addressing Dante from the Car* in the Tate Gallery[47] where the sensuous quality of the handling and colouring belies the pessimistic interpretation that, until very recently, used to be attributed to Blake in his treatment of the text.

Blake's own views on the fundamentals of life, and particularly on the predicament of man in his fallen state in the world of physical creation, led him to be highly critical of the accepted orthodoxies of his time and of those writers who, on account of their creative vision, he was tempted to illustrate. Against what he saw as the dead hand of religious and political orthodoxy he set the enlivening force of radical and spiritual energy. It was this quality that he saw in Milton who, he said, 'was a true Poet and of the Devil's party without knowing it'.[48] It is not surprising that one of Blake's most flowing water-colours of his earlier period, despite considerable fading, is that of *Satan in his Original Glory* of *c.* 1805 in the Tate Gallery.[49] This paradox is reflected in Blake's illustrations to Milton; he was also much less censorious of the sensuous idyll of Adam and Eve in the Garden of Eden than Milton himself.

In his last, Melbourne, version of *Satan Watching the Endearments of Adam and Eve* (cat. 1) Blake subtly alters the expression of Satan to stress his tragic status. Otherwise the two late water-colours in the National Gallery of Victoria follow very closely the compositions of their counterparts in the series painted in 1808 for Thomas Butts. The third of the late water-colours done for John Linnell however, *Michael Foretells the Crucifixion*, in the Fitzwilliam Museum, Cambridge, adds a glorious light emanating from the vision of the crucified Christ that suffuses the whole composition. Quite why Blake abandoned this last series is unclear. Unlike the Dante illustrations, which represent every degree of finish from rough sketch to completed, signed work, all three of the 1822 *Paradise Lost* illustrations are finished and there are no traces of any unfinished versions of the other nine compositions in the series. Perhaps at this time Blake was too busy with the *Job* illustrations, which he engraved in exquisite detail with additional marginal decorations and texts not

5 *Minos*

6 *Cerberus*

7 *The Goddess of Fortune*

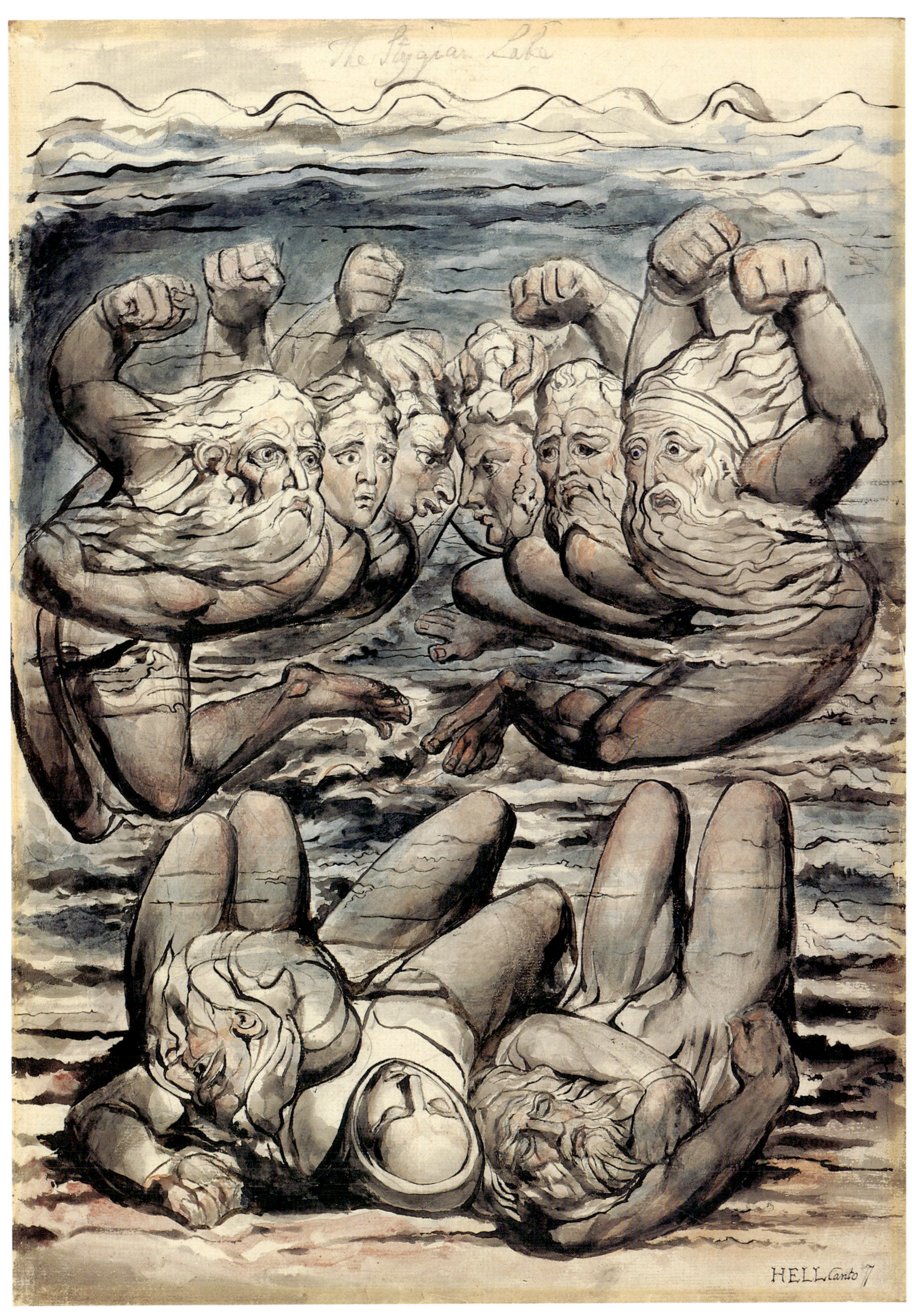

8 *The Stygian Lake, with the Ireful Sinners Fighting*

9 *The Angel Crossing the Styx*

10 *The Angel at the Gate of Dis*

11 *The Hell-Hounds Hunting the Destroyers of Their Own Goods*

12 *Capaneus the Blasphemer*

found in the various water-colour series, or perhaps the new theme of Dante's *Divine Comedy* simply held more attraction for him.

Milton, together with the Bible in the King James translation and Shakespeare, was part of the common heritage of any cultivated person in late eighteenth-century England. Blake therefore had a whole tradition to draw on, and react against. In the case of Dante he stepped outside the English tradition into a world alien both in language and religion, that of Latin Catholicism. Although there are two early drawings of Ugolino,[50] a subject popular among late eighteenth-century artists such as Reynolds and Fuseli, and although the commission to paint eighteen heads of poets for William Hayley's library at Felpham in 1800[51] included, besides Shakespeare, Milton and a number of other English poets (even Hayley's illegitimate son Thomas Alphonso Hayley), a group of foreign poets starting with Homer and, including Dante, running up to the more or less contemporary Klopstock, the large series of illustrations to Dante represented a completely new venture and one that crowned Blake's achievement. The commission was left unfinished and in various stages of completion but even so there are 102 works in the main series, together with sketches and, also unfinished, a set of seven engravings (cat. 50 a–g).

Blake, as a Protestant and, very self-consciously, an Englishman, was critical of an Italian Catholic, and the inscriptions on some of the drawings show him attacking Dante in no uncertain terms: 'Everything in Dante's Comedia shows That for Tyrannical Purposes he has made This World the Foundation of All, & the Goddess Nature Memory is his Inspirer & not Imagination . . .'.[52] In other words, Blake saw Dante's ideas of salvation through the Catholic Church as too much tied to the temporal powers of this world.

He had another basic objection to Dante's *Divine Comedy*: 'Whatever Book is for Vengeance for Sin & whatever Book is Against the Forgiveness of Sins is not of the Father but of Satan the Accuser & Father of Hell'.[53] But it has recently been demonstrated that Blake's condemnation of Dante's ideas of salvation was not as wholesale as was thought in the past.[54] Partly indeed, as in the case of Milton, Blake chose to be more impressed by the creativity of the poet than critical of the elements in the text with which he disagreed. Moreover, it is not necessary to assume that Blake would have applied every aspect of his own thought, as embodied in the personal mythology expressed in his writings, to those elements in the writings of others that paralleled his. Further discussion of the ways in which Blake departs from the text of Milton and Dante will be found in the introductory sections to the two groups of water-colours, and cases where he differs from his texts will be found in the individual catalogue entries.

Like any great work of art, the aesthetic quality of Blake's works transcends any element of criticism that may be embodied in them. Although Blake was an unequal artist, the National Gallery of Victoria is fortunate in owning examples of his work in which his powers are shown at their greatest. Even in the unfinished works, and even in an example where Blake has recourse to verbal labels to demonstrate where he differs from Dante, such as *The Queen of Heaven in Glory* (cat. 38), the quality of the general design and, in particular, the grace of the two main figures represent the aesthetic and sensuous qualities of Blake's late style.

Indeed, the graceful interplay of figures both for the purposes of design and for expressive effect is one of the characteristics of the Dante illustrations. One strand that can be followed in the series as a whole is the relationship between the figures of Dante and Virgil. Sometimes they just stand side by side reacting to the shocking scenes before them with minimal hand gestures, but sometimes the whole of the body is brought into action, as in *Dante Running from the Three Beasts* (cat. 3) and *Minos* (cat. 5), where the two figures are balanced by other charged pairs of figures on the right. The almost balletic interaction of Dante and Virgil is, however, best seen in the examples from the series in the Tate Gallery, as in *The Inscription Over Hell-Gate* and *The Ascent of the Mountain of Purgatory*.[55] A similar vigorous counterpoint of graceful figures is found in *Dante at the Moment of Entering the Fire* (cat. 33).

In contrasted mood is the dynamic force of the figures in *The Stygian Lake, with the Ireful Sinners Fighting* (cat. 8). Similarly vibrant, and helped by their relatively high degree of finish, are the giant figures in *Geryon Conveying Dante and Virgil Down Towards Malebolge* and *Ephialtes and Two Other Titans* (cat. 14, 26), and above all in what is probably the most striking image in the whole series, *Antaeus Setting Down Dante and Virgil in the Last Circle of Hell* (cat. 27). This is an example of where Blake's literal illustrations of Dante's text produce the most startling results, as also, in their horrific way, do the two depictions of *The Schismatics and Sowers of Discord* (cat. 23, 24). A more imaginative approach to the horror implicit in many of Dante's descriptions of the torments of Hell, though one still based largely on Dante's text, can be found in the series of illustrations depicting the punishment of the Thieves (see cat. 19, 20, 21), in particular the appalling transformation of Agnello Brunelleschi into a serpent.

Blake's emphatic use of the figure is partly his own invention, partly based on traditional modes of facial expression, and partly the result of using traditional 'pathos formulae' in which the whole body is turned to narrative use in a manner based on accepted antique models.[56] As Blake himself said, in his annotations to Reynolds's *Discourses*: 'no-one can ever Design till he has learn'd the Language of Art by making many Finishd Copies both of Nature & Art & of whatever comes in his way from Earliest Child hood. The difference between a bad artist & a Good One Is: the Bad Artist Seems to Copy a Great deal. The Good one Really Does Copy a Great deal'.[57] This is not just a question of finding specific sources for Blake's images in the art of his predecessors, for instance the sources found for Blake's famous *Glad Day* (or, as it is more correctly called, *Albion Rose* or *The Dance of Albion*),[58] but of recognizing that there was for artists at the end of the eighteenth century a whole 'Language of Art', as Blake put it, based on the art of the past and

13 *The Symbolic Figure of the Course of Human History Described by Virgil*

14 *Geryon Conveying Dante and Virgil Down Towards Malebolge*

particularly of antiquity, which they could use almost unconsciously to express fundamental ideas.

Blake also used compositional means for varying purposes. The whirlwind effect of *The Angel Crossing the Styx* (cat. 9) parallels that in the famous *Whirlwind of Lovers*, depicting *The Circle of the Lustful; Francesca da Rimini*, in the City Museum and Art Gallery, Birmingham.[59] In a completely different mood the almost abstract outlining in separate zones of the saints in *St Peter Appears to Beatrice and Dante* and *St Peter and St James with Dante and Beatrice* (cat. 36, 37) conveys the remoteness of Heaven from earthly time and space. On a rather different level, the way in which the composition of *The Harlot and the Giant* (cat. 34) parodies that of *Beatrice Addressing Dante from the Car*[60] stresses the condemnation of the church expressed by Blake (following Dante) in the former.

More interesting, perhaps, as an example of Blake's method of working than for revealing his final scheme in his series of Dante illustrations is the way that *Capaneus* (cat. 12) and *Geryon* (cat. 14) match each other as complementary compositions in reverse. These are not consecutive subjects in the series of illustrations but they did occur on successive pages in the large sketchbook in which Blake executed the series. Samuel Palmer, visiting Blake with John Linnell on 9 October 1824:

> found him lame in bed, of a scalded foot (or leg). There, not inactive, though sixty-seven years old, but hard-working on a bed covered with books sat he up like one of the Antique patriarchs, or a dying Michael Angelo. Thus and there was he making in the leaves of a great book (folio) the sublimest design from his (not superior) Dante.[61]

Blake himself seems to have numbered most though not all of the pages and also inscribed most pages with an elaborate system of cross-reference that has not yet been fully disentangled. It is clear that these two water-colours were done on the adjacent pages 43 and 44 and the not quite finished *Geryon* must have evolved as a counterpart to the completed and signed *Capaneus*. Page 45 has still to be traced (some of the water-colours in other collections are stuck down on their mounts and the versi bearing the page numbers are not available for inspection) but page 46 bears another figure composition on the same scale, that showing the giant *Ephialtes and Two Other Titans* (cat. 26). Similarly, two upright compositions of allegorical figures, *The Symbolic Figure of the Course of Human History Described by Virgil* and *The Goddess of Fortune* (cat. 13, 7), fall on the adjacent pages 54 and 55 respectively.

It seems that Blake moved from subject to subject without any particular system, following instead similarities in mood or general type of composition. As a generalization one can however say that he concentrated to begin with on themes from the *Inferno*, from which in any case he chose the majority of his subjects, while the bulk of the subjects from *Paradiso* occur at the end of the book. It was presumably because of his departure from the sequence of the text that he inscribed the pages with the elaborate system of cross-referencing mentioned above.

It is also clear that adjacent pages frequently employ much the same palette; perhaps indeed they were even coloured on the same day. For instance, again concentrating on the works in the National Gallery of Victoria, the same pinks, greys and greens occur on pages 62, 63, 64 and 65 (cat. 9, 25, 29, 15). Of the succeeding pages, number 67 has not been traced but the water-colours on pages 66 and 68, *Lucifer* and *The Devil Carrying the Lucchese Magistrate to the Boiling-Pitch Pool of Corrupt Officials* (cat. 28, 16) are close to each other in palette.

The best of the finished water-colours from the Dante series show Blake's richness of colour combined with the subtlety of his late technique at their finest, close to but even more accomplished than in the late illustrations to *Paradise Lost*. In *The Vestibule of Hell and the Souls Mustering to Cross the Acheron* (cat. 4) both the high finish and the depth of rich colour give expressive force to the scene of the souls about to be transported to Hell. An even higher degree of finish emphasizes the extraordinary effect of *Antaeus Setting Down Dante and Virgil in the Last Circle of Hell* (cat. 27).

However, Blake's technique was also capable of much more subtle effects. In *Ephialtes and Two Other Titans* (cat. 26) it is by light strokes of the pen and the discreet rubbing of the surface of the paper that Blake conveys the falling stones and snow. The chill of the innermost circle of Hell is similarly expressed in the layered forms across the lower half of the composition of *Lucifer* (cat. 28). Blake also used light, vigorous strokes made with the point of the brush to show the energy of the fleeing figures in the background of *Geryon Conveying Dante and Virgil Down Towards Malebolge* and *The Devils Under the Bridge* (cat. 14, 17). Blake used a firmer line, drawn with the point of a brush or by a pen, to depict the rich foliage of *The Lawn with the Kings and Angels* (cat. 31) and, from the illustrations to *Paradise Lost*, *Satan Watching the Endearments of Adam and Eve* (cat. 1).

Besides the strong, expressive colour of such finished water-colours as *The Vestibule of Hell*, *The Stygian Lake* and *Capaneus* (cat. 4, 8, 12), Blake also used the most delicate of colouring in his finished or nearly finished water-colours. Examples are *The Angel at the Gate of Dis* and *Dante at the Moment of Entering the Fire* (cat. 10, 33). Even more delicate are the tentative washes applied by Blake, as just the beginning of his intended colouring, to the last work in the series, *The Queen of Heaven in Glory* (cat. 38).

The summation of Blake's late technique, unfinished but fully evocative in its free handling and light but glowing colouring, is the water-colour of *Dante Adoring Christ* (cat. 35). This is a development, much more positive in mood however, of the famous plate in *Jerusalem* showing Albion before the crucified Jesus.[62] Whatever criticism Blake may have had of Dante, this work is one of the most convincing expressions of faith in art. Using a technique first developed when Blake enjoyed the faith of innocence, its conviction is now all the more profound through being based on experience.

15 *The Necromancers and Augurs*

16 *The Devil Carrying the Lucchese Magistrate to the Boiling-Pitch Pool of Corrupt Officials*

17 *The Devils Under the Bridge*

Notes

1 G. E. Bentley Jr, *Blake Books*, Clarendon Press, Oxford, 1977, pp. 366, 383, 385, 387, 412, Copy X.
2 Vienna, Kunst-Historisches Museum, inv. no. 9040, signed and dated 1655. This was a salutary lesson delivered by Professor Johannes Wilde at the Courtauld Institute of Art in the early 1950s: on being told that cleaning of this portrait had begun to reveal a date, the director of the museum had immediately assumed that it would read 1656, the year of Rembrandt's bankruptcy.
3 See Patrick Trevor Roper, *The World Through Blunted Sight*, Thames & Hudson, London, 1970.
4 See Bentley, *Blake Books*, pp. 364–88.
5 The best survey of Blake's relationship to contemporary events is to be found in D. Erdman, *Blake: Prophet Against Empire*, Princeton University Press, Princeton, NJ, 1954 and subsequent editions.
6 Bentley, *Blake Books*, pp. 205–6. This was to be 'Book the First' of a projected seven! See also Erdman, *Prophet Against Empire* (1977 edn), pp. 152–3.
7 Bentley, *Blake Books*, pp. 166–73.
8 See in particular M. Butlin, 'The Evolution of Blake's Large Colour Prints of 1795', in A. Rosenfeld (ed.), *William Blake: Essays for S. Foster Damon*, Brown University Press, Providence, RI, 1969, pp. 109–16, and R. Essick, *William Blake, Printmaker*, Princeton University Press, Princeton, NJ, 1980, pp. 121–52.
9 For the series see M. Butlin, *The Paintings and Drawings of William Blake*, Yale University Press, London, 1981 (hereafter referred to as Butlin 1981), nos 289–326, all repr., and for the most up-to-date thinking on the problem of Blake's own '1795' dating see Martin Butlin, *Tate Gallery Collections: William Blake 1757–1827*, Tate Gallery, London, 1989.
10 Butlin 1981, nos 387, 441, 468 and 521, repr. pl. 487 and in colour pls 534, 542 and 582.
11 Butlin 1981, nos 651 and 750, repr. pl. 877 and, in colour, pl. 966.
12 G. Keynes, *Blake, Complete Writings*, Oxford University Press, Oxford, 1969, pp. 816–18.
13 G. E. Bentley Jr, 'Thomas Butts: White Collar Maecenas', *PMLA*, vol. LXXI, 1956, pp. 1052–66.
14 Keynes, *Blake, Complete Writings*, pp. 511–13, 520.
15 Reproduced in D. Erdman, *The Illuminated Blake*, Oxford University Press, London, 1975, p. 256.
16 Butlin 1981, no. 368, repr. in colour pl. 346.
17 Keynes, *Blake, Complete Writings*, p. 852; see also M. Paley, *William Blake*, Phaidon, Oxford, 1978, p. 49.
18 G. E. Bentley Jr, *William Blake: Vala or the Four Zoas*, Clarendon Press, Oxford, 1963; C. Magno & D. Erdman (eds), *'The Four Zoas' by William Blake*, Bucknell University Press, Lewisberg, Pa., 1987.
19 Butlin 1981, pp. 317–18, 335–6.
20 Butlin 1981, nos 387 and 446, repr. pls 487 and 520.
21 Butlin 1981, nos 391 and 401, repr. in colour pls 498 and 502.
22 Butlin 1981, nos 51–69, pls 45–61, and in colour pls 177–8.
23 Butlin 1981, no. 244, repr. pls 284–93.
24 An example of the closeness of Blake's *Virgil* wood-engravings to contemporary modes of illustration can be seen by comparing them, and more particularly the preliminary drawings, with Thomas Stothard's small 1 x 1 7/8 in. (2.5 x 4.8 cm) pen and wash drawings illustrating Robert Bloomfield's poem 'The Farmer's Boy' for the *Atlas Almanack*, repr. exhibition catalogue, *British Drawings: Spring Medley 1984*, Anthony Reed, London, and Davis & Longdale, New York, April–June 1984, pp. 25–6, no. 27.
25 Butlin 1981, no. 486, repr. in colour pl. 565.
26 All the series of Blake's illustrations to Milton are listed in Butlin 1981, pp. 373–404, nos 527–46, repr. in colour pls 616–96.
27 L. Parris, 'William Blake's Mr Thomas', *Times Literary Supplement*, 5 December 1968, p. 1390.
28 Reproduced in D. Erdman, *Illuminated Blake*, p. 157; and, for examples issued separately, Butlin 1981, nos 270–1, pl. 370 and, in colour, pl. 341.
29 Butlin 1981, nos 320–22, repr. in colour pls 397–9; for a preliminary drawing see no. 259, repr. pl. 307.
30 Butlin 1981, no. 547, repr. in colour pls 590–5.
31 For the relationship between John Linnell, the 'Ancients' and Blake see G. E. Bentley Jr, *Blake Records*, Clarendon Press, Oxford, 1969, *passim*; and also the individual biographies of these artists: A. Storey, *The Life of John Linnell*, Richard Bentley, London, 1892, vol. I, pp. 147 ff.; A. H. Palmer, *The Life and Letters of Samuel Palmer*, Seeley & Co., London, 1892, pp. 13 ff.; [S. Calvert], *A Memoir of Edward Calvert Artist*, Sampson Low, Marston & Co., London, 1893, pp. 17 ff.; A. M. W. Stirling, *The Richmond Papers*, William Heinemann, London, 1926, pp. 24 ff.
32 See Butlin 1981, pp. 409–35, nos 550–9, repr. pls 733–93, and in colour pls 697–717; and, for the fullest possible treatment, D. Bindman (ed.), *William Blake's Illustrations of the Book of Job* and *Colour Versions of William Blake's Book of Job Designs*, The William Blake Trust, London, 1987, fully illustrated.
33 Butlin 1981, nos 478 and 479, repr. in colour pls 566 and 567.
34 Butlin 1981, no. 544, repr. in colour pls 684–95.
35 For the fullest treatment of Blake's illustrations to *The Grave* see R. Essick & M. Paley, *Robert Blair's 'The Grave' Illustrated by William Blake*, Scolar Press, London, 1982.
36 Butlin 1981, pp. 472–82, nos 649–64; Bentley, *Blake Records*, pp. 215–20, 225–6; and G. E. Bentley Jr, *Blake Records Supplement*, Clarendon Press, Oxford, 1988, pp. 65–8.
37 Butlin 1981, nos 653, 649, 651 and 661, repr. pls 878, 876, 877 and 888.
38 Butlin 1981, nos 803–7; *Ugolino* is no. 805, repr. in colour pl. 970.
39 These were the *Canterbury Pilgrims* and *The Spiritual Form of Nelson* and *of Pitt* (see n. 37) and were nos 280, 279 and 254 in the exhibition; the pages from *Jerusalem* were no. 324.
40 Bentley, *Blake Books*, pp. 224–30.
41 Bentley, *Blake Books*, pp. 306–9.
42 This rumour was based on a passage in the *Revue Britannique*, Paris 1833, 3e série, IV, pp. 183–6, reprinted in M. Wilson, *The Life of William Blake*, rev. edn, Oxford University Press, London, 1971, pp. 384–7; in which see also pp. 267, 268–9, 274, 344–5, 349.
43 Bentley, *Blake Records*, pp. 591, 599. There are however no records of regular payments after 1810; see Bentley, *Blake Records*, p. 578.
44 Bentley, *Blake Records*, pp. 27–8, prints a letter from John Flaxman to William Hayley in which he reports that 'Mr Hawkins a Cornish Gentleman has shewn his taste & liberality in ordering Blake to make several drawings for him, & is so convinced of his uncommon talents that he is now endeavouring to raise a subscription to send him to finish studies in Rome'.
45 Butlin 1981, no. 536, repr. in colour pls 645–56.
46 Butlin 1981, no. 543, repr. in colour pls 672–83.
47 Butlin 1981, no. 812 88, repr. in colour pl. 973.
48 *The Marriage of Heaven and Hell*, c. 1791–93, pl. 6; Keynes, *Blake, Complete Writings*, p. 150. For Blake and Milton see Paley, *William Blake*, pp. 59–65.
49 Butlin 1981, no. 469, repr. pl. 554.
50 Butlin 1981, nos 207 recto and 208, repr. pls 229 and 230.
51 Butlin 1981, no. 343 *1–18*, repr. pls 436–53; *Milton* is no. 343 *11*, pl. 446, and *Dante* no. 343 *4*, pl. 439.

52 *Homer Bearing the Sword, and his Companions*, Fogg Art Museum; Butlin 1981, no. 812 7. Keynes, *Blake, Complete Writings*, p. 785.
53 *The Circles of Hell*, British Museum; Butlin 1981, no. 812 *101*. Keynes, *Blake, Complete Writings*, p. 785.
54 For the 'orthodox' view see A. Roe, *Blake's Illustrations to the Divine Comedy*, Princeton University Press, Princeton, NJ, 1953; for David Fuller's rebuttal of the more extreme of Roe's interpretations see 'Blake and Dante', *Art History*, vol. XI, 1988, pp. 349–73.
55 Butlin 1981, nos 812 *4* and *74*, reproduced in Roe, *Blake's Illustrations to the Divine Comedy*, pls 4 and 74.
56 For pathos 'Pathos Formulae' see in particular B. Lindberg, *William Blake's Illustrations to the Book of Job*, Abö Akademi, Abö, Finland, 1973, pp. 113–22, and J. Warner, *Blake and the Language of Art*, McGill–Queen's University Press, Kingston, Ont., 1984, *passim*; neither examines the series of Dante illustrations.
57 Keynes, *Blake, Complete Writings*, pp. 455–6.
58 A. Blunt, 'Blake's "Glad Day"', *Warburg Journal*, vol. II, 1938, pp. 65–8; further examples of Blake's 'borrowings' from the antique are given in A. Blunt, *The Art of William Blake*, Oxford University Press, London, 1959.
59 Butlin 1981, no. 812 *10*, reproduced in Roe, *Blake's Illustrations to the Divine Comedy*, pl. 10.
60 See n. 47.
61 Palmer, *Life and Letters*, pp. 9–10; Bentley, *Blake Records*, p. 291.
62 Reproduced in Erdman, *Illuminated Blake*, p. 355.

Catalogue 1–38

Blake Water-Colours in the National Gallery of Victoria

Martin Butlin

Abbreviations

Literature abbreviations refer to the select bibliography at the end of this volume. Authors and dates of publication are cited for books; authors, titles and dates for journal articles.

Exhibition abbreviations refer to the following:

1876	*The Works of William Blake*, Burlington Fine Arts Club, London.
1893	Royal Academy, London.
1913–14	*Works by William Blake*, Tate Gallery, London; Whitworth Institute, Manchester; Art Museum, Nottingham Castle; with *David Scott*, National Gallery of Scotland, Edinburgh. October 1913–July 1914. (Separate catalogues, and slightly different contents, at each centre, the first two with detailed entries by Archibald G. B. Russell.)
1957–58	*William Blake 1757–1827*, National Gallery of Victoria, Melbourne. November 1957–February 1958.
1975	*William Blake 1757–1827* (British Council), Kunsthalle, Hamburg, and Städelsches Kunstinstitut, Frankfurt am Main. March–July. (Detailed catalogue entries by David Bindman, introduction by Werner Hofmann.)
1978	*William Blake*, Tate Gallery, London. March–May. (Catalogue by Martin Butlin.)
1979	*The Poetical Circle: Fuseli and the British*, Australian Gallery Directors' Council tour of Australia and New Zealand. April–November. (Catalogue by Peter Tomory.)
1980	*Dante–Virgil–Geryon*. Staatsgalerie Stuttgart. September–November.
1983	*Blake e Dante*, Casa de Dante in Abruzzo, Castello Gizzi, Torre de'Passeri, Pescara.

Measurements are given in centimetres; height precedes width.

Inscriptions are presumed to be by Blake, unless the contrary is stated. The position of the inscription is given by the abbreviations u.l. (upper left), l.r. (lower right), u.c. (upper centre), etc.

Fig. 1 William Blake, *Milton*, *c.* 1800–03. Pen and tempera on canvas, 40.1 x 90.9 cm. The City of Manchester Art Galleries

1–2 Two Illustrations to *Paradise Lost* 1822

Pen and water-colour
Each approx. 51 x 38 cm

Provenance: John Linnell; his heirs, sold Christie's 15 March 1918 (153 and 152 respectively), £787.10.0; bt Martin for the Felton Bequest for presentation to the National Gallery of Victoria.
Felton Bequest 1920 1024/3–1025/3

Exhibitions: Burlington Fine Arts Club 1876 (two out of 212, 213 and 214, each as 'Subject from Milton's "Paradise Lost" ', measurements given as 19¾ x 15¼, 20 x 15¼ and 19¾ x 16 in.); see also individual entries.

Literature. Rossetti in appendix to Gilchrist 1863, p. 212 nos 92 and 91, and 1880, p. 223 nos 112 and 111; Figgis 1925, p. 89; Keynes 1926, pp. 355–9; Peckham, 'Blake, Milton, and Edward Burney' 1950, pp. 107–26; Bentley 1969, p. 275; Pointon 1970, pp. 139–60; Rose, 'Blake's Illustrations' 1970, pp. 40–67; Keynes (1949) 1971, p. 218; Wittreich 1971, pp. 341–2; Bindman 1975, p. 197, repr. pls 98–9; Wittreich 1975, p. 93; Dunbar 1980, pp. 35–43, 56–60; Butlin 1981, pp. 388–9 no. 537; Behrendt 1983, pp. 36–7, 65, 85; Essick 1985, pp. 22–3; Werner 1986, pp. 18, 50–112; Bentley 1988, p. 106.

These are two out of three finished water-colour illustrations to Milton's *Paradise Lost* painted for John Linnell (1792–1882), the young painter who was introduced to Blake by George Cumberland's son George probably in June 1818. Linnell's journal, as copied by A. H. Palmer (Ivimy Papers), notes under 9 May 1822, 'M[r] Blake began copies from his Drawings from Miltons P.L.'. W. M. Rossetti, without giving his reasons, also dates the three water-colours to 1822.

All three water-colours are closely based in design on the corresponding subjects in the set of twelve illustrations to *Paradise Lost* painted on the same scale for Thomas Butts and each dated, with two exceptions, 1808 (Butlin 1981, no. 536). These in their turn were based, with one alteration of subject, on a set of twelve smaller water-colour illustrations to *Paradise Lost* painted for the Reverend Joseph Thomas, six of which were dated 1807 (Butlin 1981, no. 529). Presumably John Linnell commissioned water-colours of all the twelve subjects in the Butts set although, unlike the Dante series (see cat. 3–38), all of the known *Paradise Lost* water-colours are completely finished and there are no further unfinished subjects.

Blake would have known of the long tradition of illustrations to Milton's poems dating back to the late seventeenth century. In particular he would have been aware of his friend Fuseli's Milton Gallery, the series of oil paintings that were exhibited in London and were also engraved. In addition Peckham has demonstrated the influence of Edward Burney's twelve engraved illustrations to *Paradise Lost*, published in 1799 (repr. Peckham 1950 between pp. 114 and 115); both the choice of subjects and certain details of composition are similar. Blake himself had already made a large colour-print of *The House of Death* from *Paradise Lost* in 1795 (Butlin 1981, nos 320, 321 and 322, repr. in colour pls 398, 399 and 400) and as well as his various series of illustrations to *Paradise Lost* he also did eight illustrations to Milton's *Comus* for Thomas in about 1801 (Butlin 1981, no. 527) and eight more for Butts in about 1815 (Butlin 1981, no. 528), six illustrations to *On the Morning of Christ's Nativity* for Thomas in 1809 (Butlin 1981, no. 538) and again for Butts in about 1815 (Butlin 1981, no. 512), twelve illustrations to *L'Allegro* and *Il Penseroso* for Butts *c.* 1816–20 (Butlin 1981, no. 543), and twelve illustrations to *Paradise Regained* for John Linnell, also *c.* 1816–20 (Butlin 1981, no. 544). The only major work by Milton that Blake did not illustrate was *Samson Agonistes*.

At much the same time as Blake's main period of activity illustrating Milton he wrote and printed his own illuminated poem *Milton*, dated 1804 on the title-page but not completed until 1808 or later. He also painted a portrait of Milton (fig. 1) as one of a series of eighteen heads of poets done for the library of his patron William Hayley's house 'The Turret' at Felpham near Chichester in Sussex in about 1800–03 (Butlin 1981, no. 343 *11*, repr. pl. 446). His Visionary Heads include two drawings of *Milton When a Boy* and *Milton When Young*, *Milton's Elder Daughter* and *Milton's Youngest Daughter*, on pages 47, 46, 43 and 44 respectively of the larger Blake–Varley Sketchbook (repr. sale catalogue, Christie's, 21 March 1989, lot 184 (separate publication), pp. 36, 38 and 39), and *Milton's First Wife* on page 96 of the smaller Blake–Varley Sketchbook (Butlin 1981, no. 692 *96* and 97, repr. Butlin 1969).

Blake's attitude to Milton was a critical one. Although he would have been brought up on Milton's poetry (together with the Bible in the King James translation, and Shakespeare—part of the great trilogy of English literature), and admired Milton as a poet, he could not accept his views on sin and salvation. Already in *The Marriage of Heaven and Hell* of 1790–93 he noted that 'The reason Milton wrote in fetters when he wrote of Angels & God, and at liberty when of Devils & Hell, is because he was a true Poet and of the Devil's party without knowing it' (Keynes 1969, p. 150). In the same book, again largely with *Paradise Lost* in mind, Blake wrote, 'But in the Book of Job, Milton's Messiah is call'd Satan' and 'In Milton, the Father is Destiny, the Son a Ratio of the five senses, & the Holy-ghost Vacuum!' (Keynes 1969, p. 150). In 1825, closer in time to the *Paradise Lost* illustrations painted for John Linnell (now in the National Gallery of Victoria), Henry Crabb Robinson reported conversations with Blake in which the latter discussed both Dante and Milton, again in a critical and paradoxical manner; these are quoted in the introduction to cat. 3–38. On the whole, however, Blake's illustrations to *Paradise Lost* are relatively straightforward, although Satan is treated as a tragic hero rather than as a purely negative force, as in *Satan Watching the Endearments of Adam and Eve* (cat. 1). For comments on the individual designs in the National Gallery of Victoria see the catalogue entries that follow.

1 *Satan Watching the Endearments of Adam and Eve*

Pen and water-colour over pencil
51.4 x 39.3 cm, irregular; within framing line, also irregular, 51.5 x 39 cm; on trimmed paper, 51.8 x 39.7 cm
Signed 'WBlake inv' l.r.
Felton Bequest 1920 1025/3

Exh.: Burlington Fine Arts Club 1876 (212); Melbourne 1957–58 (78); Tate Gallery 1978 (228, repr.); *Poetical Circle* Australia and New Zealand 1979 (58, repr.).

Lit.: Collins Baker & Wark 1957, p. 19; Beer 1968, pp. 195, 257; Grant in Rosenfeld 1969, p. 365; Pointon 1970, pp. 147–8, 262; Taylor 1971, pp. 66–7; Wilton, 'Blake and the Antique' 1976, p. 193; Bindman 1977, p. 190; Paley 1978, p. 63; Paley in Essick & Pearce 1978, p. 178; Dunbar 1980, pp. 56–60, 196, repr. pl. 29; Butlin 1981, p. 389 no. 537 *1*, repr. in colour pl. 657; Behrendt 1983, pp. 144–8; Werner 1986, pp. 70–3, repr. pl. 41.

Paradise Lost IV, 325–535. Adam and Eve sit reclining on a 'soft downy bank damasked with flow'rs', 'Imparadised in one another's arms'. Milton lists a variety of flowers, although Blake seems to confine these to roses and lilies. Adam plucks a lily, Eve a rose. Satan, entwined by the Serpent, a significant detail not in Milton's original text, hovers above them. He looks down upon Adam and Eve and her gaze seems to be directed at Satan rather than at Adam. The sun rises or sets (according to which interpreter one follows) on the right, while the waxing or waning moon is seen on the left.

Most critics equate the Paradise of Milton's poem with, in this scene, Blake's Beulah, a state of sensuous bliss that can lead on to Eden or Paradise but from which one can also fall. Behrendt sees the group of Satan and the Serpent as a parody of that of the traditional group of Adam and Eve which, as he shows, is close to the conventional depiction of such an artist as Stephen Rigaud, who illustrated an edition of Milton published in 1801 (Behrendt 1983, p. 146, repr. fig. 46).

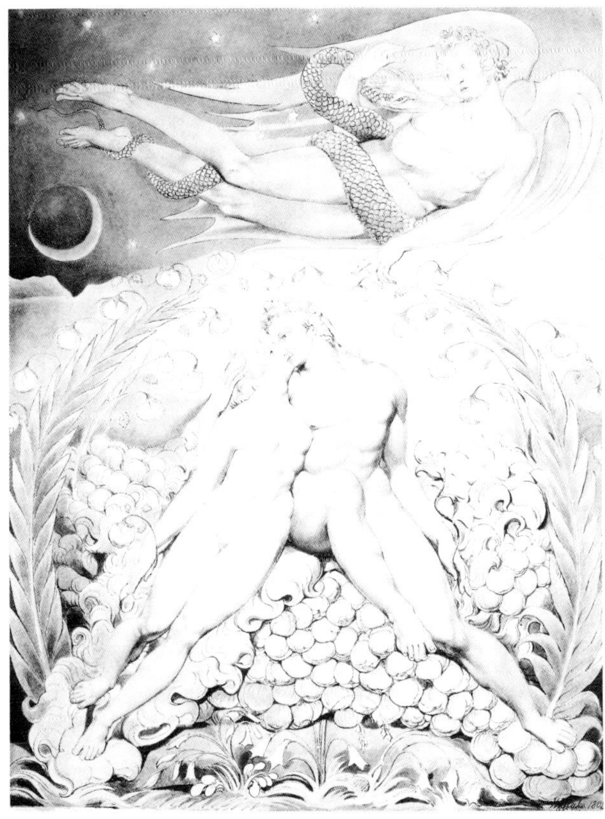

Fig. 2 William Blake, *Satan Watching the Endearments of Adam and Eve*, 1808. Pen and water-colour, 50.7 x 38.2 cm. The Museum of Fine Arts, Boston. Gift by subscription, 1890

Fig. 3 William Blake, *Satan Watching the Endearments of Adam and Eve*, 1807. Pen and water-colour, 25.8 x 21.3 cm. The Henry E. Huntington Library and Art Gallery, San Marino, California

Fig. 4 William Blake, *Satan Watching the Endearments of Adam and Eve*, 1806. Pen and water-colour, 26.7 x 20 cm. The Fogg Art Museum, Harvard University, Cambridge, Massachusetts. Bequest of Grenville L. Winthrop

In this case the Linnell water-colour is the last in an evolution of no fewer than four water-colours; there are also two related pencil drawings. The composition is close to that in the preceding water-colour (fig. 2) executed for Thomas Butts in 1808 (Museum of Fine Arts, Boston; Butlin 1981, no. 536 *4*, repr. in colour pl. 648); in the Melbourne water-colour the details of the flowers and foliage are done in a more painterly way, the stars in the sky fall onto Satan's legs as well as onto his wings, and Satan appears to gaze more directly at Eve. The differences between the large Butts water-colour and that painted for the Reverend Joseph Thomas in 1807 (fig. 3, Huntington Library and Art Gallery, San Marino, California; Butlin 1981, no. 529 *5*, repr. in colour pl. 636) are more significant. Not only is the Thomas water-colour smaller but Satan, entwined by the Serpent, is shown hovering in the opposite direction, his gaze concentrating on the Serpent; Eve is totally taken up with Adam, and indeed it would have been impossible for her eyes to meet those of Satan. In addition the positions of the sun and the moon are shown the other way round so that the moon, less suitably, is on the same side of the composition as Adam, the sun on that of Eve.

In the Thomas water-colour Adam's legs are, rather awkwardly, crossed and the foliage is more ethereal, less symmetrical. In the case of this particular subject there is a still earlier water-colour version (fig. 4), that dated 1806 and now in the Fogg Art Museum, Harvard University, Cambridge, Massachusetts (Butlin 1981, no. 531, repr. in colour pl. 644); this may also have belonged to Thomas Butts. The size is approximately the same as the version painted for Thomas but the Serpent is shown at the bottom of the composition behind Eve's feet and with one of Adam's feet resting upon its coils. Satan hovers above, his hands to his head, gazing down on the pair with a far more agonized expression than in the other water-colours. The bower in which Adam and Eve are seated is much more open and there are suggestions of an extensive landscape behind. Neither sun nor moon is shown. In this version Eve's ankles are crossed while Adam's legs are in a similar position to that in the large Butts and Linnell versions. Of the two pencil drawings one shows only Adam and Eve in their bower, much as in the earliest, 1806, water-colour (Sir Geoffrey Keynes

Collection, Fitzwilliam Museum, Cambridge; Butlin 1981, no. 532, repr. pl. 724). The other drawing (in the British Museum; Butlin 1981, no. 533, repr. pl. 723) shows Adam and Eve in the bower, with Adam's legs as in the 1806 water-colour, whereas Eve's ankles are no longer crossed and are placed more as in the 1807 and later water-colours. Satan hovers above, his body not yet twisted as in the later versions, although he appears to be looking into the eyes of the Serpent whose forms, embracing him, are barely suggested. The sun is shown on the right. This drawing therefore has elements of all stages in the evolution of the composition but was probably executed between the 1806 and 1807 water-colours.

2 *The Creation of Eve*

Pen and water-colour over pencil
50.2 x 40.4 cm; within framing line, irregular, 50.2 x 40.4 cm; on trimmed paper, 50.4 x 40.7 cm
Felton Bequest 1920 1024/3

Exh.: Burlington Fine Arts Club 1876 (213); Tate Gallery (51), Manchester (2), Nottingham (2) and Edinburgh (2) 1913–14; Melbourne 1957–58 (79); Tate Gallery 1978 (229, repr.).

Lit.: Wicksteed 1924, p. 288; Blunt, 'Blake's Pictorial Imagination' 1943, p. 208; Collins Baker & Wark 1957, p. 22; Nanavutty in Sola Pinto 1957, pp. 186–7; Blunt 1959, pp. 30–1; Pointon 1970, pp. 143–4, 262; Hagstrum in Paley & Phillips 1973, p. 137; Bindman 1977, pp. 188–91; Paley 1978, p. 63; Dunbar 1980, pp. 72–5, 197, repr. pl. 38; Butlin 1981, p. 389 no. 537 2, repr. in colour pl. 658; Behrendt 1983, pp. 157–60; Essick 1985, p. 45; Werner 1986, pp. 83–6, repr. pl. 42.

Paradise Lost VIII, 452–77. Adam recalls the creation of Eve out of his side: 'Mine eyes he closed, but open left the cell / Of fancy, my internal sight'. The Creator is shown, as in Milton's text, as Christ rather than God the Father. However, whereas in Milton the Creation is described in great physical detail, including the removal of one of Adam's ribs (streaming with his blood) to be formed into Eve, Blake, taking his cue from the fact that the scene is described by Adam from memory, shows it in a much more ethereal manner. The incident is set under a visionary night sky with crescent moon above. Eve is seen as the prefiguration of the Virgin Mary, her hands held in prayer before her.

Blake places Adam on an enormous leaf which, as in several of the other *Paradise Lost* scenes, suggests that element of material, vegetative nature that was to contribute towards the Fall. The trees behind have been identified as oaks, also associated by Blake with the material world. Again, the scene has been equated with Blake's Beulah: 'A soft Moony Universe, feminine, lovely, / Pure, mild & Gentle, given in Mercy to those who sleep . . . ' (*Vala or the Four Zoas*, written 1796–*c.* 1807; Keynes 1969, p. 266). In Blake's own mythology the creation of the first woman was a stage in the Fall: when Enitharmon separates off from Los as his emanation, 'All Eternity shudder'd at sight / Of the first female now separate' (*The First Book of Urizen*, 1794; Keynes 1969, p. 231). However the creation of woman was also a step

Fig. 5 William Blake, *The Creation of Eve*, 1808. Pen and water-colour, 50 x 40 cm. The Museum of Fine Arts, Boston. Gift by subscription, 1890

Fig. 6 William Blake, *The Creation of Eve*, 1807. Pen and water-colour, 25.3 x 20.8 cm. The Henry E. Huntington Library and Art Gallery, San Marino, California

18 *The Devils Setting Out with Dante and Virgil*

19 *The Thieves and the Serpents*

towards the redemption of man, and in his later poem *Jerusalem*, 1804–*c.* 1820, Blake wrote 'But when Man sleeps in Beulah, the Saviour in Mercy takes / Contraction's Limit, and of the Limit he forms Woman, That / Himself may in process of time be born Man to redeem' (Keynes 1969, p. 670). Blake may also have had in mind Olohon, the emanation of Milton in Blake's poem of that title (1804–*c.* 1808).

The composition of this final Linnell version of the subject is close to that painted in 1808 for Thomas Butts (fig. 5, Museum of Fine Arts, Boston; Butlin 1981, no. 536 8, repr. in colour pl. 652), although Christ's raised arm has been made somewhat thicker by a pentimento to the upper outline. A greater area of the foreground detail, and that of the wood behind, is executed in water colour washes rather than in pen, and in general the water colour is much more painterly and rich in texture; the contrast between the two versions is far stronger than that in the equivalent versions of *Satan Watching the Endearments of Adam and Eve*. In both of these versions the figures are more monumental than in the smaller water-colour painted in 1807 for the Reverend Joseph Thomas (fig. 6, Huntington Library and Art Gallery, San Marino, California; Butlin 1981, no. 529 8, repr. in colour pl. 639). In the Thomas water-colour the wood behind is shown as an undefined mass without detailed drawing, and dips in the centre rather than rising to reinforce the effect of the figure composition. On the other hand, there is slightly more detail in the foreground of the earlier version.

There is also a pencil drawing (British Museum; Butlin 1981, no. 535, repr. pl. 727). In this it appears that Adam is lying with his back towards the viewer, although this is not altogether certain, and Christ is creating Eve with either both arms or, perhaps significantly, his left arm; this has been seen as a symbol of distorted or rational creation rather than creative energy. The drawing presumably preceded the first, 1807, water-colour. Blake also painted a water-colour of *The Creation of Eve: 'And she shall be called Woman'* in *c.* 1803–05 as one of his series of water-colour illustrations to the Bible (Metropolitan Museum of Art, New York; Butlin 1981, no. 435, repr. in colour pl. 512); here the treatment is completely different although Adam is again shown lying on an enormous leaf.

3–38 Thirty-Six Illustrations to Dante's *Divine Comedy* 1824–27

Water-colour, usually with pen and/or pencil
Each approx. 37.2 x 53.7 cm or vice versa
Each watermarked: WELGAR 1796 or WE

Provenance: John Linnell; his heirs, sold Christie's 15 March 1918 (148) £7665; bt Martin for the National Art-Collections Fund; thirty-six designs bt Felton Bequest for presentation to the National Gallery of Victoria.
Felton Bequest 1920 988/3 1023/3

Literature: 'William Blake', Obituary, *Literary Gazette* 18 August 1827, p. 541; Gilchrist 1863, I, pp. 332, 334, 342; Palmer 1892, pp. 9–10; *National Art-Collections Fund Sixteenth Annual Report 1919*, London, 1920, pp. 40–4; Keynes 1921, pp. 182–5; Binyon 1922, pp. 25–8; Damon 1924, pp. 218–20; Roe 1953, series repr.; A. Blunt, review of Roe 1953, *Burlington Magazine* XCVI, 1954, p. 389; Keynes 1969, pp. 785, 869, 873, 876–7, 879; Blunt 1959, pp. 87–91; Hoff 1961, repr.; Burke, 'The Eidetic and the Borrowed Image' 1964, pp. 121–4; Keynes 1968, pp. 152, 156, 160–2, 164; Raine 1968, I, p. 423 n. 14; Beer 1969, pp. 274–81; Bentley 1969, pp. 290–1, 313, 315–16, 333, 338–9, 349–50, 403–9, 414, 417, 475, 527, 543, 589–90, 604; Keynes (1949) 1971, pp. 212, 224–8; Todd 1971, p. 146; Bindman 1977, pp. 216–19; Paley 1978, pp. 71–3; Klonsky 1980, series repr.; Butlin 1981, p. 554; Gizzi 1983, series repr.; Bentley 1988, pp. 89, 97, 98, 110–12, 114, 121, 123, 125; Fuller, 'Blake and Dante' 1988, pp. 349–73.

Blake's illustrations to Dante's *Divine Comedy* were commissioned by John Linnell. Blake began work on the series in the autumn of 1824 and it was planned to engrave the series, but the project was interrupted by Blake's death on 12 August 1827, only seven plates having been begun (see cat. 21 and, for the engravings themselves, cat. 50 a–g). The complete series consists of 102 drawings all of the same size—though some are vertical and some horizontal—in varying degrees of completion, most including water-colour; thirty-six are in the National Gallery of Victoria. In addition there are a number of related pencil sketches.

Blake's friend, and John Linnell's son-in-law, the painter Samuel Palmer (1805–81) described the circumstances of at least part of Blake's activity on the series in an account, perhaps written later, transcribed by A. H. Palmer in his life of his father:

> On Saturday, 9th October, 1824, Mr. Linnell called and went with me to Mr. Blake. We found him lame in bed, of a scalded foot (or leg). There, not inactive, though [*almost*] sixty-seven years old, but hard-working on a bed covered with books sat he up like one of the Antique patriarchs, or a dying Michael Angelo. Thus and there was he making in the leaves of a great book (folio) the sublimest design from his (not superior) Dante. He said he began them with fear and trembling. I said 'O! I have enough of fear and trembling'. 'Then', said he, 'you'll do'. He designed them (100 I think) during a fortnight's illness in bed!

However, A. H. Palmer himself doubted the date, partly because he could find no contemporary confirmation of this in Linnell's journal for October 1824 (see Bentley 1969, p. 291 nn. 1 and 3). Nevertheless, the precision of the date suggests that it could well be true, despite the fact that there is no recorded payment by John Linnell specifically for the Dante illustrations until 21 December 1825 when he paid £3 'to M[r] Blake on acc[t] of Dante' (Bentley 1969, p. 589). According to Alexander Gilchrist, Linnell continued to pay Blake as he had when Blake was working on the engravings to *The Book of Job* (see cat. 49 a–v): 'The agreement between the two friends as to the *Dante* was, that Mr. Linnell should go on paying Blake 2*L*. or 3*L*. a week, as he wanted money, Blake doing as little or as much as he liked in return'. In the second half of 1824 and 1825 Linnell

20 *Vanni Fucci 'Making Figs' Against God*

was making frequent payments to Blake for his work on *The Book of Job* and these might well have covered Blake's initial work on the Dante illustrations as well.

It is unlikely that Blake did more than the preliminary pencil drawing for his designs while confined to bed, and indeed the fact that the works are in all stages of completion, from rough sketch to finished and signed water-colours, suggests that he continued to work on the designs themselves, as well as beginning the engravings, right up to the time of his death.

What is clear, however, is that Blake's work was done while the designs were still bound up in the 'great book (folio)'. Examination of the designs as they are now distributed among various collections shows that three of the four edges of each sheet of paper have been darkened by the dirt of ages, while one of the long sides is clean where it has been cut from the book. From an examination of these edges, and from what seem to be Blake's original page numbers inscribed on nearly all the sheets, it also seems that, although Blake did most of his designs starting from one end of the book on the right-hand page of each opening, some were done on the reverse sides of the sheets. The volume must have been broken up by 1893, when a number of the designs were exhibited separately at the Royal Academy.

As bound up, each design occupied half of a complete sheet of paper bearing two watermarks, one reading 'WELGAR 1796', the other showing a fleur-de-lis design incorporating the initials 'WE'. Some of the designs have rough drawings, apparently for other designs in the series, on the back, and most also bear inscriptions in Blake's hand, including not only the page numbers referred to above but also a complex system of cross-references in some such form as 'No. 2 next at p 6' at the top edge of the paper, with the same information, erased, being given in the centre of the sheet. The number on such a sheet is different, in the case quoted being '4'. The sense of these inscriptions has been shown by Miss Mary Laing to mean that this design, although on page 4, is in fact number 2 and that the next number, 3, is on page 6. In this particular case this is not true, number 3 (cat. 27) actually being on page 2, but on the whole the cross-references tie up; the exceptions are a few of the very first numbers, and one or two cases where Blake has altered the page reference later (as on cat. 13).

It has not as yet been possible to work out exactly why Blake chose such a complicated system of numbers and no logic can be found in either sequence. Some designs are stuck down, so that not every inscription is known but, given those that have been transcribed, one can say that all the numbers, as in 'No. 2 . . . ', up to twenty-three, are subjects from the *Inferno* and that all the known page numbers up to twenty are subjects from the *Inferno*; in addition, all the known page numbers up to eleven are finished designs, suggesting that Blake began by finishing each design in his volume as he went along, later working them out as the fancy took him, wherever they might occur in the book. However, the incidence of subjects from Hell at the beginning of both numerical systems may have a simpler explanation in that, of the 102 surviving designs, seventy-two illustrate the *Inferno*, twenty *Purgatorio* and ten *Paradiso*; all the engraved subjects come from the *Inferno*. There is no evidence of how many designs were planned; clearly the *Inferno* held the most interest for Blake.

Drawn on the same paper, and probably bound into the same volume, were five illustrations to *The Book of Enoch*, all now in the National Gallery of Art, Washington, DC (Lessing J. Rosenwald Collection). One of these (Butlin 1981, no. 827 *3*) bears on the back one of the cross-reference inscriptions of the kind found on most of the Dante designs, while one of the Dante designs, *The Circle of the Gluttons, with Cerberus*, in the Fogg Art Museum, Harvard University, Cambridge, Massachusetts (Butlin 1981, no. 812 *11*) is inscribed on the back with two references to 'Enoch'. The *Enoch* drawings are clearly also late works, close in style to the least finished of the Dante designs.

The diarist Henry Crabb Robinson (1775–1867) also visited Blake while he was working on the Dante illustrations, on 17 December 1825, and his account shows that Blake was using H. F. Cary's translation of the *Divine Comedy*: 'I found him at work on Dante—The book (Cary) and his sketches both before him—He shewed me his designs, of which I have nothing to say but that they evince a power of grouping & of throw^g^ grace & interest over conceptions most monstrous & disgusting which I sho^d^ not have anticipated ' (Bentley 1969, pp. 315–16). However, Gilchrist suggests that Blake also studied to read Dante in the original:

> With characteristic fervour and activity of intellect, he, at sixty-seven years of age, applied himself to learning Italian, in order to read his author in the original. Helped by such command of Latin as he had, he taught himself the language in a few weeks; sufficiently, that is, to comprehend that difficult author substantially, if not grammatically: just as, earlier in life, he had taught himself something of Latin, French, and even Greek. (Gilchrist 1907, p. 351)

Indeed, one of the designs, *The Inscription Over Hell-Gate* in the Tate Gallery (Butlin 1981, no. 812 *4*), shows Blake improvising his own Italian inscription and translation: instead of Dante's '*Lasciate ogni speranza voi ch'entrate*' Blake has written '*Lasciate ogni speranza voi che inentrate*' (the last word is obscure but it is definitely different from Dante's original), translating this as 'Leave every hope you who in enter'.

Crabb Robinson continues his account of his visit to Blake with a record of their conversation about Dante:

> Our conversation began ab^t^ Dante[.] 'He was an atheist—A mere politician busied ab^t^ this world as Milton was till in his old age he returned back to God whom he had had in his childhood—' I tried to get out from B: that he meant this charge only in a higher sense And not using the word Atheism in its popular meaning[,] But he wo^d^ not allow this . . . From this subject we passed over to that of good &

21 *The Six-Footed Serpent Attacking Agnello dei Brunelleschi*

evil on which he repeatedly [*made*] his former assertions more decidedly—He allowed indeed that there is error mistake &c and if these be evil—Then there is evil but these are only negations—Nor would he admit that any [knowld[g] (?) of *del*] education sho[d] be attempted except that of cultivation of the imagination & fine arts—'What are called the vices in the natural world, are the highest sublimities in the spiritual world[.'] . . . And when I again remarked that this doctrine puts an end to all exertion or even wish to change anything He had no reply—We spoke of the Devil And I observed that when a child I thought the Manichaean doctrine or that of two principles a rational one. He assented to this and in confirmation asserted that he did not believe in the *omnipotence* of God—The language of the Bible on that subject is only poetical or allegorical[.] Yet soon after he denied that the natural world is any thing. It is all nothing and Satan's empire is the empire of nothing[.]

He reverted soon to his favourite expression [visions *del*] my visions—[']I saw Milton in Imagination And he told me to beware of being misled by his Paradise Lost[.] In particular he wished me to shew the falsehood of his doctrine that the pleasures of *sex* arose from the fall—The fall could not produce any pleasure[.'] I answered the fall produced a state of *evil* in which there was a mixture of good or pleasure. And in that Sense the fall may be said to produce the pleasure—But he replied that the fall produced only generation & death[.] And then he went off upon a rambling state of a Union of Sexes in Man as in God—an androgynous state in which I could not follow him—As he spoke of Milton's appear[g] to him—I asked whether he resembled the prints of him—He answered—[']All[.']—[']Of what age did he appear to be[?'] [']Various ages—Sometimes a very old man[.'] he spoke of M. as being at one time—A sort of classical Atheist—And of Dante as being now with God—

Of the faculty of Vision he spoke as One he had had from early infancy—He thinks all men partake of it—but it is lost by not being cultiv[d]. And he eagerly assented to a remark I made that all men have all faculties to a greater or less degree— (Bentley 1969, pp. 316–17)

On a visit to Blake a week earlier, Crabb Robinson had recorded Blake's statement that '*Dante* saw Devils where I see none—I see only good . . . '. Such contemporary accounts, and Blake's practice when illustrating other authors, suggests that Blake's Dante designs are not just direct illustrations but also incorporate his own ideas, interpretations and criticism of Dante's meaning. The degree of this reinterpretation has, however, been disputed. Albert S. Roe, in his pioneering book of 1953, observes parallels with Blake's own imagery and personal mythology in nearly every design. Roe sees Blake as replacing Dante's orthodox trilogy of Hell, Purgatory and Paradise with a more complex four-fold system in which the path of salvation led from Ulro through Generation to Beulah; this last was a state of relaxation from which one might either pass on to the highest state, Eden, or fall back into Ulro. According to Roe, Dante, as he portrays himself as the protagonist of the *Divine Comedy*, never reached the true salvation of Eden but chose a mistaken, materialist conception in Paradise. Dante, clothed in red, and Virgil, clothed in blue, are equated with two of Blake's four Zoas, Luvah and Los, respectively representing feeling and imagination, the two qualities of the creative artist. Kathleen Raine has glossed this by pointing out that Swedenborg, whose teachings were certainly known to Blake, associated red with love and blue with wisdom. Virgil is not allowed to follow Dante into Purgatory and Paradise—presumably at least one reason for Dante's fall from grace.

David Fuller, on the other hand, in his article on 'Blake and Dante' in *Art History* 1988, holds that Roe goes much too far in his assessment of Blake as criticizing Dante in the designs. He sees most of the designs as direct illustrations to the text, sometimes glossed with allusions to the Bible. Taking his cue from the inscriptions on certain of the designs, he does however find criticism of Dante, in particular over Dante's respect for antiquity, his respect for kingship, his stress on the Crucifixion as atonement rather than as an act of love and unconditional forgiveness, and his introduction of an erotic element in the relationship between Dante and Beatrice. He accepts that there are critical elements in—from among the designs at Melbourne—nos 16 and 99 (cat. 7 and 38); other designs with critical texts are *Homer Bearing the Sword and his Companions* in the Fogg Art Museum (Butlin 1981, no. 812 7) and *The Circles of Hell* in the British Museum (Butlin 1981, no. 812 *101*). Further designs held by Roe to be critical of Dante, such as the Tate Gallery's *Beatrice Addressing Dante from the Car* (Butlin 1981, no. 812 88), he sees as showing a positive acceptance of Dante's ideas on salvation. Additional examples of the differing interpretations, embodied in particular by Roe and Fuller, can be found in the entries on the individual designs that follow.

3 *Dante Running from the Three Beasts*

Pen, ink and water-colour over pencil
37 x 52.8 cm
Inscr. 'HELL Canto I WB' in ink l.l. and 'LAGO/de Cuor' in water l.l.; and on reverse in pencil, with page held upright, '4' u.r., 'No. 2 next at p 6' u.c. and the same, erased, in the centre
Watermark: WELGAR 1796
Felton Bequest 1920 988/3

Exh.: Melbourne 1957–58 (42); Hamburg and Frankfurt 1975 (206, repr.).

Lit.: Rossetti in Gilchrist 1863, p. 216 no. 101 a, and 1880, p. 227 no. 123a; Roe 1953, pp. 47–50 no. 1, repr.; Hoff 1961, p. 5, repr. pl. 1 and in colour on the cover; Burke, 'The Eidetic and the Borrowed Image' 1964, p. 123, repr. pl. 101 (reprinted in Essick 1973, pp. 286–7, repr. pl. 92); Klonsky 1980, pp. 25, 137, repr. in colour; Butlin 1981, p. 555 no. 812 *1*; Gizzi

22 *Ulysses and Diomed Swathed in the Same Flame*

23 *The Schismatics and Sowers of Discord: Mahomet*

24 *The Schismatics and Sowers of Discord: Mosca de' Lamberti and Bertrand de Born*

1983, p. 79, repr.; Boime 1987, pp. 29–30, 148, 151; Fuller, 'Blake and Dante' 1988, pp. 353, 371 n. 7.

Inferno I, 1–90. Dante, in the middle of the journey through life, comes to a dark wood and loses his way. After a night full of fear he sets out again at dawn but is distracted from his way by a leopard (representing for Dante worldly pleasure or Florence), a lion (pride, or the Royal House of France) and a wolf (avarice or the Papal See). Fleeing from these he encounters Virgil.

The sheet of water shown in Blake's water-colour does not appear in Dante's text but seems to have been suggested by Dante's reference to the fear that had occupied 'the lake of my heart' ('*lago del cor*') during the night, the quotation Blake inscribed in the water. Otherwise, according to Fuller, this is a direct illustration to Dante's text. Roe, however, followed by Klonsky, reads a considerable amount of Blake's own imagery into the design. Dante is the fallen Albion or man, he is lost in the forest of materialism, and he flees from the three-fold Accusers of the Moral Law (see Blake's *Jerusalem*, pl. 93); the leopard symbolizes ravening selfhood, the lion uncontrolled dependence upon reason, and the she-wolf materialism. Virgil is equated with Blake's character Los, partly because he is clad in blue, and with Christ because his arms are outstretched. The water behind is the Sea of Ulro. All this Fuller regards as over-interpretation.

The wolf was probably based on engravings of the wolf on the Capitoline Hill in Rome and, as Burke suggests, the lion may have been based on an antique sculpture in the Townley collection which could already be seen in the British Museum (see Burke 1964, pls 103–5, and 1973, pls 93–6).

4 *The Vestibule of Hell and the Souls Mustering to Cross the Acheron*

Ink and water-colour over pencil
52. 7 x 37.1 cm
Inscr. 'HELL Canto 3 WB' in ink l.l.; and on reverse in pencil, '7' u.r., 'No 30 next at p 64' u.c. and the same, erased, in centre
Watermark: WELGAR 1796
Felton Bequest 1920 989/3

Exh.: RA 1893 (2); Melbourne 1957–58 (43); Tate Gallery 1978 (320, repr.).

Lit.: Rossetti in Gilchrist 1863, p. 216 no. 101e, and 1880, p. 227 no. 123e; Roe 1953, pp. 54–5 no. 5, repr.; Hoff 1961, pp. 2, 4 n. 28, 6, repr. pl. 2; Klonsky 1980, pp. 29, 138, repr. in colour pl. 5; Butlin 1981, p. 557 no. 812 5; Gizzi 1983, p. 83, repr.; Fuller, 'Blake and Dante' 1988, pp. 352, 371 n. 7, repr. pl. 4.

Inferno III, 22–83. Dante, led by Virgil, has entered the Vestibule of Hell through the great gate inscribed 'abandon Hope all ye that enter here' (Blake illustrated this in the previous design, now in the Tate Gallery; Butlin 1981, no. 812 *4*). He reaches the shores of the river Acheron where the souls of those who lived without blame and without praise wait to be ferried across in Charon's bark; above them mourn the choir of angels who neither rebelled nor were faithful to God, and who were chased from Heaven but refused by Hell. Dante describes the ensign with a banner leading the souls, and the hornets and wasps that attack them. Dante recognizes 'the shadow of him who from cowardice made the great refusal', probably Pope Celestine V, who was elected Pope in 1294 but resigned nine months later in favour of Boniface VIII.

According to Dante the figures are naked but Blake has clothed them in rich garments to suggest worldly rank and power. The female figure on the left resembles his depictions of the Whore of Babylon in a water-colour of 1809 (British Museum, Butlin 1981, no. 523, pl. 584) and another water-colour from the Dante series also in Melbourne (cat. 34). Otherwise the water-colour is a direct illustration of Dante's text.

5 *Minos*

Pen and water-colour over pencil and black chalk
37.4 x 52.8 cm
Inscr. 'HELL Canto 5/WB' l.r. in ink; and on reverse in pencil, with paper held as an upright, '10' u.r., 'No. 16 next at p. 44' u.c. and the same, erased, in centre
Watermark: WELGAR 1796
Felton Bequest 1920 990/3

Exh.: RA 1893 (3); Melbourne 1957–58 (44).

Lit.: Rossetti in Gilchrist 1863, p. 216 no. 101g, and 1880, p. 228 no. 123g; Roe 1953, pp. 61–3 no. 9, repr.; Hoff 1961, pp. 2, 3 n. 24, 7, repr. pl. 3; Klonsky 1980, pp. 33, 139, repr. in colour pl. 9; Butlin 1981, pp. 558–9 no. 812 9; Gizzi 1983, p. 87, repr. and in colour; Fuller, 'Blake and Dante' 1988, p. 371 n. 7.

Inferno V, 1–24. Dante and Virgil have descended from the first circle of Hell down into the second, that of the Carnal Sinners. Minos charges the souls as they appear according to how they clasp each other, sending them to a suitable punishment. He warns Dante to beware where he is entering and also whom he trusts; Virgil tells Minos not to impede their progress.

There is a free sketch for the composition in the British Museum (Butlin 1981, no. 813 verso, pl. 1061), and what appears to be a much closer sketch, trimmed at the top and on both sides and damaged through immersion in water and having had other drawings stuck to it, in a private collection (Butlin 1981, no. 814 recto, pl. 1063).

6 *Cerberus*

Pen, ink and water-colour over pencil and black chalk
37.3 x 52.7 cm
Inscr. 'HELL Canto 6' in ink over pencil l.r.; and on reverse in pencil, with paper held as an upright, '19' u.r. and 'Pg Canto 25' along right-hand edge
Watermark: WELGAR 1796
Felton Bequest 1920 991/3

Exh.: ? RA 1893 (5); Melbourne 1957–58 (45); Hamburg and Frankfurt 1975 (207, repr.).

Lit.: Rossetti in Gilchrist 1863, p. 217 no. 101m, and 1880, p. 228 no. 123m; Roe 1953, p. 68 no. 13, repr.; Hoff 1961, p. 8, repr. pl. 4; Klonsky 1980, pp. 37, 140, repr. in colour pl. 13; Butlin 1981, p. 560 no. 812 *13*; Gizzi 1983, p. 91, repr.; Fuller, 'Blake and Dante' 1988, p. 371 n. 7.

25 *The Pit of Disease: Gianni Schicchi and Myrrha*

Inferno VI, 13–33. This is one of two water-colours showing Cerberus, the other being in the Tate Gallery (Butlin 1981, no. 812 *12*); the monster also appears in the background of *The Circle of the Gluttons with Cerberus* in the Fogg Art Museum (Butlin 1981, no. 812 *11*). A sketch formerly in the collection of the late Hugo Schwab (Butlin 1981, no. 818 verso, pl. 1068) is closest to the Melbourne version which, Roe suggests, was done before that in the Tate Gallery but abandoned because it failed to show Cerberus in a sufficiently formidable guise. However, the Melbourne version may show a slightly later moment in the story, when the monster Cerberus, who presides over the third circle of Hell, that of the Epicures and Gluttons, is prevented from devouring Virgil and Dante by Virgil feeding the beast with handfuls of earth. Some of Cerberus's victims, howling like dogs after their flesh has been flayed and rent by the monster, lie in the foreground. Blake depicts the cold setting, with rain and snow, but places the monster under a heavy arch absent from the text. Roe suggests that Cerberus is shown in a cave, which indicates the weight of the fallen world and blocks off any glimpse of eternity.

There are a few pencil lines on the back that may be the beginnings of a landscape setting for the *Purgatorio* scene of the inscription, but this may be to over-interpret marks made purely by accident.

7 *The Goddess of Fortune*

Pencil, pen and water-colour
52.7 x 37.3 cm
Inscr. 'HELL Canto 7' in ink and again in pencil l.r., 'Celestial Globe' and 'Terrestial Globe', both partly erased, in pencil on the two globes in the centre; and 'The hole of a Shithouse / The Goddess Fortune is the devils Servant ready to Kiss any ones Arse' in pencil above the figure of Fortune; and on reverse in pencil, '55' u.r., 'No 19 next at p 80', u.c., and 'HELL Canto 12' along right-hand edge
Watermark: WELGAR 1796
Felton Bequest 1920 993/3

Exh.: Melbourne 1957–58 (46).

Lit.: ? Rossetti in Gilchrist 1863, p. 216 under no. 101, and 1880, p. 227 under no. 123; Roe 1953, pp. 70–1 no. 16, repr.; Hoff 1961, p. 9, repr. pl. 5; Butlin 1981, p. 561 no. 812 *16*; Gizzi 1983, p. 93, repr.; Fuller, 'Blake and Dante' 1988, p. 371 n. 7.

Inferno VII, 25–96. This design should precede Roe no. 15 (cat. 8). Blake combines Dante's description of the two opposing circles of the Avaricious and the Prodigal, who roll enormous weights against each other, with Virgil's description of Dame Fortune, who has governed their lives. The group of the Avaricious on the left are priests, popes and cardinals, and Blake marks the weight with which they fight 'Celestial Globe'; the other group fight with a weight inscribed 'Terrestial Globe'. Fuller sees this as a literal illustration to the text, although both Roe and Klonsky relate it to Blake's own mythology, the weight or globes for instance representing limited vision in the Fallen World. Klonsky suggests that Fortune is sitting in a privy.

Vague chalk lines and an area of shading on the back may be the beginnings of another drawing but, like similar marks on the backs of several of the drawings, may equally well be purely accidental.

8 *The Stygian Lake, with the Ireful Sinners Fighting*

Pen, ink and water-colour over pencil
52.7 x 37.1 cm
Inscr. 'HELL Canto 7' in ink over pencil l.r., and 'The Stygian Lake' in pencil over 'HELL Stygian Lake [?] Canto 7' all in pencil, erased, u.c.; and on reverse in pencil, '6' u.r., 'No 4 next at p 49' and '14 x 49' u.c., and 'HELL Canto 3' along right-hand edge
Watermark: WELGAR 1796
Felton Bequest 1920 992/3

Exh.: RA 1893 (6); Melbourne 1957–58 (47); Hamburg and Frankfurt 1975 (208, repr.); Pescara 1983.

Lit.: Rossetti in Gilchrist 1863, p. 217 no. 101o, and 1880, p. 228 no. 123o; Roe 1953, pp. 69–70 no. 15, repr.; Hoff 1961, p. 10, repr. pl. 6; Bindman 1977, p. 217; Klonsky 1980, pp. 40, 140, repr. in colour pl. 16; Butlin 1981, pp. 560–1 no. 812 *15*; Gizzi 1983, p. 94, repr. and in colour.

Inferno VII, 106–26. Dante and Virgil enter the fifth circle of Hell and come to the Stygian marsh or Styx, in which they see the Wrathful and the Sullen smiting each other not just with their hands but also with their heads, bodies and feet; the sobs of those below the water make its surface bubble. In the text the figures are naked but Blake shows them in tight-fitting garments and, in some cases, with head-gear, including that of a monk in the centre of the three figures at the bottom. It is not altogether clear whether all the figures are below the surface of the water or, as in Dante's text, whether some can be seen above it. Roe states that the three figures at the bottom are dead, which seems unlikely as they are already in Hell, while Klonsky describes them as only temporarily *hors de combat*. Roe sees the water as the Sea of Ulro, Klonsky as the Sea of Time and Space, and for both it is a symbol of materialism, a suitable setting for the fighting that marks the Fallen World.

9 Recto: *The Angel Crossing the Styx*
Verso: Slight sketch, possibly for *The Laborious Passage Along the Rocks*

Pen and water-colour over pencil (recto), pencil and wash (verso)
37.3 x 52.7 cm
Inscr. 'HELL Canto 8' in ink l.r. and 'Hell Canto 8' in pencil, erased, u.r.; and on reverse in pencil, with paper seen as an upright, '62' or '63' erased u.r. and 'Canto 24 v 60' partly erased l.l.
Watermark: WELGAR 1796
Felton Bequest 1920 994/3

Exh.: Melbourne 1957–58 (48).

Lit.: Rossetti in Gilchrist 1863, p. 217 no. 101r, and 1880, p. 228 no. 123r; Roe 1953, pp. 74–5 no. 19, recto repr.; Hoff 1961, p. 11, recto repr. pl. 7;

26 *Ephialtes and Two Other Titans*

27 *Antaeus Setting Down Dante and Virgil in the Last Circle of Hell*

28 *Lucifer*

Klonsky 1980, pp. 43, 141, recto repr. pl. 19; Butlin 1981, p. 562 no. 812 *19*; Gizzi 1983, p. 97, recto repr.; Fuller, 'Blake and Dante' 1988, p. 353.

Inferno VIII, 67–75 and IX, 64–84. Dante and Virgil, still in the fifth circle, approach the City of Dis, its mosques glowing red in the eternal fire of Hell. Dante describes the sound at the approach of the Heavenly Messenger as of a wind; Blake illustrates this literally with a whirlwind which snatches up the figures of the damned as in the famous *Whirlwind of Lovers* also from this series (Birmingham City Art Gallery; Butlin 1981, no. 812 *10*). In the background can be seen two of the great rock bridges that connect the various circles of Hell. All critics are agreed that this is a relatively straightforward illustration to Dante's text, although Roe, as before, equates the Styx with Blake's Sea of Ulro and in addition the fortified city as the World of Generation or the Mundane Shell.

The sketch on the back, to be seen with the paper held upright, shows flames along the curve of a hill. Nicholas Draffin has suggested that it is perhaps connected with a later composition in the series *The Laborious Passage Along the Rocks* (British Museum; Butlin 1981, no. 812 *45*), an illustration to Canto XXIV, 19–63, to which the inscription might well refer.

A rough sketch for the composition on the recto, with considerable differences, is in the Geoffrey Keynes Collection, now in the Fitzwilliam Museum, Cambridge (Butlin 1981, no. 819, pl. 1062), and a drawing of *An Angel Taking Huge Strides in the Air Among Stars* in the Victoria and Albert Museum (Butlin 1981, no. 820 recto, pl. 1074) may be related to the figure of the Heavenly Messenger on the left.

10 Recto: ***The Angel at the Gate of Dis***
Verso: Slight sketch, perhaps of hills

Pen and water-colour over pencil and black chalk (recto), chalk (verso)
37.2 x 52.8 cm
Inscr. 'HELL Canto 9' in ink l.r.; and on reverse in pencil, with page seen as an upright, '11' u.r.
Watermark: WELGAR 1796
Felton Bequest 1920 995/3

Exh.: RA 1893 (7); Tate Gallery (41vi), Manchester (48vi), Nottingham (42xi) and Edinburgh (62) 1913–14; Melbourne 1957–58 (49).

Lit.: Rossetti in Gilchrist 1863, p. 217 no. 101s, and 1880, p. 228 no. 123s, as 'The Gorgon-head, and the Angel opening the Gate of Dis'; Roe 1953, pp. 75–6 no. 20, recto repr., as 'The Gorgon-Head and the Angel Opening the Gate of Dis'; Hoff 1961, p. 12, recto repr. pl. 8; Beer 1969, p. 277; Grant, 'The Fate of Blake's Sun-Flower' 1974, pp. 46–7, recto repr. pl. 7; Klonsky 1980, pp. 44, 141, recto repr. in colour pl. 20; Butlin 1981, p. 562 no. 812 *20*; Gizzi 1983, p. 98, recto repr.; Fuller, 'Blake and Dante' 1988, p. 372 n. 17.

Inferno IX, 36–60 and 88–90. The Heavenly Messenger or Angel has now arrived at the Gate of Dis which is guarded by the three hellish Furies, the Erinnyes—Megaera on the left, Alecto on the right and Tisiphone in the middle; they call upon the Gorgon Medusa to come and turn the Angel into stone and Virgil covers Dante's eyes so that he shall not share the same fate. Roe, followed by Klonsky, interprets the central figure above the gate as Medusa. The snake-like hair of the Furies is shown and they hold torches, though Roe incorrectly sees these as trumpets and identifies the figures as the Daughters of Albion representing the Female Will, three being a number of evil import. From this he develops the idea that the gateway and the Angel's staff have a sexual symbolism and that the poets are turning their heads away from this expression of sexual repression. Fuller quotes this interpretation as an example of Roe's over-interpretation derived from a misreading of what Blake has actually drawn.

There is a pentimento in the left of the Angel's head, where the paper has been rubbed, and also on his legs and staff. The faint sketch on the back, similar to that on the back of the previous design (cat. 9), is perhaps the beginning of a vertical composition of overlapping hills.

11 ***The Hell-Hounds Hunting the Destroyers of Their Own Goods***

Pen, ink and water-colour over black chalk and pencil
37.3 x 52.8 cm
Inscr. 'HELL Canto 13' in ink l.r.; and on reverse in pencil, with page seen as an upright, '78' l.r. and 'N 14 next at p 68' l.c., the same, erased, in centre, and 'HELL Canto 8' along right-hand edge
Watermark: WELGAR 1796
Felton Bequest 1920 996/3

Exh.: Tate Gallery (41vii), Manchester (48vii), Nottingham (42xii) and Edinburgh (61) 1913–14, all as 'The Harpies and the Hell-Hounds'; Melbourne 1957–58 (50).

Lit.: Rossetti in Gilchrist 1863, p. 218 no. 101x, and 1880, p. 229 no. 123x; Roe 1953, pp. 80–1 no. 25, repr.; Hoff 1961, p. 13, repr. pl. 9; Burke, 'The Eidetic and the Borrowed Image' 1964, p. 123, repr. pl. 91 (reprinted in Essick 1973, pp. 283–4, repr. pl. 84); Klonsky 1980, pp. 50, 143, repr. pl. 26; Butlin 1981, p. 564 no. 812 *25*; Gizzi 1983, p. 104, repr.; Boime 1987, pp. 137–8; Fuller, 'Blake and Dante' 1988, p. 371 n. 7.

Inferno XIII, 109–29. The poets are now in the second ring of the seventh circle, the Wood of the Self-Murderers, the subject of the preceding design showing the Harpies and the Suicides (Tate Gallery; Butlin 1981, no. 812 *24*). Dante and Virgil have been listening to Pier delle Vigne, who has been embedded in the trunk of a tree, when they are interrupted by sounds as of a boar hunt; two notorious spendthrifts, Giacomo da Sant' Andrea and Lano da Sienna, dash into view, pursued by Hell-Hounds. Two Harpies look down from the trees. The frozen pose of Lano da Sienna, seen between the trees, suggests that the figure is based on an antique motif, perhaps from a Niobe group.

There are pentimenti around the figure of Lano da Sienna, and the outlines of the head and leg of the left-hand hound have been reinforced in pencil. The placing of the inscriptions on the reverse, upside down as compared with the usual placing, suggests

29 *The Rest on the Mountain Leading to Purgatory*

30 *The Souls of Those Who Only Repented at the Point of Death*

31 *The Lawn with the Kings and Angels*

that the water-colour may have been painted on the left-hand leaf of a page opening, and with the top of the composition at the left-hand, free edge, rather than Blake's more usual process, which was to paint his designs on the right-hand page of an opening, with the top of the composition at the gutter between the two pages.

12 ***Capaneus the Blasphemer***

Pen, ink and water-colour
37.4 x 52.7 cm
Inscr. 'HELL Canto 14/WB' with the point of the brush in ink l.l.; and on reverse in pencil, with the page seen as an upright, '43' u.r., 'N 27 next at p 80' u.c., the same, erased, in centre, and 'Hell Canto 17' along right-hand edge
Watermark: WE
Felton Bequest 1920 997/3

Exh.: Melbourne 1957–58 (51); Hamburg and Frankfurt 1975 (209, repr.); Tate Gallery 1978 (322, repr.); Pescara 1983.

Lit.: Rossetti in Gilchrist 1863, p. 218 no. 101z, and 1880, p. 229 no. 123z; Roe 1953, pp. 82–3 no. 27, repr.; Hoff 1961, pp. 2, 4 n. 27, 14, repr. pl. 10; Burke, 'The Eidetic and the Borrowed Image' 1964, p. 123, repr. pl. 95 (reprinted in Essick 1973, p. 286, repr. pl. 89); Klonsky 1980, pp. 53, 143–4, repr. in colour pl. 29; Butlin 1981, p. 564 no. 812 27; Gizzi 1983, p. 107, repr. and in colour.

Inferno XIV, 46–72. Dante and Virgil are now in the third ring of the seventh circle, where those who have done violence against God, nature or art are punished. Capaneus, who had committed violence against God, was one of the seven kings who besieged Thebes. He defied Jupiter and was killed by a thunderbolt. Dante describes him as lying proud and disdainful, apparently unaffected by the flames. According to Roe, Blake shows him as Satan, the limit of opacity, ruling in pride over the Fallen World. Blake refers to Capaneus in his annotations (probably done *c.* 1800) to Boyd's translation of Dante's *Inferno*, published in Dublin in 1785: 'The grandest Poetry is Immoral, the Grandest characters Wicked, Very Satan—Capanius, Othello a murderer, Prometheus, Jupiter, Jehovah, Jesus a wine bibber. Cunning & Morality are not Poetry but Philosophy; the Poet is Independent & Wicked; the Philosopher is Dependent & Good' (Keynes 1969, p. 412).

Ursula Hoff has related the figure of Capaneus to the antique figure of the Nile in the Vatican (repr. Burke 1964, pl. 96, and 1973, pl. 88), and also to J. A. Koch's drawing of Capaneus in the series of Dante illustrations he did *c.* 1805 for the Reverend George Frederick Nott.

This is one of the most highly finished water-colours in the series. Blake has created highlights in the streaks of lightning, on Capaneus's right arm and elsewhere by rubbing away the water-colour to expose the white of the paper. A few indefinable chalk marks on the back of the paper are probably accidental.

William Rossetti, in his catalogue at the back of Gilchrist's *Life of William Blake*, lists two drawings which he tentatively entitled 'Capaneus, from Dante (?)', one described as showing three men, the other four; from the descriptions neither seems to be related to the Melbourne water-colour (Rossetti 1863, p. 249 list 2, nos 103 and 104, and 1880, p. 268 list 2, nos 131 and 132; one may be the drawing in the British Museum, Butlin 1981, no. 790, pl. 1029; the other is untraced, Butlin 1981, no. 791).

13 Recto: ***The Symbolic Figure of the Course of Human History Described by Virgil***
Verso: Slight sketch for *The Goddess of Fortune* (?)

Pen, ink and water-colour over pencil and ? black chalk
52.7 x 37.3 cm
Inscr. 'HELL Canto 14' in ink l.l. and 'Hell Canto 14/ the Italian [?] [illegible]' in pencil, partly erased, u.l.; and on reverse in pencil, '54' u.r., 'No 12 next at p ['14' erased] 6' u.c., 'No 12 next at p 14' in centre, and 'Hell Canto 7' along right-hand edge
Watermark: WELGAR 1796
Felton Bequest 1920 998/3

Exh.: Melbourne 1957–58 (52).

Lit.: Rossetti in Gilchrist 1863, p. 218 no. 101a[1], and 1880, p. 229 no. 123a[1]; Blunt, 'Blake's Pictorial Imagination' 1943, p. 198, recto repr. pl. 55b; Roe 1953, pp. 83–4 no. 28, recto repr.; Hoff 1961, pp. 2, 3 n. 23, 15, recto repr. pl. 11; Burke, 'The Eidetic and the Borrowed Image' 1964, p. 123, recto repr. pl. 97 (reprinted in Essick 1973, p. 286, recto repr. pl. 90); Klonsky 1980, pp. 15, 54, 144, recto repr. pl. 30; Butlin 1981, p. 565 no. 812 28; Gizzi 1983, p. 108, recto repr.; Fuller, 'Blake and Dante' 1988, p. 359.

Inferno XIV, 94–119. Dante and Virgil, in the third ring of the seventh circle, come across a blood-red stream. Dante explains that the rivers of Hell, Acheron, Styx and Phlegethon, are formed by tears falling from the giant old man encased in the mountain of Ida on the island of Crete, the centre of the known world. For Dante this figure embodied the course of human history and his description was based on Nebuchadnezzar's dream in Daniel II and also on the passage in Ovid's *Metamorphoses* I. His head is of gold, his arms and breast of silver, his lower abdomen brass, and below that he is of iron save that his right foot is of clay; this denotes the decay of the world from the Golden Age before the Fall to Dante's own time, the clay foot representing the degenerate church. Blake, while failing to distinguish between the various elements that make up the body, endows the figure with a crown, an orb and a sceptre to show that in his view the decay of the world was the result of political oppression—kingship and tyranny.

Anthony Blunt suggests that the pose of the figure and its crowned head are taken from an ancient statue of Helios (repr. Burke 1964, pl. 99, and 1973, pl. 91), but that 'Blake has transformed his model by giving it a terror quite contrary to the spirit of ancient sculpture'. A more immediate source is Blake's own drawing of *Old Parr When Young* of 1820 (Henry E. Huntington Library and Art Gallery, San Marino; Butlin 1981, no. 748, repr. pl. 960).

On the back there are faint indications of a drawing identified by Nicholas Draffin as for cat. 7, *The Goddess of Fortune*, an illustration to Hell Canto

7 as suggested by the inscription. However, this is very difficult to make out and the placing of the inscription implies that if it does apply to the drawing then that is of a horizontal format.

14 *Geryon Conveying Dante and Virgil Down Towards Malebolge*

Pen, ink and water-colour over pencil and chalk (recto)
37.2 x 52.7 cm
Inscr. 'HELL Canto 17 [altered from '16']' in pencil l.r.; and on reverse in pencil, with paper held as an upright, '44' u.r., 'N 17 next at p 84' u.c., the same, erased, in centre, and 'Hell Canto 10' along right-hand edge
Watermark: WE
Felton Bequest 1920 999/3

Exh.: RA 1893 (9); Melbourne 1957–58 (53); Tate Gallery 1978 (323, recto repr.); *Poetical Circle* Australia and New Zealand 1979 (59, recto repr.); *Dante–Virgil–Geryon* Stuttgart 1980 (44); Pescara 1983.

Lit.: Rossetti in Gilchrist 1863, p. 218 no. 101d[1], and 1880, p. 229 no. 123d[1]; Roe 1953, pp. 86–7 no. 31, repr.; Hoff 1961, p. 16, repr. pl. 12; Klonsky 1980, pp. 57, 144, repr. in colour pl. 33; Butlin 1981, p. 566 no. 812 *31*; Gizzi 1983, p. 111, repr. and in colour; Fuller, 'Blake and Dante' 1988, p. 371 n. 7.

Inferno XVII, 1–27 and 79–123. Virgil and Dante are carried on the back of the monster Geryon from the third ring of the seventh circle down to Malebolge in the eighth circle. In antiquity Geryon was a monster with three heads, six arms and three bodies joined together at the waist; he was slain by Hercules. In the middle ages, however, Geryon was equated with fraud, with the face of a just man but the body of a reptile. In the background on the left can be seen the Panders and Seducers, fleeing from the Demons, the subject of the next illustration in the series, *Demons Tormenting the Panders and Seducers in Malebolge* (Fogg Art Museum, Harvard University, Cambridge; Butlin 1981, no. 812 *32*).

There are pentimenti to Geryon's claws and to the heads of Dante and Virgil. Nicholas Draffin interprets the barely distinguishable marks on the back of the drawing as a sketch for *Farinata degli Uberti*, an illustration to Canto X (British Museum; Butlin 1981, no. 812 *21*). The marks seem, however, to be merely smudged chalk offsets from another sheet of paper.

15 *The Necromancers and Augurs*

Pen, ink and water-colour over pencil and black chalk
52.7 x 37.2 cm
Inscr. 'HELL Canto' in ink and 'Hell Canto 20' in pencil, partly erased, l.r.; and on reverse in pencil, '65' u.r., 'Hell Canto 34' l.r. and 'N 61 last in the Inferno / unless from [?] Inferno [?] Dante lifted / by Virgil past [?] Lucifer [??]', erased, in centre
Watermark: WE
Felton Bequest 1920 1001/3

Exh.: Melbourne 1957–58 (55).

Lit.: Rossetti in Gilchrist 1863, p. 218 no. 101h[1], and 1880, p. 230 no. 123h[1]; Roe 1953, p. 92 no. 36, repr.; Hoff 1961, p. 17, repr. pl. 13; Klonsky 1980, pp. 61, 145–6, repr. in colour pl. 37; Butlin 1981, p. 567 no. 812 *36*; Gizzi 1983, p. 115, repr.; Fuller, 'Blake and Dante' 1988, p. 371 n. 7.

Inferno XX, 1–56. This is an incident in the fourth chasm of the eighth circle, where the Sorcerers and Fortune-tellers receive their punishment, which consists of having their heads twisted backwards. Dante names seven figures in all, one of them a woman, Manto, after whom Virgil's birthplace Mantua was named; one of the men is probably her father Tiresias. Virgil and Dante look down from the rock bridge above.

The inscription on the back is difficult to read but suggests that the drawing on his p. 61 was to be the last subject from the *Inferno* unless he added the subject of Lucifer, also at Melbourne, whose body provided the route by which the poets emerged from Hell at the threshold of Purgatory (see cat. 28). This occurs at the end of Canto 34. Unfortunately the preceding scene, from Canto 33, showing *Ugolino and his Sons in Prison*, is stuck down and it is not possible to see the number on the back (British Museum; Butlin 1981, no. 812 *68*).

16 *The Devil Carrying the Lucchese Magistrate to the Boiling-Pitch Pool of Corrupt Officials*

Pen, ink and water-colour over pencil and black chalk
52.8 x 37.1 cm
Inscr. 'HELL Canto 21' in ink l.r.; and on reverse in pencil, '68' u.r., 'No 15 next at p 10' u.c., the same erased in centre, and 'Hell Canto 8' along right-hand edge
Watermark: WE
Felton Bequest 1920 1002/3

Exh.: Melbourne 1957–58 (56).

Lit.: Rossetti in Gilchrist 1863, p. 218 no. 101i[1], and 1880, p. 230 no. 123i[1]; Roe 1953, p. 93 no. 37, repr.; Hoff 1961, p. 18, repr. pl. 14; Klonsky 1980, pp. 62, 146, repr. pl. 38; Butlin 1981, p. 568 no. 812 *37*; Gizzi 1983, p. 116, repr.; Fuller, 'Blake and Dante' 1988, p. 371 n. 7.

Inferno XXI, 29–42. This scene is set in the fifth chasm of the eighth circle, preceding cat. 17. Bonturo Dati's fellow magistrate, probably Martino Bottaio, is being carried by a demon and is about to be thrown into the boiling pitch before being attacked with hooks, as in the other scene.

For a possible sketch see the reverse of *The Souls of Those Who Only Repented at the Point of Death*, cat. 30.

17 *The Devils Under the Bridge*

Pen and water-colour over chalk and pencil
37.3 x 52.7 cm
Inscr. 'HELL Canto 18' in ink l.l.; and on reverse in pencil, with paper seen as an upright, '82' and 'N 30 next at p 64 . . . p 30' u.c., the same, erased in centre, and 'HELL Canto 22' along right-hand edge
Watermark: WE
Felton Bequest 1920 1000/3

32 *The Angel Inviting Dante to Enter the Fire*

33 *Dante at the Moment of Entering the Fire*

Exh.: Tate Gallery (41viii), Manchester (48viii), Nottingham (42xiii) and Edinburgh (64) 1913–14, all as 'Bridges and Lakes in the Eighth Circle'; Melbourne 1957–58 (54); Tate Gallery 1978 (324, repr.).

Lit.: Rossetti in Gilchrist 1863, p. 218 no. 101j[1], and 1880, p. 230 no. 123j[1]; Roe 1953, pp. 89–91 no. 34, repr.; Hoff 1961, p. 19, repr. pl. 15; Klonsky 1980, pp. 63, 146, repr. pl. 39; Butlin 1981, p. 567 no. 812 *34*; Gizzi 1983, p. 117, repr.; Fuller, 'Blake and Dante' 1988, p. 371 n. 10.

Inferno XXI, 46–57. Despite Blake's reference to Canto 10 this shows the scene in the fifth chasm of the eighth circle, with the devils jabbing at the Lucchese Magistrate Bonturo Dati, head of the popular party at the time and the worst of all his fellows at barratry or fraud. In the distance the Seducers pursued by demons can still be seen, as in cat. 14 and the following design, which perhaps accounts for Blake's mistake. Dante described great rock bridges as characteristic of Malebolge but Blake depicts them as being made from petrified, giant pieces of human anatomy. Klonsky states that this may have been suggested to Blake by the remark of Pope Nicholas III, the 'Simoniac Pope' of the well-known design from this series at the Tate Gallery that also shows the eighth circle (Butlin 1981, no. 812 *35*): 'Below my head are dragged other popes guilty of simony, flattened through the fissures of the rock' (Canto XIX, 73–5). For Roe they represent Fallen Man at his furthest remove from Divine Energy.

18 Recto ***The Devils Setting Out With Dante and Virgil***
Verso: Slight sketch for *Cacus*

Pen, ink and water-colour over pencil (recto), chalk or pencil (verso)
37.2 x 52.8 cm
Inscr. 'HELL/Canto 21' l.r.; and on reverse in pencil, with paper seen as an upright, the same in ink l.r.c. and in pencil, '52' u.r., 'N 45 next at p 77' u.c., and 'Hell Canto 25 Cacus' partly erased along right-hand edge
Watermark: WE
Felton Bequest 1920 1003/3

Exh.: Melbourne 1957–58 (57); Pescara 1983.

Lit.: Rossetti in Gilchrist 1863, p. 218 no. 101 l[1], and 1880, p. 230 no. 123 l[1]; Roe 1953, p. 94 no. 39, recto repr.; Hoff 1961, p. 20, recto repr. pl. 16; Klonsky 1980, pp. 65, 146–7, recto repr. in colour pl. 41; Butlin 1981, p. 568 no. 812 *39*, verso repr. pl. 1054; Gizzi 1983, p. 119, recto repr. and in colour; Fuller, 'Blake and Dante' 1988, p. 371 n. 7.

Inferno XXI, 97–139. The devils who have been harassing the Lucchese Magistrate and other barrators turn towards Dante and threaten him, but one of their number, Malalcoda, stops them and instructs them to escort Dante and Virgil as they continue their way through the eighth circle. The beginning of this scene is shown in *Virgil Abashing the Devils* in the British Museum (Butlin 1981, no. 812 *38*). Among the devils escorting the poets are Barbariccia, leading them, and Ciriatto, recognizable by his tusks.

The drawing on the back is for another water-colour in the series, *The Centaur Cacus*, who appears in the seventh chasm of the eighth circle (British Museum; Butlin 1981, no. 812 *50*).

19 ***The Thieves and the Serpents***

Pen, ink and water-colour over pencil and black chalk (recto)
37.2 x 52.8 cm
Inscr. 'HELL Canto 24' in ink l.r., and 'Hell' u.r. to be seen with sheet held vertically, and on reverse in pencil, with the paper held as an upright, '74', 'No 47 next at p 73' l.c., the same erased, in centre, and 'Canto 25' u.c.
Watermark: WE
Felton Bequest 1920 1004/3

Exh.: Melbourne 1957–58 (58).

Lit.: Rossetti in Gilchrist 1963, p. 219 no. 101t[1], and 1880, p. 230 no. 123t[1]; Roe 1953, pp. 101–4 no. 47, repr.; Hoff 1961, p. 21, repr. pl. 17; Klonsky 1980, pp. 73, 148, repr. pl. 49; Butlin 1981, pp. 570–1 no. 812 *47*; Gizzi 1983, repr.; Fuller, 'Blake and Dante' 1988, pp. 369–70, 371 n. 7.

Inferno XXIV, 82–96. The two poets have crossed over the cliff into the seventh chasm of the eighth circle, where the Thieves are punished by serpents, the subject of no fewer than nine of Blake's water-colours and two of the engravings he made from them (Butlin 1981, nos 812 *47–54* and *102*). As Fuller points out, the Thieves, who have failed to respect other people's property, are punished by losing the right of property over their own bodies. He agrees with Roe and Klonsky that it was the serpents that particularly fascinated Blake, and in finding parallels with the symbolism of the serpents that appear in Blake's own writings. Not only was the serpent the instigator of the Fall in the Bible, it also appeared, embodied as Orc, as a symbol of sexual energy; in *The Four Zoas* manuscript Orc is transformed from a human being into a serpent.

In this generalized impression the five figures may represent the five senses and do not seem to be identifiable with any particular figures in the text. A similar generalized impression, with the figures much larger in scale, is found in *The Punishment of the Thieves* in the Tate Gallery (Butlin 1981, no. 812 *102*).

Roe suggests that the two small figures in the background on the right are not by Blake, but the style seems to be compatible with his. A figure holding a cross pushes another figure over the cliff into the abyss, an incident that does not appear in Dante's text. The chalk marks on the back of the drawing have been taken as the beginnings of a very rough sketch, but seem in fact to be merely smudges.

20 Recto: ***Vanni Fucci 'Making Figs' Against God***
Verso: Possible sketch of hills

Pen, ink and water-colour (recto), pencil (verso)
52.7 x 37.2 cm
Inscr. 'HELL Canto 25' in ink l.l.; and on reverse in pencil, '34' u.r. and 'Pg-Canto 9' along right-hand margin
Watermark: WE
Felton Bequest 1920 1005/3

34 *The Harlot and the Giant*

Exh.: RA 1893 (12); Melbourne 1957–58 (59).

Lit.: Rossetti in Gilchrist 1863, p. 219 no. 101v[1], and 1880, p. 231 no. 123v[1]; Roe 1953, pp. 104–5 no. 49, recto repr.; Hoff 1961, p. 22, recto repr. pl. 18; Klonsky 1980, pp. 76, 149, recto repr. pl. 52; Butlin 1981, p. 571 no. 812 *49*; Gizzi 1983, p. 130, recto repr.; Fuller, 'Blake and Dante' 1988, pp. 369–70, 371 n. 7.

Inferno XXV, 1–15. In the previous illustration (British Museum; Butlin 1981, no. 812 *48*) Vanni Fucci had been bitten by a serpent, instantly transformed into ashes, and then reconstituted into his former shape like the phoenix. This was his punishment for robbing the treasury of San Jacopo in the Church of San Zeno, Pistoia, in 1293. In the Melbourne design Vanni Fucci blasphemes against God with an obscene gesture. The flames rain down on him from the dark cloud above and serpents renew their attacks on him.

The pencil lines on the back may, as Nicholas Draffin has suggested, be the beginning of a sketch of a landscape with low hills, to be seen with the paper held horizontally. There are also chalk smudges, and indeed the whole effect may be accidental.

21 Recto: ***The Six-Footed Serpent Attacking Agnello dei Brunelleschi***
Verso: Sketch of a head

Pen, ink and water-colour over black chalk (recto), chalk (verso)
37.2 x 52.7 cm
Inscr. 'HELL Canto 25' in ink and 'line 45' in pencil (probably not by Blake but imitating the hand of the inscription in ink), l.r.; and on reverse in pencil, with page held as an upright, '76' l.l., 'N 42 next at p 95' l.c. both inverted, the same, erased, in centre, and 'Vanni Fucci/Hell Canto 24' erased along right-hand edge
Watermark: WELGAR 1796
Felton Bequest 1920 1006/3

Exh.: RA 1893 (13); Melbourne 1957–58 (69); Pescara 1983.

Lit.: Rossetti in Gilchrist 1863, p. 219 no. 101x[1], and 1880, p. 231 no. 123x[1]; Roe 1953, pp. 107–8 no. 51, recto repr.; Hoff 1961, pp. 2, 4 n. 26, 23, recto repr. pl. 19; Klonsky 1980, pp. 78, 149, recto repr. pl. 54; Butlin 1981, pp. 571–2 no. 812 *51*; Gizzi 1983, recto repr. and in colour; Fuller, 'Blake and Dante' 1988, pp. 369–70, 371 n. 7, 372 n. 17.

Inferno XXV, 49–78. Cianfa de' Donati, at this moment transformed into a six-footed serpent, attacks Agnello dei Brunelleschi and their bodies fuse, as is shown in the next design, now in the Fogg Art Museum, Harvard University, Cambridge (Butlin 1981, no. 812 *52*). Their fellow Florentines Puccio Sciancato and Buoso (either Buoso degli Abati or Buoso de' Donati) stand on the right in horror, while Dante and Virgil stand on the left.

The sketch on the back suggests a head, together with the serpent and landscape features, presumably the beginning of another scene from this part of Hell, perhaps indeed showing Vanni Fucci as is suggested by the inscription.

The recto was one of the designs to be engraved by Blake (see cat. 50 d). There are also two pencil sketches of the whole composition, one in the Fondazione Horne, Florence (Butlin 1981, no. 821 recto, repr. pl. 1072), the other in the Henry E. Huntington Library and Art Gallery, San Marino, California (Butlin 1981, no. 822, repr. pl. 1073). The first seems to precede the Melbourne water-colour, whereas that in the United States appears to have been done after the water-colour in preparation for the engraving. The faint sketch on the back of another of the water-colour illustrations to Dante, *Virgil Repelling Filippo Argenti from the Boat of Phlegyas* (Butlin 1981, no. 812 *18*) may also be related.

Roe suggests that Brunelleschi represents man totally transformed into his material aspect, 'Man in his Spectre's power' (*Jerusalem*, pl. 37/41), but Fuller sees no reason to find any extra significance beyond Dante's own imagery. For Ursula Hoff the figure corresponds to that of Cadmus in Goltzius's *Cadmus and the Dragon*; Dante relates this incident to Ovid's description of the transformation of Cadmus in lines 97–9 of the same canto.

22 ***Ulysses and Diomed Swathed in the Same Flame***

Pen, ink, black chalk and water-colour over pencil
52.8 x 37.2 cm
Inscr. 'HELL/Canto 26' in ink l.l.; and on reverse in pencil, '58' u.r. and 'Pg canto 13' along right-hand edge
Watermark: WE
Felton Bequest 1920 1007/3

Exh.: Melbourne 1957–58 (61).

Lit.: Rossetti in Gilchrist 1863, p. 220 no. 101b[2], and 1880, p. 231 no. 123b[2]; Roe 1953, pp. 110–12 no. 55, repr.; Hoff 1961, p. 24, repr. pl. 20; Klonsky 1980, pp. 82, 150, repr. pl. 58; Butlin 1981, p. 573 no. 812 *55*; Gizzi 1983, p. 136 repr.; Fuller, 'Blake and Dante' 1988, pp. 358, 371 n. 7.

Inferno XXVI, 25–63. Virgil and Dante are now in the eighth chasm of the eighth circle, where occurs the punishment of Evil Councillors, which is to be swathed in individual flames, likened by Dante to fireflies. Ulysses and Diomed are punished for deceiving the Trojans with the Wooden Horse. Rose sees the flame in which they are swathed as representing the Fallen World or Mundane Shell, shutting off their perception of eternity with the opacity of unrelieved reason.

There are faint chalk smudges on the back, apparently accidental.

23 Recto: ***The Schismatics and Sowers of Discord: Mahomet***
Verso: Slight sketch, perhaps for *The Whirlwind of Lovers*

Pen and water-colour over pencil (recto), pencil (verso)
37.3 x 52.7 cm
Inscr. 'WB/HELL Canto 28' in ink l.r.; and on reverse in pencil, with paper held as an upright, '17' u.r., 'No 9 next at p 18' u.c., 'No 9 next at p 18', erased, in centre, 'One of the Whirlwinds of love' c.r. and

35 *Dante Adoring Christ*

36 *St Peter Appears to Beatrice and Dante*

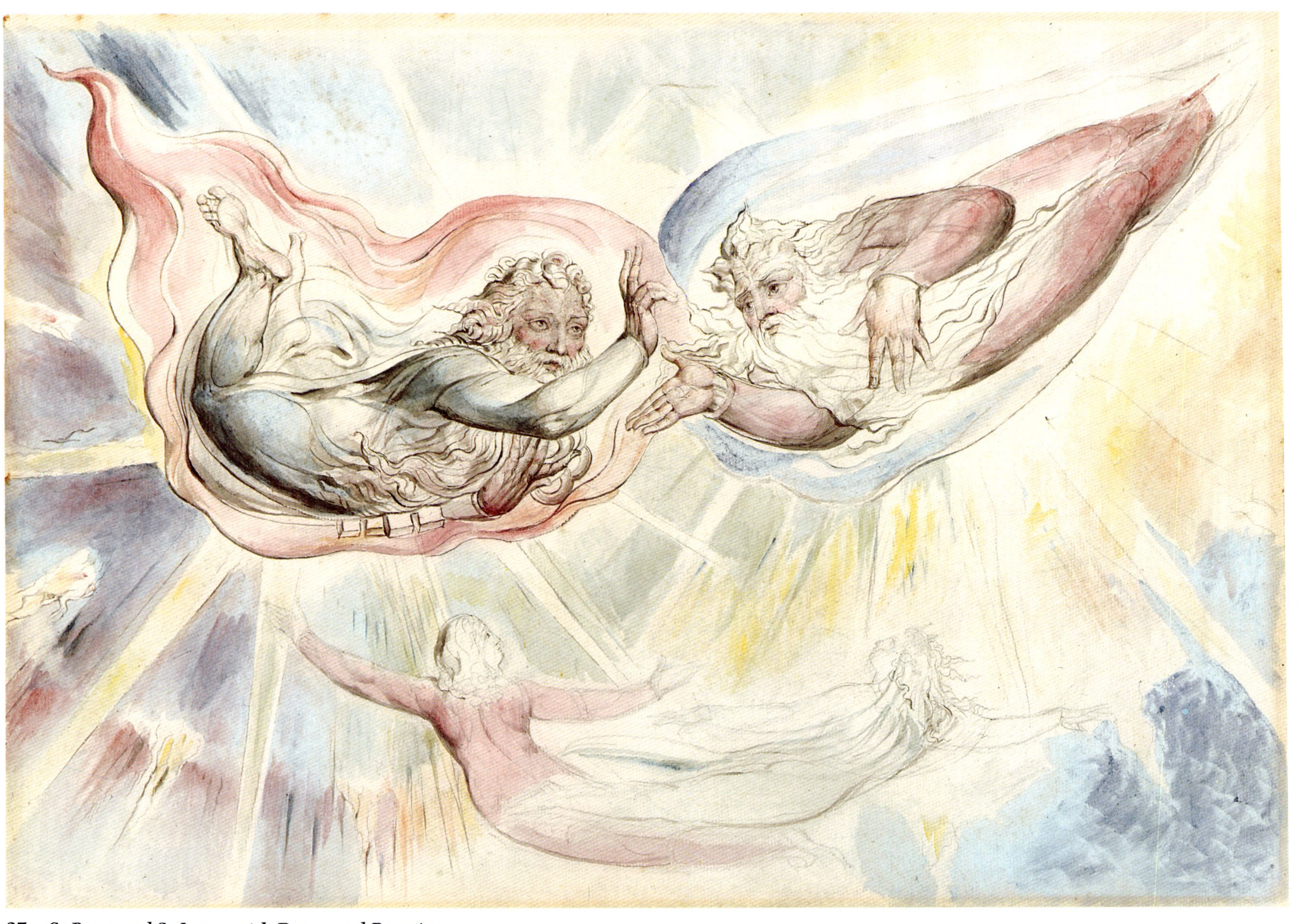

37 *St Peter and St James with Dante and Beatrice*

38 *The Queen of Heaven in Glory*

'Hell Canto 5/Paulo and Francesca' l.r., both with paper held as an oblong
Watermark: WELGAR 1796
Felton Bequest 1920 1008/3

Exh.: ? RA 1893 (15); Melbourne 1957–58 (62).

Lit.: Rossetti in Gilchrist 1863, p. 220 no. 101c², and 1880, p. 231 no. 123c²; Roe 1953, pp. 112–13 no. 56, recto repr.; Hoff 1961, p. 25, recto repr. pl. 21; Burke, 'The Eidetic and the Borrowed Image' 1964, p. 123, recto repr. pl. 93 (reprinted in Essick 1973, pp. 283–4, recto repr. pl. 86); Klonsky 1980, pp. 83, 150, recto repr. pl. 59; Butlin 1981, p. 573 no. 812 *56*; Gizzi 1983, p. 137, recto repr.; Fuller, 'Blake and Dante' 1988, pp. 358, 371 n. 7, repr. pl. 43.

Inferno XXVIII, 19–42. The poets are in the ninth chasm of the eighth circle, that of the Sowers of Discord, whose punishment is to be mutilated. Mahomet shows his entrails to Dante and Virgil while to the left stands his son Ali, his head cleft from chin to forelock. A winged devil with swords stands on the right. In the distance, behind Mahomet, can be seen Bertrand de Born carrying his head in his hand.

Klonsky points out that there was a legend at the time of Dante that Mahomet (*c.* AD 570–632) had been a Christian convert and had even risen to become a cardinal and a candidate for the papacy; he had then defected to found his own religion. The assassination of Ali in 661 had led to further schism. Fuller notes that for Blake 'all religions are one' and that he would have been far more tolerant of Mahomet; in fact Blake's *Visionary Head of Mahomet* shows him as an idealized, if resolute, young man (Santa Barbara Museum of Art; Butlin 1981, no. 720, repr. pl. 936). Nevertheless Blake, far from showing his disapproval of Dante's ideas in this design, followed his imagery.

The sketch on the back runs along the lower half of the paper. No whirlwind is shown but the inscriptions suggest that it may have been the beginning of the sketch for the famous design from earlier in this series, *The Whirlwind of Lovers* in the City Museum and Art Gallery, Birmingham (Butlin 1981, no. 812 *10*).

24 ***The Schismatics and Sowers of Discord: Mosca de' Lamberti and Bertrand de Born***

Pen, ink and water-colour over pencil
37 x 52.7 cm
Inscr. 'WB/HELL Canto 28' in ink over pencil l.r., '28 HELL Canto 28' in chalk, partly erased, u.r.; and on reverse in pencil, with paper held as an upright, '21' u.r., 'N 57 next at p 22' u.c., and the same, erased, in centre
Watermark: WE
Felton Bequest 1920 1009/3

Exh.: ? RA 1893 (15); Melbourne 1957–58 (63); Hamburg and Frankfurt 1975 (211, repr.); Pescara 1983.

Lit.: Rossetti in Gilchrist 1863, p. 220 no. 101d², and 1880, p. 231 no. 123d²; Roe 1953, pp. 113–15 no. 57, repr.; Hoff 1961, p. 26, repr. pl. 22; Klonsky 1977, p. 118, repr.; Klonsky 1980, pp. 84, 150, repr. in colour pl. 60; Butlin 1981, pp. 573–4 no. 812 57; Gizzi 1983, p. 138, repr. and in colour; Fuller, 'Blake and Dante' 1988, p. 371 n. 7.

Inferno XXVIII, 103–42. Still in the ninth chasm of the eighth circle, Dante and Virgil are shown with Bertrand de Born on the left, now holding out his head like a lantern, and Mosca de' Lamberti, raising the stumps of his handless arms. Bertrand de Born had set Henry II of England against his son, while Mosca de' Lamberti's murder of Buondelmonte had begun the conflict between the Guelph and Ghibelline factions in Florence. The devil that appears in the previous design is shown from behind in the background.

The same general colouring is used in this design and the preceding scene, suggesting that they were done at much the same time. The paper has been rubbed away around the heads of Dante and Virgil, presumably changing their outlines, and also around Bertrand de Born's head and in the diagonal slope of rock above the flames on the left. There are some faint chalk marks on the reverse, probably accidental.

25 Recto: ***The Pit of Disease: Gianni Schicchi and Myrrha***
Verso: Slight sketch, perhaps for *The Mountain Leading to Purgatory*

Pen, ink and water-colour over pencil (recto), pencil (verso)
52.7 x 37.2 cm
Inscr. 'HELL Canto 30' in ink l.c.r.; and on reverse in pencil, '63' u.r. and 'Pg Canto 4', the figure perhaps reworked, along right-hand edge
Watermark: WELGAR 1796
Felton Bequest 1920 1010/3

Exh.: Melbourne 1957–58 (64).

Lit.: Rossetti in Gilchrist 1863, p. 220 no. 101f², and 1880, p. 231 no. 123f²; Roe 1953, pp. 117–19 no. 59, recto repr.; Hoff 1961, p. 27, recto repr. p. 23; Klonsky 1980, pp. 86, 150–1, recto repr. pl. 62; Butlin 1981, p. 574 no. 812 59; Gizzi 1983, p. 140, recto repr.; Boime 1987, pp. 26, 28; Fuller, 'Blake and Dante' 1988, p. 353.

Inferno XXX, 22–45. A scene in the tenth chasm, of the Falsifiers, in the eighth circle. Dante sees two pale and naked shadows rushing out biting as if hungry swine thrust out from their sty. One, Gianni Schicchi, grabs Capocchio by the neck with his fangs. Capocchio, who is also shown scratching himself in the previous design, *The Pit of Disease: The Falsifiers* now in the Tate Gallery (Butlin 1981, no. 812 58), is probably the Florentine alchemist who was burned alive in Sienna in 1281. Gianni Schicchi disguised himself as the just dead Buoso Donati and remade his will at the instigation of Buoso's relations but in fact largely in his own favour (as in Puccini's one-act opera). The other animal-headed figure on the left is Myrrha, daughter of King Cinyras of Cyprus with whom she had an incestuous relationship, also in disguise.

The figure lying on the ground, who may be Griffolino of Arezzo, is based on *The Strong Wicked Man* engraved from Blake's design by Schiavonetti for

Robert Blair's *The Grave*, published by R. H. Cromek in 1808.

There are pentimenti down Dante's back and on the figure of Myrrha. The faint indications of a horizontal composition on the back may be, Nicholas Draffin has suggested, a sketch for another of the Dante illustrations, *The Rest on the Mountain Leading to Purgatory* (cat. 29), or, less likely, *The Ascent of the Mountain of Purgatory* (Tate Gallery; Butlin 1981, no. 812 74).

26 *Ephialtes and Two Other Titans*

Pen, ink and water-colour over black chalk and pencil
37.3 x 52.7 cm
Inscr. 'HELL/Canto 31' in ink l.l.; and on reverse in pencil, with page seen as an upright, '46' u.r., 'No 60 next at p 65' u.c., the same, erased, in centre, and 'Hell Canto 32' along right-hand edge
Watermark: WELGAR 1796
Felton Bequest 1920 1011/3

Exh.: Melbourne 1957–58 (65); Pescara 1983.

Lit.: Rossetti in Gilchrist 1863, p. 220 no. 101i², and 1880, p. 232 no. 123i²; Roe 1953, pp. 122–4 no. 62, repr.; Hoff 1961, p. 28 repr. pl. 24; Klonsky 1980, pp. 89, 151, repr. in colour pl. 65; Butlin 1981, p. 575 no. 812 62; Gizzi 1983, p. 143, repr. and in colour.

Inferno XXXI, 84–111. The poets are now crossing the bank that separates the eighth circle or Malebolge from the ninth circle or central pit. This is guarded by Giants, standing waist deep in a ditch around its edge. After conversing with Nimrod they come across Ephialtes, the son of Neptune who made war against the gods and was killed by Apollo, possibly with Hercules, while attempting to pile Mount Pelion upon Mount Ossa. Ephialtes is chained as in Dante's text but Blake adds two other giants, perhaps, as Roe suggests, so that the design can depict the fallen state of three of the four Zoas: the chained Ephialtes is Orc or the fallen Luvah, the old giant on the left is Urizen, and the youth on the right Tharmas; Los, who embodies the Imagination through which alone salvation can be found, is represented by the two poets. Klonsky identifies a fourth giant lying on his back among the rubble that fills the lower third of the design; similar giants are found in the design of *Lucifer* (cat. 28).

Blake illustrates the passage in which Dante describes Ephialtes shaking himself, like an earthquake with falling stones, an effect partly achieved by rubbing the paper. The effect also suggests snow, perhaps to indicate how Jove continues to threaten the Giants with a thunderous and stormy sky.

There are a few lines on the back in chalk but these do not seem to be a deliberate sketch.

27 *Antaeus Setting Down Dante and Virgil in the Last Circle of Hell*

Pen and water-colour
52.6 x 37.4 cm
Inscr. 'HELL Canto 31' in ink l.r.; and on reverse in pencil, '2' u.r., 'N 3 next at p 3' u.c. and the same, erased, in centre
Watermark: WE
Felton Bequest 1920 1012/3

Exh.: RA 1893 (18); Tate Gallery (41xiii), Nottingham (42xvii) and Edinburgh (67) 1913–14; Melbourne 1957–58 (66); Tate Gallery 1978 (328, repr.); *Poetical Circle* Australia and New Zealand 1979 (60, repr.); Pescara 1983.

Lit.: Rossetti in Gilchrist 1863, p. 220 no. 101j², and 1880, p. 232 no. 123j²; Blunt, 'Blake's Pictorial Imagination' 1943, p. 211, repr. pl. 62d; Hoff 1940, p. 93, repr.; Roe 1953, pp. 124 5 no. 63, repr.; Blunt 1959, p. 90, repr. pl. 59a; Hoff 1961, p. 29, repr. pl. 25; Burke, 'The Eidetic and the Borrowed Image' 1964, pp. 121–2, repr. pl. 90 (reprinted in Essick 1973, pp. 279–80, repr. p. 83); Hoff & Plant 1968, p. 104, repr. in colour p. 105; Klonsky 1980, pp. 90, 151–2, repr. pl. 66; Butlin 1981, pp. 575 6 no. 812 63; Gizzi 1983, p. 144, repr. and in colour; Dean 1986, p. 76, repr. in colour; Lister 1986, no. 61, repr. in colour; Fuller, 'Blake and Dante' 1988, p. 371 n. 7.

Inferno XXXI, 112–43. After their encounter with Ephialtes the poets go further on and come upon Antaeus, the son of Gaea and Poseidon who, invincible as long as he remained in contact with the earth, was conquered by Hercules lifting him off the ground and squeezing him to death in mid-air; as he had not joined in the Giants' attack on the Olympian gods he was left unbound in Hell. Virgil asks Antaeus to set the poets down in the last circle.

Ursula Hoff has pointed out how Blake parallels Dante's imagery of the Carisenda, one of the leaning towers in Bologna, as seen when a cloud is going over it, and also the imagery of a ship's mast in his rigid right arm. Anthony Blunt compares the effectiveness of the Blake giant's clumsy gesture and immense size with the tame depiction in Flaxman's engraving of the same scene (repr. Blunt 1959, pl. 59 b).

This is one of the most finished water-colours of the whole series and shows the sophistication of Blake's last technique in the use of stippling and rubbing and scratching out to produce virtuoso effects. There are pentimenti around the figures of Dante and Virgil and Antaeus's right hand.

The page seems to have been damaged when it was removed from the original volume and has been made up along the left-hand edge. There are a few lines on the back but not enough for one to be certain that these were deliberate.

28 Recto: *Lucifer*
Verso: Slight sketch, perhaps for *Virgil Abashing the Devils*

Pen, ink and water-colour over pencil and black chalk (recto), chalk (verso)
52.7 x 37.2 cm
Inscr. 'HELL/Canto 34' in ink l.r.; and on reverse in pencil, '66' u.r., 'N 33 next at p 51' u.r., the same, erased, in centre, and 'Hell Canto 21' along right-hand edge
Watermark: WE
Felton Bequest 1920 1013/3

Exh.: Melbourne 1957–58; Pescara 1983.

Lit.: Rossetti in Gilchrist 1863, p. 221 no. 101p², and 1880, p. 232 no. 123p²; Roe 1953, pp. 134–6 no. 69, recto repr.; Hoff 1961, p. 30, recto repr. pl. 26;

Burke, 'The Eidetic and the Borrowed Image' 1964, p. 124, recto repr. pl. 98 (reprinted in Essick 1973, p. 290, recto repr. pl. 102); Klonsky 1980, pp. 96, 153–4, recto repr. in colour pl. 72; Butlin 1981, pp. 577–8 no. 812 69; Gizzi 1983, p. 150, recto repr. and in colour.

Inferno XXXIV, 10–81. Dante and Virgil are now in the ninth and last circle, that of the Traitors, and have reached the inner of four concentric rings where traitors to their lords and benefactors are frozen in a kind of building, shining like straw in glass. At the centre stands Lucifer, frozen from the waist down, with three heads and bat-like wings, the flapping of which freezes the heart of Hell, Cocytus. In each mouth he chews on a sinner: Judas Iscariot, Brutus and Cassius.

Roe identifies Lucifer as the three-fold Accuser or Spectre of the Giant Albion and the frozen giant figures as the four Zoas. He also identifies the small figure above the giant's head on the left as Dante, suggesting that Blake shows him in the Pit of Error. Fuller, however, sees the design as a straightforward illustration of Dante's text, and indeed Dante seems to be shown as described in the text at the point when, at Virgil's instigation, he has climbed down Lucifer's shaggy sides to the top of his thighs and Virgil seizes him by the hair and twists him upside down before dragging him out of Hell through an opening in the rock, whereupon Dante sees Lucifer upside down. The small figure is clothed in Dante's characteristic pink.

Joseph Burke has postulated that the figure of Lucifer is based on a print of the Indian goddess Durga which Blake could have seen in Moor's *Hindu Pantheon* (repr. Burke 1964, p. 100; 1973, pl. 101).

The slight sketch on the back could perhaps, as Nicholas Draffin has suggested, be a sketch for *Virgil Abashing the Devils* in the British Museum (Butlin 1981, no. 812 38). Alternatively, it could be related to *The Souls of Those Who Only Repented at the Point of Death* (cat. 30), one of what appear to be two upright figures being shown with arms raised as in that design.

29 Recto: ***The Rest on the Mountain Leading to Purgatory***
Verso: Slight sketch for *The Necromancers and Augurs* (?)

Pen, ink and water-colour over black chalk and pencil (recto), black chalk (verso)
52.7 x 37.2 cm
Inscr. 'P–g Canto 4' in ink l.l.c.; and on reverse in pencil, '64' u.r., 'N 31 next at p 67' u.c., the same erased in centre, and 'Hell Canto 20' along right-hand edge
Watermark: WELGAR 1796
Felton Bequest 1920 1014/3

Exh.: None

Lit.: Rossetti in Gilchrist 1863, p. 221 no. 102d, and 1880, p. 232 no. 124d; Damon 1924, p. 219; Roe 1953, pp. 141–2 no. 73, recto repr.; Hoff 1961, p. 31, recto repr. pl. 27; Klonsky 1980, pp. 101, 154, recto repr. in colour pl. 77; Butlin 1981, p. 579 no. 812 73; Gizzi 1983, p. 155, recto repr.; Fuller, 'Blake and Dante' 1988, pp. 371 n. 7, 372 n. 17.

Purgatorio IV, 46–57. The poets are climbing the steep path that encircles the mountain leading to Purgatory. In the previous design in the Tate Gallery (Butlin 1981, no. 812 74), Dante has called to Virgil in his weariness; now they sit down on a terrace, looking down over the sea. In the text Dante wonders at the direction of the sun but Blake shows it obscured by mist or clouds. Roe suggests that these bands of mist or cloud, which occur in several of the illustrations to Purgatory, represent the different stages of limited vision to be overcome along the way. For Fuller this symbolism derives from Dante's own use of clouds in Canto XVI where the unpurged sins of anger prevent the Wrathful from seeing the sun. The colouring of this design is cooler than in the illustrations to the *Inferno*, being dominated by pinks and greens. For a possible sketch see cat. 25 verso.

There is a slight sketch on the back, apparently of an arm and hand with outspread fingers. According to Nicholas Draffin it may relate to one of the figures in *The Necromancers and Augurs*, also in the National Gallery of Victoria (cat. 15).

30 ***The Souls of Those Who Only Repented at the Point of Death***

Pen, ink and water-colour over pencil and black chalk
37.2 x 52.7 cm
Inscr. 'P–g Canto 5 & 6' in ink l.r.; and on reverse in pencil, with paper held as an upright, '51' u.r., 'N 34 next at p 83' u.c., the same erased in centre, and 'Hell Canto 21' along right-hand edge
Watermark: WE
Felton Bequest 1920 1015/3

Exh.: RA 1893 (20); Melbourne 1957–58 (69); Hamburg and Frankfurt 1975 (212, recto repr.); Tate Gallery 1978 (329, recto repr.).

Lit.: Rossetti in Gilchrist 1863, p. 221 no. 102f, and 1880, p. 233 no. 124f; Roe 1953, pp. 143–4 no. 75, repr.; Hoff 1961, p. 32, repr. pl. 28; Klonsky 1980, pp. 102, 154–5, repr. pl. 78; Butlin 1981, pp. 579–80 no. 812 75; Gizzi 1983, pl. 156, repr.; Fuller, 'Blake and Dante' 1988, p. 353.

Purgatorio V, 37–57 and VI, 28–48. Although Dante describes the souls of those who only repented at the point of death as running, Blake illustrates Dante's simile of flaming vapours and shows the souls as airborne, turning in a great circle. He also seems to show them in pairs, male and female. Roe interprets this as Blake depicting the souls as pairs of Spectres with their Emanations, plunging downwards towards the waters of Ulro, only to be deflected upwards again towards Dante, representing Imagination, who receives them with a gesture of benediction. In fact it is Virgil who receives them while, as Adrian Flick has pointed out, Dante, in red and standing on the right, already looks up towards the summit of the mountain where, Virgil has promised him, he shall see Beatrice, who is to be his guide to Paradise. Fuller denies that there is any particular symbolism here, suggesting that Blake is merely illustrating the text with an extreme literalism; he quotes Yeats's description of Blake as a 'literal realist of imagination' (Fuller, p. 353). The colouring is close to that in cat. 29.

Nicholas Draffin interprets the faint chalk marks on the reverse as perhaps preliminary notes for *The Devil Carrying the Lucchese Magistrate to the Boiling-Pitch Pool of Corrupt Officials*, also at Melbourne (cat. 10), but it seems more likely that they are accidental.

31 *The Lawn with the Kings and Angels*

Pen, ink and water-colour over pencil
37.3 x 52.7 cm
Inscr. 'P–g /Canto 7 & 8' in ink l.c. and '8' in pencil u.r.; and on reverse in pencil, with paper seen as an upright, '33' u.r., 'N 44 next at p 52' u.c., the same, erased, in centre, and 'Vanni Fucci' and 'Hell Canto 25' along right-hand edge
Watermark: WELGAR 1796
Felton Bequest 1920 1016/3

Exh.: Melbourne 1957–58 (70); Tate Gallery 1978 (330, repr.).

Lit.: Rossetti in Gilchrist 1863, p. 221 no. 102g, and 1880, p. 233 no. 124g; Roe 1953, pp. 145–6 no. 76, repr.; Hoff 1961, p. 33, repr. pl. 29; Klonsky 1980, pp. 103, 155, repr. pl. 79; Butlin 1981, p. 580 no. 812 *76*; Gizzi 1983, p. 157, repr.; Fuller, 'Blake and Dante' 1988, p. 371 n. 7.

Purgatorio VII, 64–90 and VIII, 22–48 and 94–108. The poets are now accompanied by Virgil's fellow Mantuan, the poet Sordello and, still in the Anti-Purgatorio, they have come to a lawn scooped out in the mountainside. Here they see a group of Negligent Rulers singing the *Salve Regina* and the evening hymn *Te lucis ante terminum*.

Two angels appear with blunted, flaming swords to guard the kings from a serpent, likened to that which tempted Eve. Dante describes the richly coloured grass and flowers but, as Roe points out, Blake shows the kings in a grove of trees, the symbol of error; this, according to Roe, prevents them from seeing the angels. Fuller, however, sees the design as a straight illustration of the text.

The general colouring is similar to that in the previous two designs at Melbourne. There are pentimenti to the heads of the three poets and also to the angels. One of the inscriptions on the reverse appears to relate to the illustration to the *Inferno* also at Melbourne (cat. 20) but there are no signs of any preliminary sketch.

32 *The Angel Inviting Dante to Enter the Fire*

Pen, ink and water-colour over pencil and black chalk
52.7 x 37.3 cm
Inscr. 'P–g Canto 27' in ink over pencil l.l.; and on reverse in pencil, '40' u.r. and 'Pg Canto 27' along right-hand edge
Watermark: WELGAR 1796
Felton Bequest 1920 1017/3

Exh.: Melbourne 1957–58 (71).

Lit.: Rossetti in Gilchrist 1863, p. 222 no. 102o, and 1880 p. 233 no. 124o; Roe 1953, pp. 157–8 no. 84 and p. 164 n., repr.; Hoff 1961, p. 34, repr. pl. 30; Klonsky 1980, pp. 111, 157 repr. pl. 87; Butlin 1981, p. 582 no. 812 *84*; Gizzi 1983, p. 165, repr.; Fuller, 'Blake and Dante' 1988, p. 371 n. 7, 372 n. 17.

Purgatorio XXVII, 5–36. Blake's previous illustration to *Purgatorio* is for Canto 13 (*The Terrace of Envious Souls*, Fogg Art Museum, Harvard University, Cambridge; Butlin 1981, no. 812 *83*), leaving a large gap, although Blake might well have filled this had he completed the series of illustrations to Dante. Virgil and Dante are now accompanied by the Roman poet Statius, whose *Thebaid* was modelled on Virgil's own *Aeneid*. They are near the summit of the mountain of Purgatory mounting a path the inner side of which is filled with flames, and are confronted by an angel who tells them that the only way forward is by passing through fire. Dante is terrified but Virgil reassures him that, even though he will feel pain, he cannot be destroyed; moreover, beyond the flames he will find Beatrice. Roe suggests that Dante can only leave Beulah through the purging fire of Imagination; the sun of Eden is just partly visible. He sees parallels with the closing passages of both *The Four Zoas* and *Jerusalem*, in which the soul is purged with fire just before its reunion with God. Fuller, on the other hand, considers the design to be a direct illustration of Dante's text.

Blake seems to have changed his design considerably, there being a number of pentimenti in the water to the right of the edge of the cliff, and the sun appears to have been sketched in first at the level of the angel's head.

33 *Dante at the Moment of Entering the Fire*

Pen, ink and water-colour over black chalk and pencil
52.8 x 36.9 cm
Inscr. 'P–g/Canto27' in ink over pencil l.c.; and on reverse in pencil, '20' u.r., 'N 51 next at p 27' u.c., the same, erased, in centre, and 'Hell Canto 28' along right-hand edge
Watermark: WE
Felton Bequest 1920 1018/3

Exh.: RA 1893 (24); Melbourne 1957–58 (72); Tate Gallery 1978 (331, repr.); Pescara 1983.

Lit.: Rossetti in Gilchrist 1863, p. 222 no. 102p, and 1880, p. 233 no. 124p; Roe 1953, pp. 158–9 no. 85, 164 n., repr.; Hoff 1961, p. 35, repr. pl. 31; Klonsky 1980, pp. 15–16, 112, 157, repr. in colour pl. 88; Butlin 1981, pp. 582–3, no. 812 *85*; Gizzi 1983, p. 166, repr. and in colour; Boime 1987, p. 148; Fuller, 'Blake and Dante' 1988, p. 371 n. 7, 371 n. 17.

Purgatorio XXVII, 46–8. The scene immediately follows that in cat. 32 at Melbourne; indeed, it has been suggested, because the path encircling the mountain is now shown ascending in the opposite direction, that this was designed as an alternative to the unfinished cat. 32. Virgil has just entered the flames and has asked Statius to follow Dante in third place rather than coming second. The angel hovers above. Roe suggests that the four female figures floating in the flames ahead of the poets are the Daughters of Beulah or Inspiration, leading the way to Eden. Fuller, however, points out that earlier, in Canto XXV, 121–39, Dante had described spirits in the flames singing hymns.

As in the previous design the colours are now richer than in the earlier depictions of *Purgatorio*, but this design is much more finished. Again there are pentimenti, but none of the drastic reworkings of the previous design, these being confined largely to the two left-hand figures in the flames and Virgil's left arm, although pencil lines suggest further flames in the sky on the left. There is a pencil sketch for the whole composition in the British Museum (Butlin 1981, no. 825, repr. pl. 1076).

34 *The Harlot and the Giant*

Pen, ink and water-colour over pencil and black chalk
37.2 x 52.7 cm
Inscr. 'P–g Canto 32' in ink over pencil l.r.; and on reverse in pencil, with page seen as an upright, '30' u.r. and 'N 36 next at p 92' u.c.
Watermark: WE
Felton Bequest 1920 1019/3

Exh.: Melbourne 1957–58 (73); Hamburg and Frankfurt 1975 (216, repr.); Tate Gallery 1978 (335, repr.); Pescara 1983.

Lit.: Rossetti in Gilchrist 1863, p. 222 no. 102t, and 1880, p. 234 no. 124t; Roe 1953, pp. 171–4 no. 89, repr.; Hoff 1961, pp. 2, 26, repr. pl. 32; Damon 1965, p. 83; Bindman 1977, pp. 218–19; Klonsky 1980, pp. 116, 159, repr. pl. 92; Butlin 1981, p. 584 no. 812 89; Gizzi 1983, p. 170, repr. and in colour; Boime 1987, pp. 109–10, 138, 152, repr. pl. 48; Fuller, 'Blake and Dante' 1988, pp. 365, 371 nn. 7 and 9.

Purgatorio XXXII, 85–7 and 142–53. Dante has entered the Terrestial Paradise or Garden of Eden and Beatrice has replaced Virgil as Dante's guide, addressing him from the car or chariot shown in the two previous designs, *Beatrice on the Car, Matilda and Dante* (British Museum; Butlin 1981, no. 812 87) and *Beatrice Addressing Dante from the Car* (fig. 7, Tate Gallery; Butlin 1981, no. 812 88). After passing through the river of Lethe and seeing Beatrice unveiled for the first time since her death ten years earlier, Dante, still with Statius, follows the divine pageant of the vision shown in the previous designs until they reach the mystic tree of the knowledge of good and evil. Dante then falls asleep and when he awakes the vision has gone and he finds Beatrice seated at the foot of a tree, the roots of which represented for Dante the Roman Empire and the new foliage the church with which it had become united.

However, for Dante, as indeed for Blake, the relationship between church and state had become perverted and the chariot or car of the divine pageant is transformed into a seven-headed beast, probably denoting the seven capital sins, surmounted by the Harlot characterizing the papacy during the 'Babylonian Captivity' at Avignon; the giant represents Phillip the Fair of France, under whose power the papacy had fallen. Dante was immediately concerned with this event, being involved in the political repercussions in Italy. For Blake, a Protestant, the condemnation was more general, the Harlot being seen as the Catholic Church while one of the beast's heads wears a papal tiara. Blake's design is, to a considerable extent, a parody of his *Beatrice Addressing Dante from the Car*, although the figures are on a larger scale. Blake retains the figures of Faith, Hope and Charity from the previous design; they now stand, appalled, on the right.

Blake had already depicted the Whore of Babylon in a water-colour of 1809 (fig. 8), but there it is as an illustration to Revelation XVII, 1–4 (British Museum; Butlin 1981, no. 523, repr. in colour pl. 584).

Fig. 7 William Blake, *Beatrice Addressing Dante from the Car*, 1824–27. Pen and water-colour, 37.1 x 52.7 cm. The Tate Gallery, London

Fig. 8 William Blake, *The Whore of Babylon*, 1809. Pen and water-colour, 26.6 x 22.3 cm. The British Museum, London

35 Recto: ***Dante Adoring Christ***
Verso: Sketch of the Redeemed?

Pen, ink and water-colour over pencil and black chalk (recto), pencil (verso)
52.7 x 37.2 cm
Inscr. '97' in pencil u.r.; and on reverse in pencil, '96' u.l., and, to be seen with left-hand edge as bottom, 'N 43 next at p 33' and 'Vanni Fucci' l.c., '24' and 'Vanni Fucci' l.r., and, with right-hand edge to be seen as bottom, 'Canto 23 Paradiso', erased
Watermark: WELGAR 1796
Felton Bequest 1920 1020/3

Exh.: RA 1893 (28); Melbourne 1957–58 (74); Tate Gallery 1978 (336, recto repr.); Pescara 1983.

Lit.: Rossetti in Gilchrist 1863, p. 222 no. 103a, and 1880, p. 234 no. 125a; Damon 1924, p. 219; Roe 1953, pp. 175–8 no. 90, recto repr.; Kiralis, 'A Possible Revision in Blake's *Jerusalem*' 1955, pp. 203–4; Hoff 1961, p. 37, recto repr. pl. 38; Bindman 1977, p. 219; Klonsky 1980, p. 118, recto repr. in colour pl. 94; Butlin 1981, pp. 584–5 no. 812 *90*; Gizzi 1983, p. 172, recto repr. and in colour; Fuller, 'Blake and Dante' 1988, pp. 365–6, repr. pl. 48.

Paradiso XIV, 97–111. This is the first of Blake's illustrations to *Paradiso*, but he could of course have intended further illustrations from earlier cantos. Dante is shown before the vision of Christ in the heaven of Mars. In the text the vision starts as one of the Cross itself, from which Christ glows out, but Blake omits the Cross, merely showing Christ in the position of the Crucified. Fuller suggests that this demonstrates Blake's view of the Crucifixion as an act of love rather than of atonement, and, like Roe, he likens it to the visions at the end of Blake's writings—*The Four Zoas*, *Milton* and *Jerusalem*; in particular Blake's design is similar to that of plate 76 of *Jerusalem*. Blake also omits the figure of Beatrice, possibly to show Dante worshipping Christ without the intervention of the church. Conversely, Blake goes beyond Dante in showing Christ standing on a glowing sun with two more globes, perhaps the moon on the left and, again, the sun on the right behind his outstretched hands.

The pencil sketch on the reverse probably shows the hosts of the Redeemed from Canto XXIII. Seen the opposite way up to the inscriptions relating to Vanni Fucci (these appear to have no relation to the design) one can see a semi-circle of figures in an arch across the whole design, with rays filling the corners above. In the foreground there seem to be two figures seen from behind, perhaps Dante and Beatrice; that on the right holds its arms outstretched in wonder while the companion's arms are held down by the sides of the body. There are stars between the foreground figures and the semi-circle of the Redeemed beyond.

Unlike most of the pages used by Blake for his Dante illustrations, this seems to have been the left-hand side of an opening, with the inner edge down the right hand side of the composition.

36 ***St Peter Appears to Beatrice and Dante***

Pen, ink and water-colour over black chalk and pencil
37.1 x 52.7 cm
Inscr. on reverse in pencil '99' u.r.
Watermark: WE
Felton Bequest 1920 1021/3

Exh.: Melbourne 1957–58; Pescara 1983.

Lit.: Rossetti in Gilchrist 1863, p. 222 no. 103e, and 1880, p. 234 no. 125e; Roe 1953, pp. 182–3 no. 94, repr.; Hoff 1961, p. 38, repr. pl. 34; Beer 1969, p. 279; Klonsky 1980, pp. 121, 160–1, repr. pl. 97; Butlin 1981, p. 586 no. 812 *94*; Gizzi 1983, p. 175, repr. and in colour; Fuller, 'Blake and Dante' 1988, pp. 351, 371 n. 7.

Paradiso XXIV, 19–33. Dante and Beatrice have risen up through the various spheres of Heaven from Mars by way of Jupiter and Saturn to the eighth sphere, that of the Stellar Heaven in the constellation of Gemini, Dante's natal sign. This is the sphere of the redeemed souls, which appear as flames. St Peter, as so blissful a flame that it eclipses all the others, appears and wheels around Beatrice three times addressing her in divine song. Roe interprets St Peter (shown as old and bearded) as the redeemed Urizen, but Fuller dismisses this interpretation as a mechanically applied intellectual code.

The heads of Dante and Beatrice were originally sketched higher and there are other pentimenti to St Peter's feet.

37 Recto: ***St Peter and St James with Dante and Beatrice***
Verso: Indecipherable sketch

Pen, ink and water-colour over pencil (recto), pencil (verso)
37.1 x 52.7 cm
Inscr. on reverse in pencil, with paper seen as an upright, '102' or '103' or '100' u.r.
Watermark: WE
Felton Bequest 1920 1022/3

Exh.: Melbourne 1957–58 (76).

Lit.: Rossetti in Gilchrist 1863, p. 222 no. 103f, and 1880, p. 234 no. 125f; Roe 1953, pp. 183–4 no. 95, recto repr.; Hoff 1961, p. 39, recto repr. pl. 35; Beer 1969, p. 279; Klonsky 1980, p. 122, 161, recto repr. in colour pl. 98; Butlin 1981, p. 586 no. 812 *95*; Gizzi 1983, p. 176, recto repr.; Dean 1986, p. 78, recto repr. in colour; Fuller, 'Blake and Dante' 1988, p. 371 n. 7.

Paradiso XXV, 13–24. St James appears from out of the sphere containing Christ's first vicars and joins Peter. He questions Dante on Hope, just as Peter had questioned him on Faith. Roe equates St James with another of Blake's four Zoas, Luvah, again in the unfallen state; Fuller regards the design as a direct illustration to Dante's text.

There are traces of a rough pencil sketch on the reverse but it is impossible to make out what this depicts. The last digit of the page number has been damaged and now looks much like a reversed 'C'; a '2' seems the most likely.

38 ***The Queen of Heaven in Glory***

Pen and water-colour over pencil and black chalk
37.1 x 52.8 cm
Inscr. with identifying details of composition: 'Mary' holding 'Scepter' and 'Looking [Glass]'; 'Sun' u.r.; 'Laws' (?), or 'Teams' or 'Thrones' (?) u.l., holding book inscribed 'corded round'; 'Dominions' (?) or 'Dominus' (?) u.r., holding book inscribed 'Bible/ Chaind round'; 'Homer' and 'Aristotle' on two further books c.l. and c.r.
Watermark: WELGAR 1796
Felton Bequest 1920 1023/3

Exh.: Melbourne 1957–58 (77); Hamburg and Frankfurt 1975 (217, repr.); Tate Gallery 1978 (339, repr.); Pescara 1983.

Lit.: Rossetti in Gilchrist 1863, p. 223 no. 103j, and 1880, p. 234 no. 125j; Damon 1924, pp. 219–20; Roe 1953, pp. 193–6 no. 99, repr.; Hoff 1961, p. 40, repr. pl. 36; Beer 1969, p. 280; Roe in Rosenfeld 1969, pp. 158–9, repr. pl. 11; Grant, 'The Fate of Blake's Sun-Flower' 1974, pp. 47–8, repr. pl. 8; Mellor 1974, p. 73; Klonsky 1980, pp. 13–14, 126, 162, repr. in colour pl. 102; Butlin 1981, pp. 587–8 no. 812 99; Gizzi 1983, p. 180, repr. and in colour; Erdman, 'Redefining the Texts of Blake' 1983–84, p. 13; Boime 1987, p. 161; Fuller, 'Blake and Dante' 1988, pp. 360–2, repr. pl. 45.

Paradiso XXX, 97–126; XXXI, 1–21, 55–73 and 112–42; and XXI, 1–9. This is the last of Blake's illustrations to Dante's *Divine Comedy* and it was left unfinished. It shows Dante's vision of the church triumphant. The Redeemed are depicted as a great rose with Beatrice seated in the centre below the Virgin Mary. All commentators are agreed in seeing in this design some condemnation by Blake of Dante's ideas on salvation, although Roe goes considerably further than Fuller. Roe interprets the design as the representation of the evil domination of the Female Will in the form of the Virgin Mary, who is given the attributes of Vala, and Beatrice, seated in a sunflower rather than Dante's mystic rose. The chained 'Bible' on the right is held by a figure that appears to be labelled 'Dominions', while the companion volume on the left, which is 'corded round' and perhaps represents the Old as opposed to the New Testament, is held by a figure labelled almost illegibly with a word that has been read variously as 'Laws', 'Teams', 'Thrones', or even 'Trains' or 'Frame'. While the Testaments are closed, the two other books labelled 'Homer' and 'Aristotle' are open, reflecting Blake's condemnation of Dante's acceptance of the classical tradition.

A similar condemnation is found in Blake's inscription on another design in the Dante series, *Homer Bearing the Sword, and his Companions* (Fogg Art Museum, Harvard University, Cambridge, Massachusetts; Butlin 1981, no. 812 7) and in his preface to *Milton* (Keynes 1969, p. 480). Blake also expressed his views on Aristotle in his annotations—done in about 1820—to Berkeley's *Siris* of 1744, in which he distinguishes Aristotle's idea of God, 'as abstracted or distinct from the Imaginative World', from that of Jesus, Abraham and David; Aristotle also provoked Blake to exclaim 'God is not a Mathematical Diagram' (Keynes 1969, p. 774).

The Virgin Mary is given the usual symbol of her chastity, a lily (as in Flaxman's depiction of the same scene in plate 31 of his illustrations to Dante), but Blake has labelled it 'Scepter', suggesting to Roe that this is an attack on the wordly power of the church triumphant, and to Fuller even that this is an indication that chastity is an instrument of sexual oppression. To Roe the mirror is the 'Vegetable Glass of Nature' in which the material world perceives indirectly rather than clearly the reality of eternal salvation (*A Vision of the Last Judgement*, 1810; Keynes 1969, p. 605).

According to Roe the design parallels plate 53 of *Jerusalem*, in which Vala is shown seated on a sunflower, but Fuller denies the resemblance, particularly pointing out that the rose in this design is nothing like the sunflower in *Jerusalem*. But he does accept that the design is an attack on Dante's classicism and on the erotic element in Dante's text. However, although he sees criticism of Dante's acceptance of the classical past in certain of the other designs, such as *Beatrice Addressing Dante from the Car* (Tate Gallery; Butlin 1981, no. 812 *88*), he points to other representations of Beatrice in which she appears as the ideal love that is part of spiritual salvation, as in *Beatrice and Dante in Gemini Amid the Spheres of Flame* (Ashmolean Museum, Oxford; Butlin 1981, no. 812 *93*).

'Eternity in an Hour': The Prints of William Blake

Ted Gott
Research Associate, Department of Prints and Drawings,
National Gallery of Victoria

A Family of New South Wales

It is curious that while William Blake's commercial engravings form such a large part of his *oeuvre*, they have only recently received due attention, and still await a complete catalogue.[1] The more than 380 commercial prints Blake executed, however, shaped his art and outlook in fundamental ways. His attitudes to the craft by which he supported himself were ambivalent and often contradictory. His own reproductive work he considered superior to the norm, enabling him to declare complacently that he had 'no objection to Engraving after another Artist'.[2] But the work of many of his peers filled him with distaste, moving him to exclaim: 'Whoever looks at any of the Great & Expensive Works of Engraving that have been Publish'd by English Traders must feel a Loathing & disgust' (N 63).[3]

At the age of fifteen, in 1772, Blake was apprenticed to James Basire (1730–1802), engraver to the Society of Antiquaries. Here he received a thorough training in the preparation, etching and engraving, and printing of copper-plates for reproductive illustration. Blake was bound to James Basire for seven years, and probably lived in his house, in Lincoln's Inn Fields, throughout this long apprenticeship. Basire's style of antiquarian engraving demanded expertise at rendering firm and determinate outlines, and the ability to record clear and accurate detail within the limitations of the medium's linear conventions. The engravings of medieval tomb sculptures in Westminster Abbey which Blake executed at this time for Richard Gough's *Sepulchral Monuments in Great Britain*, under his master's direction and in his concise linear manner, show his complete absorption of Basire's graphic principles.

After leaving Basire's workshop in 1779 Blake was admitted into the Royal Academy's Antique School, where with youthful idealism he conceived a career for himself as a history painter. Economic necessities, however, required him to undertake repeated commissions for commercial book illustration, and he probably ceased formal attendance at the academy after a few months. Blake worked principally for the book publishers Joseph Johnson and Harrison and Company, frequently engraving designs by Thomas Stothard (1755–1834), a painter whom he had befriended while at the academy. When his father died in 1784 he may have used a small inheritance to open a print shop with a fellow apprentice of Basire, James Parker; and it may also have been at this time that Blake acquired the rolling press on which he was to print his own original graphics for the remainder of his life. The two plates known to have been signed by Blake and Parker as print-publishers are commercial stipple engravings after Stothard. The partnership was short-lived, however, and had apparently ended by Christmas 1785. Thereafter Blake relied once more on the reproductive commissions provided by Joseph Johnson and other book publishers.

Blake's *A Family of New South Wales* (cat. 40), engraved in 1792 after a sketch by Philip Gidley King (fig. 9) for John Hunter's *Historical Journal* (1796), provides a good example of his classic reproductive engraving style.[4] Blake had been trained by James Basire in the 'mixed method' of journeyman engraving, involving a combination of both etching and burin engraving on the same copper-plate. The basic outlines of the design, and intricate areas such as the myriad minute curls of vegetation, were drawn freely onto a wax-covered plate by scratching the required design out of the wax with an etching needle. The plate was then placed in an acid bath, and the areas of copper exposed by the 'needle drawing' were corroded away or bitten down by the acid. The high degree of finish on the Aboriginal figures was completed with an engraving burin, a knife-like steel tool which is pushed through the bare copper, ploughing furrows which print as smooth, clean-edged lines. Curved lines were made by placing the copper-plate on a sandbag and turning it into the incising burin; and different widths of line were achieved by holding the burin at various angles while cutting. To build up mass and texture Blake also used the 'dot and lozenge' engraving technique, whereby the interstices between crossing engraved lines are filled with short flicks of the burin which 'colour' the overall effect conveyed to the eye.

The physical and mental exigencies of engraving led, by the end of the eighteenth century, to a rigid systematization of the technique. The linear freedom of sketching or etching was codified to the point of abstraction in engraving. The engraver's apprentice learned to reduce the discrete parts of any composition to an almost mathematical sequence of linear formulae, which demanded an unquestioning submission in handling the burin. Robert Essick has succinctly analysed the way in which Blake's original and innovative printmaking efforts were constantly steered by an attempt to escape from the reductive mechanization of 'this quantified world of eighteenth-century copy engraving'. In Essick's view, Blake's 'labours as a technical innovator were a search for graphic processes that overcame the mechanical and illusionistic division of space into dots and grids, and the assembly-line division of the artist's life into an unimaginative repetition of commercial tasks'.[5] Ironically, throughout his life

A FAMILY OF NEW SOUTH WALES

40 *A Family of New South Wales*, 1792

Blake would be required to work in the constraining reproductive mode simply in order to earn a living.

John Hunter (1737–1821) arrived in Australia with the First Fleet in January 1788 as second captain of the *Sirius* under the command of Captain Arthur Phillip. He helped Phillip survey the area around Port Jackson where Sydney was founded. When the *Sirius* under his command was wrecked off Norfolk Island in February 1790, he lived there with his crew for eleven months. In 1792 he returned to England to stand trial over the sinking of the *Sirius*, and during the return voyage reworked his Australasian diaries for publication. *An Historical Journal of the Transactions at Port Jackson and Norfolk Island*, ornamented with seventeen 'Maps, Charts, Views, & other embellishments', appeared in 1793. At his court-martial Hunter was exonerated of all blame for the loss of the *Sirius*, and his *Historical Journal*, for which some 500 advance subscriptions had been collected, became a respectable publishing success.

Philip Gidley King (1758–1808) also sailed to Australia with Phillip's First Fleet, on the *Supply*, and had been appointed commander of the settlement on Norfolk Island, a position he still held when the *Sirius* was wrecked on its shores in 1790. Hunter had been carrying orders for King's recall to England when his ship went down on the island's reefs. While Hunter and his men remained on Norfolk Island, King was able to reach Sydney aboard the *Supply*, and thence make his way back to London to report on the progress of the colony. He may have taken his drawing of *A Family of New South Wales* with him then, or given it to Hunter at this time. His own journal of life on the First Fleet voyage and in the new colony from 1787 to 1790 was published as an appendix to Hunter's *Historical Journal*. Even as King was sailing back to London, a dispatch was on its way to Sydney from the British secretary of state appointing him lieutenant-governor of Norfolk Island, a position he formally assumed in November 1791. Thus he is referred to as 'Governor King' on Blake's engraving.

John Hunter and Philip Gidley King were both to play a significant role in Australia's early settlement. In September 1795 Hunter was again posted to Sydney, as governor of the colony, an authority he struggled to keep against the power of John Macarthur and the military clique of the New South Wales Corps. King took over from Hunter as governor of New South Wales in 1800, and he also battled unsuccessfully with Macarthur and the Corps until his own retirement in 1806 in favour of the ill-fated Captain William Bligh.[6]

Hunter's *Historical Journal* was published twice in the same year. A deluxe quarto edition with the full complement of plates was released in January 1793; Blake's engraving was bound here opposite page 414. At some time around July 1793 Hunter's narrative was republished as a small quarto volume, accompanied by only four plates. Blake's *Family* was again included in the octavo issue, but folded in half to fit into the smaller book. The National Gallery of Victoria's impression of the *Family* is apparently from a dismembered copy of the quarto edition.[7]

Bernard Smith has pointed to the classical idealization King's plain sketch underwent in Blake's

Fig. 9 Philip Gidley King, *Preliminary Drawing for 'A Family of New South Wales'*. Wash drawing, 23.5 x 15.8 cm. Mitchell Library, Sydney

meticulously crafted engraving. The lean, stringy limbs of King's Aborigines have been more elegantly moulded; pendulous breasts have been firmed up; and sharply caricatured features are, on the mother and elder child at least, smoothed into crisp Grecian profiles. In part, Smith argued, these changes were due to the lavish nature of the publication for which the engraving was executed. Hunter's *Journal* was one of those 'expensive quartos handsomely produced by subscription and designed to interest virtuosi and men of taste for whom the image of the native as a noble savage still held a strong quasi-aesthetic appeal'.[8] He also related the nobility and dignity of these Aborigines to the purity and grace of Blake's treatment of the human body and human emotions in the *Songs of Innocence*. It is possible, however, that this romantic classicizing of the Aborigines' physical appearance was not entirely due to Blake himself, and that he worked from an already idealized finished copy-drawing of King's sketch from another journeyman's hand. This is suggested by the fact that the coastline and seascape background in King's sketch—motifs Blake had used to great atmospheric advantage when engraving Surinam Negroes for John Stedman at roughly the same time—are absent from his *Family* and replaced by repetitive patches of etched vegetation. It would be unusual for Blake to have sacrificed a novel antipodean setting for such a nondescript alternative.[9]

Fig. 10 William Blake (probably after John Stedman), *A Negro Hung Alive by the Ribs to a Gallows*, 1792. Etching and engraving, 18 x 13.1 cm. Collection of Robert N. Essick

If Blake was entirely responsible for refining King's scrawny figural group, then he may well have been influenced by his concurrent engravings after Stedman. By at least December 1791 he was at work for Joseph Johnson, transferring to copper sixteen illustrations to Captain John Gabriel Stedman's *Narrative, of a Five Years' Expedition, Against the Revolted Negroes of Surinam, in Guiana, on the Wild Coast of South America; from the year 1772 to 1777*. Stedman's volume did not reach completion until 1796, but Blake's plates were engraved between 1791 and 1793, and four of them are dated 1 December 1792, almost exactly contemporaneous with the *Family of New South Wales*. Stedman's *Narrative* detailed numerous instances of the harrowing punishments inflicted on rebel Surinam Negroes by vengeful slave-owners. And Blake copied Stedman's blunt and compelling designs depicting these unspeakable tortures. His *Negro Hung Alive by the Ribs to a Gallows* (fig. 10) is a typical example.

The year 1792 marked a high point in the Abolitionists' campaign to end the slave trade, although it was ultimately to be defeated in the British parliament. Blake had worked very closely with Stedman throughout the production of his *Narrative*, and by 1795 was a trusted friend and confidant of the author. David Erdman has argued that Blake's strong attack on slavery in his illuminated poem *Visions of the Daughters of Albion* (1793) was influenced by Stedman's forceful condemnation of 'the clang of the whip and the dismall yells' of the crucifixions, floggings and mutilations he witnessed at Surinam.[10] But Stedman himself was opposed not to slavery as an institution, merely to the legal excesses of European 'justice'. Nevertheless Blake's abhorrence, expressed in the *Visions*, of 'the voice of slaves beneath the sun, and children bought with money', should be borne in mind when considering the elegant nobility, nurtured by the blessings of freedom, with which he has endowed his *Family of New South Wales*.[11]

Songs of Innocence

Blake's artistic yearnings were to lead him down paths dramatically different from those normally traversed by a reproductive journeyman engraver. In the early 1780s he was welcomed into the literary salon of Harriet Mathew, wife of the Reverend A. S. Mathew, where his creative talents blossomed. J. T. Smith later recalled the commanding impression Blake made in this milieu:

> At that lady's most agreeable conversaziones I first met William Blake, the artist, to whom she and Mr. Flaxman had been truly kind. There I have often heard him read and sing several of his poems. He was listened to by the company with profound silence, and allowed by most of the visitors to possess original and extra-ordinary talent.[12]

Clearly impressed, the Mathews financed a small printing of Blake's poetical juvenilia, released as *Poetical Sketches by W. B.* in 1783, 'the production of untutored youth' as the Reverend Mathew put it in the volume's preface. The following year Blake's satirical parody (probably of the Mathews's coterie), surviving as a unique manuscript known as *An Island in the Moon* (Fitzwilliam Museum, Cambridge), was interspersed with burlesque verses and children's songs. Between 1784 and 1789 the latter were expanded into the exquisite corpus of poems celebrating pastoral tranquillity and childhood innocence, published in 1789 as the *Songs of Innocence*.[13]

In these same years Blake was struggling to find a reproductive technique which would deliver him from dependence on the commercial publishing world. *An Island in the Moon* once contained a section on 'Illuminating the Manuscript'; its only surviving fragment records the boast of an unidentified speaker that 'I would have all the writing Engraved instead of Printed, & at every other leaf a high finish'd print—all in three Volumes folio—& sell them a hundred pounds apiece. They would print off two thousand'.[14] In January 1784 George Cumberland, later to become a close friend of the artist, was also writing of 'my new mode of Printing' which 'is capable of Printing 2000 if I wanted them'.[15] Cumberland's discovery was the facility of etching texts instead of setting them in movable type, and the coincidence of both accounts suggests that he and Blake were already acquainted and working together towards streamlining graphic techniques. The solution which Blake eventually hit

39 c *The Divine Image*

39 e *A Cradle Song* (first plate)

39 d *Infant Joy*

39 f *A Cradle Song* (second plate)

upon was dramatically described by J. T. Smith:

> Blake after deeply perplexing himself as to the mode of accomplishing the publication of his illustrated songs, without their being subject to the expense of letterpress, his brother Robert stood before him in one of his visionary imaginations, and so decidedly directed him in the way in which he ought to proceed, that he immediately followed his advice, by writing his poetry, and drawing his marginal subjects of embellishments in outline upon the copper-plate with an impervious liquid, and then eating the plain parts or lights away with aquafortis considerably below them, so that the outlines were left as a stereotype. The plates in this state were then printed in any tint that he wished, to enable him or Mrs. Blake to colour the marginal figures up by hand in imitation of drawing.[16]

The relief plates created in this manner were revolutionary in the context of a market organized around the division of labour between artist, engraver, printer and publisher. By etching his own plates, printing them on his own rolling press, colouring them, and stitching them up for sale himself, Blake was attempting a more profitable unification of labour. At the same time hand-colouring and deliberate variations in the printing made each page a unique artistic object, thereby liberating Blake from the mathematical regularity of formula reproductive engraving. Two small collections of aphorisms, *There is no Natural Religion* and *All Religions are One*, record Blake's initial relief-printing experiments in 1788. The *Songs of Innocence* (cat. 39 a–n) and *The Book of Thel* (also 1789) were his first major publications utilizing the new technique.

Modern scholarship is agreed on the basic principles of the relief etching method Blake used for the *Songs of Innocence*. Both text and design were apparently painted onto the copper-plate in an acid-resistant stopping-out varnish which was applied with a thin brush. Before hardening, this stopping-out ground could easily be scraped and shaped to accommodate corrections of text or image. After the varnish had hardened the plate was covered with acid, which etched away all areas of exposed copper. The design painted with stopping out mixture remained untouched, and stood raised in relief. Once the stopping-out mixture had been cleaned off the plate this relief surface could be inked up and printed much like a wood-block.

A fragment of a rejected plate from Blake's prophetic book *America* (fig. 11) illustrates the type of raised surface from which the *Songs of Innocence* designs were printed. Rather than immersing the copper-plate in an acid bath, Blake used the dike method of etching, building a wall of sealing wax around the edges of the plate and then pouring the acid directly onto the copper. This process left irregular borders of unetched metal around the plate where the wax had protected the copper; even though Blake clean-wiped the plates before printing, these borders can still be faintly seen on certain designs of the Melbourne *Songs* (for example, *The

Fig. 11 William Blake, *Fragment of a Cancelled Plate from 'America, A Prophecy'*, 1793. Relief-etched copper-plate, 8 x 5.7 cm. National Gallery of Art, Washington, DC. Rosenwald Collection

Divine Image*). Occasionally Blake opened up portions of a stopped-out design with white-line etching, drawing thin lines with a needle through the acid resist. These were then etched through and, when the image was printed in relief, showed as networks of thin white lines against the dark relief plateaus. Such white-line etched areas are found on a number of the *Songs of Innocence* plates.[17]

Scholars have clashed, however, over the particularities of Blake's illuminated printmaking. Working at Stanley William Hayter's Atelier 17 in New York in the 1940s, Hayter, Joan Miró and Ruthven Todd concluded that Blake could not have written his texts backwards on the plate, but must have transferred them from a damp sheet of paper on which the writing was executed normally with stopping-out varnish. Pointing to the peculiar reticulations of the ink on some of Blake's relief prints and the shallowness of the etched basins on the *America* fragment, they argued that Blake could not have inked the plate with a dabber or roller (which would have fouled the whites), but must have transferred the pigment from another inked but blank plate pressed sandwich-style onto the relief-etched design.[18]

In the early 1970s John Wright also experimented with counter-proving Blake's text areas from dampened paper and, more significantly, analysed Blake's method of step-etching, whereby plates were repeatedly removed from the action of the acid and their designs repainted with acid-resistant varnish to protect delicate images or letters during the next biting.[19] Most recently, Robert Essick has argued persuasively that Blake *did* write his poems

Fig. 13 William Blake, *The Little Black Boy* (first plate), single leaf from *Songs of Innocence*, 1789. Relief etching finished with water-colour, 11 x 6.9 cm. The Fitzwilliam Museum, Cambridge. Estate of Sir Geoffrey Keynes, 1985

39 a–n ***Songs of Innocence*** **1789 (coloured before 1794)**

39 a *The Little Girl Lost* (second plate); *The Little Girl Found* (first plate)

Fig. 14 William Blake, *The Little Black Boy* (second plate), single leaf from *Songs of Innocence*, 1789. Relief etching finished with water-colour, 11.1 x 6.8 cm. The Fitzwilliam Museum, Cambridge. Estate of Sir Geoffrey Keynes, 1985

39 b *The Little Girl Found* (second plate)

backwards onto the plate with a feather or brush charged with stopping-out varnish—not a difficult feat when one considers that 'as a professional engraver, Blake was trained from the age of 15 to design, write, see, and think in reverse'.[20] Essick has also convincingly shown that Blake inked his plates with a sheepskin-covered type-printer's inking ball, which would produce the reticulated surfaces that characterize many of his designs.

The history of the various printings of the *Songs of Innocence* is complex and confusing. The earliest copies evidently contained thirty-one plates bound in varying orders. By 1794 Blake had completed his companion group of *Songs of Experience*, and published *Songs of Innocence and of Experience Shewing the Two Contrary States of the Human Soul* as a total of fifty plates (later expanded to fifty-four plates). *The Little Girl Lost* and *The Little Girl Found* were now transferred to *Experience*, and are absent after 1794 from the separate copies of the *Songs of Innocence* which Blake continued to issue throughout his life. Keynes and Wolf, supplemented by Gerald Bentley, recorded a total of twenty-five extant copies of the separate *Songs of Innocence* (numbered A to Y for identification) and twenty-seven copies of the combined *Songs of Innocence and of Experience* (numbered A to AA). Bentley listed a bewildering thirty-four separate ways in which the plates of the *Songs* were arranged by Blake in different copies of the books.[21]

Melbourne's Copy X (cat. 39 a–n) is one of only ten known copies of the *Songs of Innocence* printed before the addition of *Songs of Experience* in 1794. Its restrained and delicate coloration is characteristic of these early versions, in which the poems are printed on both sides of each leaf. Pale water-colour washes are applied sparingly and non-illusionistically to the principal motifs of each design. Text areas are left bare and therefore emphatically legible (exceptions being 'On Another's Sorrow' and 'The Voice of the Ancient Bard'). The austerity and simplicity of Blake's use of water-colour here parallels the 'innocence' and openness of his poetic language, providing a gentle visual lyricism which accords with the *Songs*' 'Sweet dreams of pleasant streams / By happy silent moony beams' ('A Cradle Song'). Blake continued to print separate copies of the *Songs of Innocence* after 1794. The poems seem to have been printed on only one side of the leaf from 1796 onwards, and their illumination moved towards brighter colours and heavier visual effects. The *Innocence* designs in Copy I of the combined *Songs of Innocence and of Experience* (Widener Library, Harvard) are printed in a strong, dark brown ink and brightly coloured, with bold pink, blue and yellow tints juxtaposed dramatically. The text areas are filled in with alternating layers of coloured wash.

Fig. 12 William Blake, *Songs of Innocence*, 1789. Relief etchings finished with water-colour. Copy X before disbinding. National Gallery of Victoria. Felton Bequest, 1988

Later copies of the *Songs* became ever more gorgeous in printing and coloration. Joseph Viscomi has defined an 'evolution from print-as-page to print-as-painting' in the late versions of Blake's illuminated books, arguing that 'by reprinting his books on only one side of the sheet, Blake changed the focus of attention' and 'forced the reader to experience the book as a physical, beautiful artifact, not just as a vehicle for narrative and pictorial ideas'.[22] And Gerald Bentley noted that some of Blake's contemporaries seem to have preferred the imagery of the *Songs*' designs over the actual poems, which may account for certain later copies where the text is virtually illegible beneath layers of intense illumination.[23] Copy AA of the combined *Songs of Innocence and of Experience* (*c.* 1815–25, Fitzwilliam Museum, Cambridge), purchased from Blake by Mrs Eliza Aders in 1825, is richly and sombrely painted. Dark blue, green and purple washes cover the plates entirely, orange framing lines are painted around every image, and the titles and many details of each design are picked out in gold. The deep muted blues, warm orange printing ink and gold highlights combine with luxurious effect, giving the volume a jewel-like character evocative of medieval illuminated missals.

The fragmentary Copy X of the *Songs of Innocence* (cat. 39 a–n) was unrecorded until 1964, when it appeared at auction in London as a group of seven separate leaves, unbound; and it has never been fully described or reproduced. Sold in 1964 by an anonymous owner, it was acquired by the London dealer Alan G. Thomas, and then sold to Raymond Lister. After a light cleaning, Lister had the leaves elegantly bound in cream morocco leather by Gray of Cambridge (fig. 12). The plates were carefully tipped to Japan stubs rather than sewn to a new spine, thus retaining the integrity of the original sheets, and Raymond Lister's book-plate was pasted into the front of this modern binding. In this format it was exhibited twice, at Frankfurt and Hamburg in 1975, and at Cambridge in 1984. By 1985 this copy of the *Songs of Innocence* had returned to the sale rooms, first offered by Shanaugh Fitzgerald and then by Sotheby's, London. In 1988 Copy X was acquired for the National Gallery of Victoria by the Felton Bequest from the London dealers Garton and Company. The leaves have now been removed and mounted separately for display. The sensitivity and practicality of Gray's binding, however, will allow

39 k *Holy Thursday*

39 m *Spring* (second plate)

39 l *The Voice of the Ancient Bard*

39 n *The School-Boy*

39 g *The Little Boy Lost*

39 h *The Little Boy Found*

39 i *Nurse's Song*

39 j *On Another's Sorrow*

Copy X to be re-formed as a book without interference to the delicate condition of the surviving leaves.[24]

All the plates of Copy X are printed on similar sheets of unbleached wove paper. The fourth leaf bears the faint watermark E & P, an abbreviation of the paper-making firm Edmeads and Pine. Each design is printed in a pale green ink, which appears brownish in certain areas. The plates are generally well-printed, with the ink displaying the slight reticulation (or surface mottling) which Essick has shown to be characteristic of tacky ink printed onto dry paper.[25] On six of the designs individual letters in the text have been strengthened with blue wash, but overall the text areas stand out clearly and distinctly, free of tinted background washes. The fourteen designs are printed on both sides of the extant leaves, and Blake has clean-wiped the dike-etch borders of the copper-plates before printing, although their outlines still show clearly on some leaves. This care was not extended to the registration. The plates were pulled through a rolling press with sufficient pressure to emboss the plate edges into the paper, causing them to be seen on the reverse of the sheet. Little attention was paid to aligning the edges of one plate with those showing through from the plate printed on the verso of the same leaf. This can produce disconcerting combinations of angles around the borders of the poems, an effect Blake appears to have allowed to reinforce the hand-made aesthetic of the early *Songs of Innocence*. As in other early copies of the *Songs*, Blake has occasionally made the parameters of the water-coloured designs smaller than the overall plate mark.

The leaves of Copy X have been numbered by a modern hand at the upper right corner of each page. These numbers follow Keynes's and Wolf's standardization for the *Songs of Innocence and of Experience*, which was based on the continuous foliation Blake himself provided for late printings of both volumes after 1815; this numbering system was also used by Erdman.[26] Since these ethereal sheets evidently derive from an early printing and colouring of the separate *Songs of Innocence* rather than a later composite copy, they should perhaps have been annotated with the standard plate numbers Keynes and Wolf allotted to the earlier copies of the *Songs of Innocence*, which are given here in the catalogue entries. At any rate, neither numbering system enables us to reconstruct the order in which the sheets were first sewn up by Blake, nor to conjecture the original size of the volume (although presumably Copy X did once include the first plates of *The Little Girl Lost* and *Spring*).

The *Songs of Innocence* were originally bound very humbly, with the various leaves simply gathered together and stitched by Blake between plain paper covers. Copies E and G, belonging to the New York Public Library and Mr Paul Mellon respectively, retain their original buff and blue-grey paper wrappers; most surviving copies, however, have either been dismembered subsequently or rebound in more elaborate materials. Since the sheets for each volume were sewn together as a distinct group by Blake or his wife, their leaf sizes and the distances between their stitch-holes provide DNA-like data vital to the assembly of scattered remnants.

A single leaf in the Fitzwilliam Museum, Cambridge, surely once formed part of Melbourne's Copy X of the *Songs of Innocence* (figs 13, 14).[27] Bearing the two designs for *The Little Black Boy* on its recto and verso, it is printed in green ink on a sheet of similar pale cream wove paper measuring 18.9 x 13.6 cm. This does not accord with the size of the leaves in the other surviving early copy printed in green (Copy I, Huntington Library, California), but matches the Melbourne leaves. The spacing of the three stitch-holes on the Cambridge leaf (the first hole 5.3 cm from the top of the sheet, and the others 3.8 and 3.9 cm apart), also agrees exactly with the holes found on the seven Melbourne leaves, which would seem to rule out coincidence. The Cambridge leaf is also printed in a pale green ink, which appears brownish in parts in a fashion similar to several of the plates of Copy X; and its *Little Black Boy* plates are tinted with delicate, classically restrained and cool water-colour washes which relate closely to the mood and execution of the National Gallery of Victoria's fourteen designs. The Fitzwilliam's single leaf once formed part of the collection of the great Blake scholar Geoffrey Keynes, who noted by way of provenance only that it had been removed from an extra-illustrated copy of Gilchrist's 1863 *Life of Blake*.[28] There is therefore no present evidence pointing to when the Cambridge leaf was separated from the Melbourne group.

The appearance of the *Songs of Innocence* is deceptively simple and fresh, belying the complexity of its genesis. The *Songs* have been analysed in the context of a strong eighteenth-century tradition of moralizing hymns for the instruction of children, and their language related to the structural simplicity and metaphorical richness of the biblical Psalms.[29] Blake's attempts to combine the roles of artist and publisher with his innovative stereotype printing have been linked to the rise of new industrial design techniques. The elaborately floral motifs which weave through the borders of poems such as 'Infant Joy' and 'A Cradle Song', have been compared with eighteenth-century embroidery and the commercially successful patterns of the English textile-printing industry.[30] The increasingly elaborate water-colour finishing of the *Songs* is due, it has been argued, to Blake's appreciation of medieval manuscript illumination.[31] And the importance of standard eighteenth-century illustrated book design has been signalled as the constrictive convention against which Blake rebelled with the 'hand-made' and idiosyncratic aesthetic of his own illuminated books.[32]

Geoffrey Keynes succinctly described the mood of the *Songs of Innocence* as 'the unalloyed joy and discovery of beauty, truth, and love', which he contrasted with Blake's 'disappointment upon a second look at the world' in the poems of *Songs of Experience*. David Erdman, however, maintained that 'the cultivation of innocence is itself a form of social criticism', while Northrop Frye has argued that the *Songs of Innocence* 'satirize the state of experience'.[33] Recent scholarship has pursued the reading of sinister undercurrents beneath the surface gaiety of the *Innocence* cycle.[34]

Thoughts on Outline

Sales of the illuminated books alone were not sufficient to support Blake financially. For most of his career he was still obliged to rely on commercial engraving to guarantee some source of regular income. Frequently commissions came from friends who shared Blake's aesthetic outlook or were aware of his financial plight.

George Cumberland (1754–1848) was a dilettante author, collector and amateur artist who had come into a modest independent income. As a student at the Royal Academy in the 1770s he befriended Thomas Stothard, and he had probably made Blake's acquaintance by 1784 when, as noted earlier, his idea for etching text on copper may have influenced Blake's experiments with relief printing. Upon receiving his inheritance Cumberland moved to Italy, and spent five years, from 1785 to 1790, studying classical sculpture and collecting Italian old master prints.

He returned to England deeply committed to the promotion of art as a catalyst for the betterment of society. His *Some Anecdotes of the Life of Julio Bonasone, a Bolognese Artist* (1793) offered as an appendix 'A Plan for the Improvement of the Arts in England', in which he argued for the founding of a national gallery to display Greek sculpture. Cumberland's *Thoughts on Outline*, likewise 'stimulated by the purest affection for the Fine Arts' (p. 1), was a polemical tract in which he argued for a return to strong, pure outline, the element of genius in both classical sculpture and the works of Michelangelo and Raphael, and the sole salvation of British art and design. To help explicate his at times obscure discourse, Cumberland incorporated twenty-four line engravings into the volume; these were based on his own drawings, pseudo-antique designs blending composite memories of vases and statues he had seen on his travels, and inspired in part by Greek and Latin verse. Blake was commissioned to engrave eight of these compositions (cat. 41 a–h).[35]

Cumberland found in Blake a strong supporter of his passion for both strong outlines and the monuments of classical antiquity. Blake had earlier drawn careful copies after Pierre François d'Hancarville's *Collection of Etruscan, Greek and Roman Antiquities from the Cabinet of the Honorable William Hamilton* (1766–67), a series of plates after Greek vases printed on a red ground to simulate the original pottery (fig. 15).[36] Cumberland may have known of these, and certainly would have seen the four engravings Blake undertook for James Stuart and Nicholas Revett's *Antiquities of Athens* (a commission he evidently secured for Blake in 1791), as well as his copies of the Portland Vase engraved for Erasmus Darwin's *Botanic Garden* (1791).[37]

Ideologically, Blake was ideally suited to collaborate with Cumberland. The author's concern to restore 'the pure line of sober rectitude, and flourishing improvement' (p. 7) accords with Blake's

Fig. 15 William Blake, *Figures from a Greek Vase, After d'Hancarville*. Pen over pencil, 27.4 x 41.9 cm. The British Museum, London

41 a–h ***Thoughts on Outline*** **1794–95**

41 a *Psyche Disobeys*

artistic credo of 1809 'that the more distinct, sharp, and wirey the bounding line, the more perfect the work of art' and references to the virtue of 'the hard and wirey line of rectitude'.[38] For Cumberland 'pure Outline' was perfectly embodied in the engravings of Marcantonio Raimondi after Raphael in which 'freedom united with correctness [was] indelibly transmitted to posterity' (p. 27); Blake similarly exhorted 'Ye English Engravers' in the 'Public Address' section of his *Notebook* to 'come down from your high flights' and 'condescend to study Marc Antonio & Albert Durer' (N 56). While Blake's comments were set down fifteen years later, in 1809–10, he surely discussed these ideas with Cumberland much earlier, and studied Cumberland's vast collection of prints by Raimondi and dozens of other early Italian engravers.

It has recently been proposed that Cumberland's enthusiasm for Cennino Cennini's *Libro dell'Arte* (or *Craftsman's Handbook*) *c.* 1400, which he had studied in Italy, sparked Blake's experimentation with 'fresco' pictures in the second half of the 1790s, and this gives us some measure of their conversations on Italian art during the *Thoughts on Outline* project.[39] As late as 1827, when he finally published a full catalogue of his collection (which Blake had seen in 1823), Cumberland was still extolling Raimondi's Italianate outline: 'no one has better understood depth, character or correctness of outline, (that absolutely necessary quality), in which so many have been deficient'.[40]

Cumberland was clearly an amateur in the complex field of printmaking, and he received Blake's instruction on numerous aspects of the craft during the production of *Thoughts on Outline*. Blake sent him advice on 'laying on the Wax' ground on etching plates and 'the pressure necessary to roll off the lines' when printing, while Cumberland in turn wrote out memos such as his account of '*Blakes* Instructions to Print Copper Plates'.[41] Blake's own notes—'To Engrave on Pewter', 'To Woodcut on Pewter' and 'To Woodcut on Copper'—were also probably jotted down in his *Notebook* around 1794 (N 4), as David Erdman cites Cumberland's memorandum on the back of a letter of 16 December 1794 that 'Blakes method [was] biting whites'.[42] But most of Blake's input related to the fashioning and printing of *engraved* lines, as only his own pair of *Psyche* plates (cat. 41 a, b) contain etched cameo settings, 'backgrounded so as to imitate the Greek vases' as

41 b *Psyche Repents*

Cumberland later put it.[43] Cumberland himself acknowledged this collaboration in an appendix added to *Thoughts on Outline*:

> Neither do I presume to say, that all the lines were the result of study, as, indeed, they ought to have been;—but one thing may be asserted of this work, which can be said of few others that have passed the hands of an engraver, which is that *Mr. Blake* has condescended to take upon him the laborious office of making them, I may say, fac-similes of my originals: a compliment, from a man of his extraordinary genius and abilities, the highest, I believe, I shall ever receive:—and I am indebted to his generous impartiality for the instruction which encouraged me to execute a great part of the plates myself; enabling me thereby to reduce considerably the price of the book. (pp. 48–9)

And there is no doubt that both Cumberland and the 'look' of *Thoughts on Outline* benefited from Blake's involvement in the project. Most of the plates executed by Cumberland are marked by the ineptness of his engraving: awkward, broken contours appear where he has been unable to return the engraving tool evenly to the plate, and overlapping outlines show his hesitation and imprecision when cutting the metal. While sometimes unable to rise above the mediocrity of Cumberland's designs, Blake's plates all reveal the manual confidence, the free assurance in cutting smooth rounded lines of a skilled craftsman. Occasionally, as in the ninth plate, Cumberland himself succeeds in rendering a stronger, smoother outline; this suggests Blake's influential presence, surely showing his friend how to turn the copper-plate cleanly before the engraving tool instead of lifting the tool at each shift of contour.

Thoughts on Outline was entered at Stationer's Hall on 22 November 1796. Although the title-page bears the imprint 'Sold by Messrs. Robinson, Paternoster-Row; and T. Egerton, Whitehall', Gerald Bentley has documented that for reasons unknown Cumberland soon withdrew the *Thoughts* from Egerton, and never sent the volume to Robinson. At some stage Cumberland also made a correction to the motto on the title-page—'*Anche io son pittore*' being pasted over the printing error '*Ainsi io son pittore*'. It is doubtful that Cumberland was even moderately successful in marketing *Thoughts on*

41 c *Venus Councels Cupid*

From an original Invention by G. Cumberland. Eng.d by W Blake. Publishd as the Act directs Nov.r 5. 1794

41 d *The Conjugal Union of Cupid*

41 e *Cupid and Psyche*

Outline, and he may often have just given the volume away. In 1804 he handed over the surviving stock of *Thoughts* to the publisher Longman, who by 1811 had managed to dispose of only ten of a total of ninety-nine taken; while from 1813 to 1815 a bookseller, White, had sold only seven copies.[44] The remaining copies were either distributed as gifts or destroyed. Undeterred by this lack of public success, however, Cumberland embarked on a sequel volume, *Outlines from the Antients, Exhibiting their Principles of Composition in Figures and Basso-Relievos taken chiefly from Inedited Monuments of Greek and Roman Sculpture*, prepared in 1824 and published in 1829; four of Blake's plates after Cumberland from *Thoughts on Outline* (cat. 41 c, d, g, h) were reprinted in this complementary work.

The National Gallery of Victoria's copy of *Thoughts on Outline* is inscribed 'H. I. Reveley' on the front-end flyleaf, and its title-page is stamped with the collector's mark of Henry Reveley (1737–98). Reveley was an avid collector of old master drawings and engravings, and built up an enormous collection which was eventually dispersed by his heirs at auction in 1852 and 1884. His *Notices Illustrative of the Drawings and Sketches of some of the most distinguished Masters* was published posthumously by his son Hugh in 1820. There is no evidence of any direct link between Blake or Cumberland and Reveley. Reveley did, however, own a copy of Blake's illuminated book *Visions of the Daughters of Albion* (1793).[45] Reveley may also have been related to the Willey Reveley who edited the third volume of Stuart and Revett's *Antiquities of Athens*, published in 1794. And this would provide a plausible link between Henry Reveley and George Cumberland, as it was through Willey Reveley that Cumberland had been able to obtain Blake's 1791 commission to engrave plates for the *Antiquities*.[46]

If this connection does exist, then the Melbourne *Thoughts* could have been a gift from Cumberland to Henry Reveley, a fellow enthusiast for Raimondi and Dürer with whom he would have had much in common. As a keen purchaser of old master prints himself, Cumberland had perhaps long been aware of Henry Reveley's distinguished collection. The misprinted motto on the Melbourne title-page is half erased and corrected in pencil to read '*Anch'io son pittore*', which may suggest that it was an early copy sent out by Cumberland before the addition of the pasted-over correction slip. The inscription on the title-page—'from the Author 1833'—need not overrule this conjecture, but could signify Hugh

41 f *Iron Age*

Reveley's later recognition of a relationship between Cumberland and his father. However, the volume has endpapers watermarked 1819 and appears to have only been bound between boards at this date. The signature 'H. I. Reveley', which occurs on one of these 1819 sheets, is therefore probably that of Hugh Reveley. If this copy of the *Thoughts* was a gift from Cumberland to Hugh Reveley, then Hugh evidently continued to stamp books with his father's collector's mark.[47]

Albert Boime has succinctly pointed to the manner in which 'Cumberland identified himself with the commercial classes, and understood the outline method as the only aesthetic approach compatible with British naval, political and industrial supremacy'.[48] The close association of the neo-classical outline method of engraving with the emerging forces of industrial design underscored the political and commercial implications of Cumberland's arguments in *Thoughts on Outline*. It is against this background that we should consider Cumberland's claim that:

> I have treated principally of *Outline*, for until . . . it be understood, *that there can be no art without it*, and that no man deserves to be called an artist, who is defective in this best rudiment; we may continue to model, carve, and paint; but, without it, we shall never have Artists, Sculptors, nor Painters . . . and it requires but little discernment to perceive, that *form* stamps a value on the meanest materials, without a right knowledge of which all our justly-boasted manual skill can be of little or no utility, either to this country, or its *commerce*, the source of all our wealth, our pride, our folly, and our crimes; but which, alas! seems to have become necessary to our very existence.
> (pp. 8, 12)

Blake clearly saw himself, both in his reproductive and original output, as the kind of skilled saviour of the arts and *ipso facto* English commercial prosperity Cumberland was seeking. In 1799 he had begged Cumberland to:

> Pray let me intreat you to persevere in your Designing . . . Go on, if not for your sake, yet for ours, who love & admire your works; but, above all, For the Sake of the Arts. Do not throw aside for any long time the honour intended you by Nature to revive the Greek workmanship. I study your outlines as usual, just as if they were antiques.

The following year his approbation of Cumberland's proposal for a national gallery, which would of course display Greek antiquities, revealed his recognition of the commercial implications of Cumberland's neo-classical philosophy:

> All your wishes shall in due time be fulfilled; the immense flood of Grecian light & glory which is coming on Europe will more than realise our warmest wishes . . . such must be the plan if England wishes to continue at all worth notice; as you yourself have observ'd only now, we must possess Originals as well as France or be Nothing.[49]

Blake's identification with Cumberland's quest for industrial strength through graphic purity must have exacerbated his bitterness over the failure of his own

19

ARISTOPHANES CLOUDS. SCENE. I.

Θεραπων

Στρεψιαδης

Φειδιππιδης

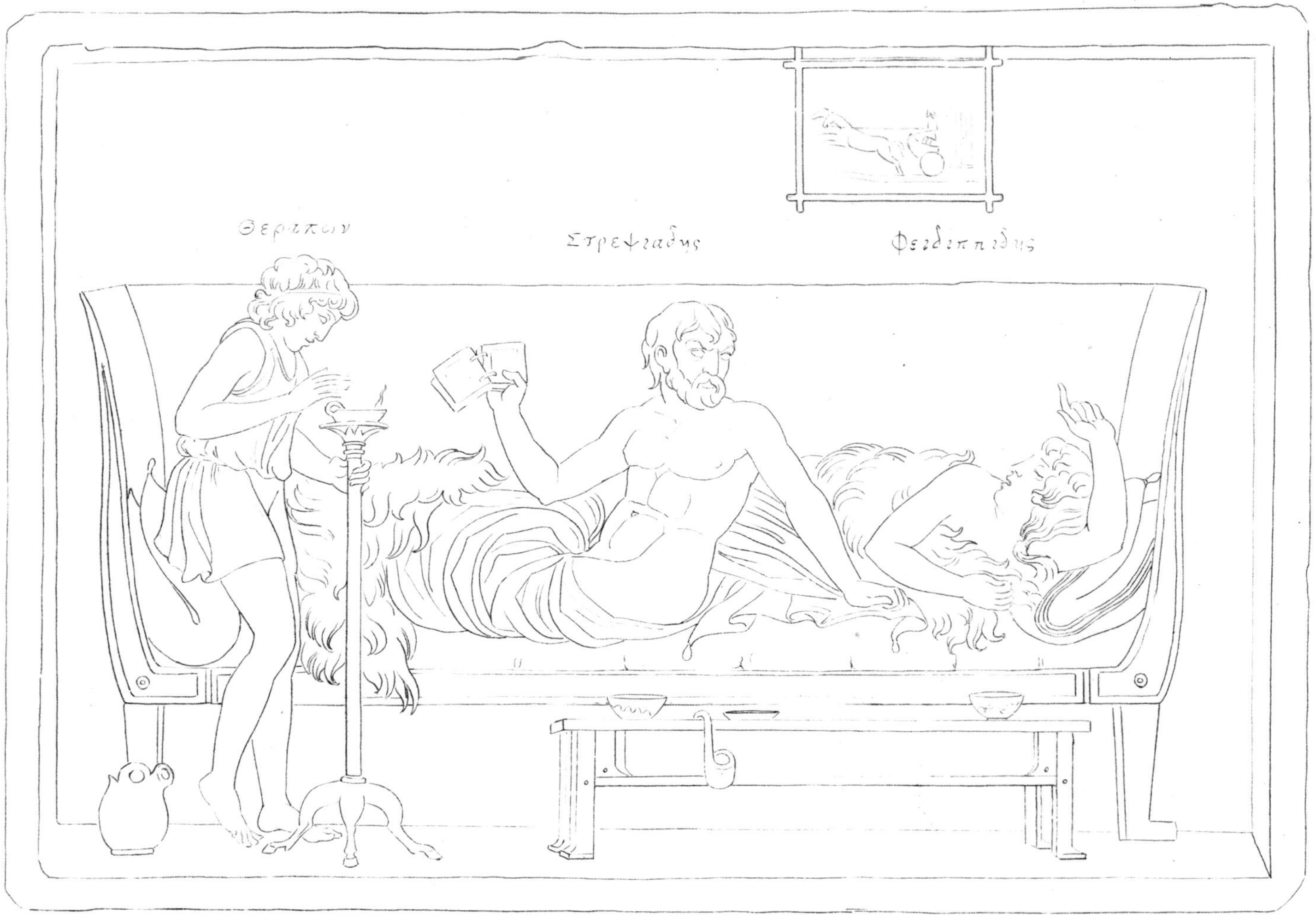

From an original Invention by G. C. Eng.d by W. B. Published January 1st 1795

41 g *Aristophanes' Clouds, Scene I*

41 h *Anacreon, Ode LII*

commercially-oriented ventures in illuminated printing, coupled with his perceived rejection and alienation from numerous reproductive commissions after 1800. Around 1808 a venomous epigram in his *Notebook*, directed against those who had abjured his compositions, was still couched in terms which depicted him as a defender of Cumberland's principles: 'They never can Rafael it, Fuseli it, nor Blake it, / If they can't see an outline, pray how can they make it?' (N 40).

The captions inscribed on Cumberland's *Thoughts on Outline* designs make pointed reference to some of the most noted Greek and Roman dramatists, lyric poets and epic writers: Anacreon, Aristophanes, Petronius, Ovid. This is entirely in keeping with the classicizing philosophy of the whole volume. And it may well be that Cumberland, as much as William Hayley (discussed later), lay behind Blake's decision to plunge into the classics a few years later. In 1803 Blake wrote to his brother James: 'I go on Merrily with my Greek & Latin; am very sorry that I did not begin to learn languages early in life as I find it very Easy . . . I read Greek as fluently as an Oxford scholar'.[50] It seems likely that at the time of the *Thoughts on Outline* project Cumberland would have urged Blake to read some of the classical authors to whom his designs pay discreet homage.

Five of the plates Blake engraved for Cumberland illustrate the myth of Cupid and Psyche, a celebrated episode from *The Golden Ass* of Apuleius (active *c.* AD 155). Two depict the climax of Apuleius's story when Psyche, who has only been visited by Cupid in the dark and has been strictly forbidden to look upon her divine lover, steals towards Cupid's sleeping form with a lamp. Another pair show Psyche turning the tables on the god of love, subjecting him to earthly bondage and physical torment. Kathleen Raine and Irene Chayes have both argued that the male/female sexual struggles of the Cupid and Psyche myth can be traced through much of Blake's poetry of the 1780s and 1790s, from *The Book of Thel* to the treatment of Vala in *The Four Zoas*.[51]

Prophetic Books

The reproductive engraving work Blake undertook for the publisher Joseph Johnson in the 1780s brought him into contact with the radical writers Thomas Paine, William Godwin and Mary Wollstonecraft, whose zeal for political freedom was fired by the French Revolution. According to Gilchrist, as 'a vehement republican and sympathiser with the Revolution, hater and contemner of kings and king-craft', Blake now wore France's red cap of liberty openly in the streets.[52] Johnson himself had Blake's poem *The French Revolution* typeset in 1791, but its publication appears to have been suspended in response to the changing political situation at home. There was little place for Blake's celebration of the overthrow of tyranny in a conservative market-place soon to react with revulsion to the execution of Louis XVI in January 1793.

Ten days after Louis XVI went to the guillotine, Britain, then led by William Pitt, declared war on France. As the French Terror aroused panic in the British parliament, radical groups were persecuted.

Fig. 16 William Blake, *Arise O Rintrah!*, plate 8 from *Europe: A Prophecy*, 1794. Relief etching (posthumous printing), 23.4 x 16.6 cm. The Fitzwilliam Museum, Cambridge

Free-thinkers like Paine were either imprisoned or forced to flee into exile. It was in this climate that Blake, working at Lambeth (at that stage still a relatively rural area of London), began his great series of Prophetic Books, sometimes known as the Lambeth Prophecies. Extending the techniques of illuminated printing developed in the *Songs of Innocence*, the Prophetic Books did not receive wide exposure, which paradoxically may have afforded Blake some measure of political protection in an era of censorship and reaction.

America (1793) sang the rise of revolutionary liberty in the colonies in the face of English regal oppression and prophesied its spread across the world. In *Europe, A Prophecy* (1794), as David Erdman has skilfully shown, 'Blake enlarges on the idea that the British attempt to accuse, judge and execute revolutionary France is equivalent to an invitation to the universal revolution'.[53] While peopled by the invented characters of Blake's private mythology, the political import of *Europe*'s verses is clear. The poem's catalyst is the fiery 'Rintrah, furious king', probably a veiled parody of William Pitt, who calls forth the legions of war and death. A number of emblematic designs in *Europe* depict the consequences of Rintrah's repressive acts—war, famine and plague. *Arise O Rintrah!* (cat. 42) symbolizes the horrors of invasion, with its

42 *Arise, O Rintrah!*, plate 8 from *Europe: A Prophecy*, 1794

43 *Los, Enitharmon and Orc*, plate 21 from *The First Book of Urizen*, 1794

Fig. 17 William Blake, *'Urizen' Plate 21*, from *A Large Book of Designs*, *c.* 1794. Colour-printed relief etching finished in pen and water-colour, 16.5 x 10.2 cm. The British Museum, London

compelling image of an aged man stretching his arms forward feverishly as if to ward off the unspeakable. A young woman clutches at his knees in terror, as dark clouds billow ominously in the background.[54]

Arise O Rintrah! provides a good example of the new technique of colour-printing which Blake developed during the early production of the Prophetic Books. The full extent of the relief-etching work on the plate can be seen in a posthumous impression inked normally and printed in a single hue (fig. 16). In addition to the relief etching and white-line etching familiar from the *Songs of Innocence*, Blake has also applied the burin directly to the metal plate, incising sharper 'white' engraved lines into the image; these are most noticeable when they cut across the dike-etch borders of the design. In his colour-printing process Blake often initially inked the plate with a base colour of printing ink (blue on the Melbourne *Rintrah* impression). Before this layer of ink dried he then painted over it with another opaque, gouache-like pigment, and printed both sets of tints together to create a simultaneous coloured relief print and monotype. The shallowness of the biting on his relief-etched copper-plates also enabled Blake to achieve a monotype printing from both the raised and lowered surfaces of the plate at once. Finishing details were then applied with pen and ink or water-colour. The thickness and tackiness of the pigments used for the colour-printing gives these prints a characteristic mottled or reticulated surface. The opacity and 'darkness' of the process are at the opposite end of the scale from the clarity and lightness of touch so evident in the early *Songs of Innocence* plates, a brooding effect which Blake no doubt preferred for the dark themes of the Prophetic Books.[55]

The First Book of Urizen abandons contemporary or historical references and steps directly into Blake's visionary universe. The poem is complex and convoluted and contrasts dramatically with Blake's earlier inviting verse due to what Mitchell has termed its 'movement away from epigrammatic wit and lyric immediacy into the rarefied atmosphere of cosmology and sacred history'.[56] Summarized briefly, it utilizes Blake's own powerful mythology to recount the Creation, the Fall of the Creator, and the appearance of man as a flawed divinity. *The First Book of Urizen* shares with the other Prophetic Books Blake's central belief that the Creation was a fall from grace which allowed the domination of reason over the poetic imagination, and his condemnation of organized religion as an evil and soul-destroying legalism.

At the heart of *The First Book of Urizen* is Urizen the law-giver, 'his hand / On the rock of eternity unclasping / The Book of brass', who falls from the realm of the Eternals and weaves the ensnaring 'Net of Religion'. His balancing counterpart is Los, Blake's archetype of the Imagination, who fashions a human form for Urizen in order to limit his repression to the physical world. In turn Los meets his own Fall through pity for Urizen. This leads to his sexual division, and the emergence of his female emanation Enitharmon. Their child is Orc, the spirit of rebellion and revolution, whose very existence threatens Los and consumes him with jealousy.[57] *Los, Enitharmon and Orc* (cat. 43) depicts Los's jealousy for Orc, which binds him fast with weighted chains of passion. David Bindman has equated the imagery of this plate with Renaissance depictions of Venus, Vulcan and Cupid at the forge, which also confront the themes of sexual jealousy and oppression.[58]

Melbourne's *Urizen* sheet may not have been intended to join a complete copy of the prophetic book, but was perhaps printed to accompany a separate group of images now known as *A Large Book of Designs*. These Blake himself described as 'a selection from the different Books of such [plates] as could be Printed without the Writing', which he organized for Ozias Humphry around 1796.[59] Humphry's copy of this purely visual selection of eight designs from *Urizen*, *America* and elsewhere is now in the British Museum Print Room. A number of separate colour-printed impressions of the same plates have sometimes been considered as intended for a putative second copy of *A Large Book of Designs*, and it is to this group that the Melbourne sheet may belong.

The sheet's relationship to the same design in the British Museum *Large Book* (fig. 17) is certainly striking. The London impression was very thickly colour-printed with heavy, opaque pigments imparting a dark and sombre mood. It was then finished with both water-colour and body colour, possibly painted on with the colour-printed pigment still wet to augment the reticulated surfaces Blake often favoured. By contrast the Melbourne version is brighter and more 'open' in feel, and finished in a much more meticulous fashion with careful pen-and-ink work and delicate water-colour stippling. The patterns of the colour-printed areas are extremely close on both impressions, however, particularly in the sky at upper left, in the area behind Los's head in the top right corner, and in the mottled green and yellow-ochre hues along the baseline. This seems to suggest that the National Gallery of Victoria's *Los, Enitharmon and Orc* was printed immediately after the British Museum impression, as a lighter second pull from a single inking of the plate (or with only minor re-inking of a few areas). Nothing of the original relief-etched work can be detected beneath the extensive water-colour finish of the Melbourne design. But the plate was pulled through the rolling press with extreme pressure, leaving a strong and quite legible embossing of the relief-etched design on the verso of the sheet. This heavy press-work would answer Blake's need for additional force to gain a reasonable second impression from the thinner layer of pigment left on the plate without re-inking.

Blake continued sporadic printings of the Prophetic Books over the following decades. The two Melbourne sheets were possibly acquired directly from him by his young patron John Linnell sometime after 1818 (although Linnell continued to collect works by Blake after the artist's death). Linnell also owned a full copy of *Europe*, the elaborately coloured and gilded late Copy K (watermarked 1818, 1820). George Cumberland purchased Copy F of *The First Book of Urizen*. On the whole the Prophetic Books did not bring Blake great financial returns, being acquired principally, as were these examples, by his small circle of friends.

Blair's *Grave*

Blake's fortunes waned considerably in the closing years of the eighteenth century. His most ambitious commercial undertaking of this period, the engravings of Edward Young's *Night Thoughts*, executed for the book publisher Richard Edwards, failed to attract buyers. The friendship of Thomas Butts, who ordered a stream of biblical water-colours and tempera paintings from 1799 onwards, ensured him some steady income none the less.

In 1800 Blake and his wife accepted an invitation from William Hayley, a prominent poet and biographer, to take up residence in the country at Felpham under Hayley's patronage. Initially euphoric, Blake eventually was to feel desperately misunderstood at Felpham, where Hayley held his original work in low esteem and steered him constantly towards dull commercial engraving projects. In August 1803 Blake was involved in a tussle with a drunken soldier named John Scolfield, who subsequently charged him with sedition. The

Fig. 18 William Blake, *Death's Door*, 1805. White-line etching, tinted with India ink, 16 x 11.4 cm. Collection of Robert N. Essick

Blakes moved back to London in September, returning to Felpham only for the sedition trial in January 1804, at which Blake was acquitted. It was at Felpham, despite Blake's problems with Hayley, that he began his last great Prophetic Books, *Milton* and *Jerusalem*.

In November 1805 Blake wrote excitedly to William Hayley that:

> Mr Cromek the Engraver came to me desiring to have some of my Designs; he nam'd his Price & wish'd me to Produce him Illustrations of The Grave, A Poem by Robert Blair; in consequence of this I produced about twenty Designs which pleas'd so well that he, with the same liberality with which he set me about the Drawings, has now set me to Engrave them. He means to Publish them by Subscription with the Poem as you will see in the Prospectus which he sends you.[60]

Presumably Blake was referring to the printed *Prospectus*, released in this same month, advertising 'Fifteen prints from designs invented and to be engraved by William Blake'. Robert Hartley Cromek (1770–1812) had trained as an engraver before turning to publishing around 1805. The exact date of his meeting with Blake is not known, but the two had

44 a–m Blair's *Grave* 1808 (see frontispiece for cat. **44 a**)
44 b *The Skeleton Re-Animated*

44 c *The Descent of Christ into the Grave*

44 d *A Family Meeting in Heaven*

Fig. 19 Luigi Schiavonetti (after Angelica Kauffmann), *Two Gentlemen of Verona*, 1792. Etching, engraving and stipple engraving, 44.2 x 59.2 cm. National Gallery of Victoria. Felton Bequest, 1926

mutual friends in George Cumberland and John Flaxman, and Hayley had also been for some time professionally aware of Cromek's engraving talents.

Robert Blair (1699–1746), a Scottish preacher and poet, published *The Grave* in London in 1743. A short poem of less than 800 lines, this 'strong, stern, rapid, and concentrated sketch of the grisly gulf' between life and death related to a long tradition of morbid poems utilizing the graveyard and its attendant associations as a motif for moral instruction.[61] Death's destruction of love, wealth, beauty and happiness; the tomb as the great leveller of king and pauper alike; and the physical decay of the body after death are the recurrent themes in Blair's elegant verse. *The Grave* had run to its forty-ninth edition as early as 1798, and must have seemed to Cromek a sure vehicle for commercial success.[62]

Blake's hopes were soon to be dashed, however. A second *Prospectus* issued by Cromek, also dated November 1805, announced 'A new and elegant edition of Blair's *Grave*, illustrated with twelve very spirited engravings by Louis Schiavonetti, from designs invented by William Blake', contrasting markedly with the spirit and letter of Blake's happy report to Hayley.[63] Cromek had gradually reduced the number of designs to be engraved from twenty to fifteen, then to twelve. Apparently startled by a powerful, radical white-line etching of the *Death's Door* composition which Blake had produced for him (fig. 18), he now transferred the engraving commission to the commercially reliable hand of Luigi Schiavonetti, who was proofing the first plate by February 1806.[64] Blake's name was still included on the title-page (cat. 44 b), and Cromek added a frontispiece portrait of Blake by Thomas Phillips (cat. 44 a), and a four-page commentary 'Of the Designs', probably written by Blake's friend Benjamin Heath Malkin.

But Blake, at a time when in Cromek's own words he was 'reduced so low as to be obliged to live on half a guinea a week!',[65] was jostled out of the lucrative engraving work he had initially been promised. While Cromek paid him 20 guineas for the twelve designs eventually used in the volume, Schiavonetti could command a fee of up to 60 guineas for engraving a single plate. Blake's bitterness practically etched through the pages of his *Notebook* in acidly scribbled verses: 'Cr[omek] loves artists as he loves his Meat. / He loves the Art, but 'tis the Art to Cheat'; and, 'A petty Sneaking Knave I knew— / O M^{r} Cr[omek], how do ye do?' (N 29).

Born in Bassano, Luigi Schiavonetti (1765–1810) trained in Italy until his mid-twenties. By then, according to legend, he had already acquired a ready

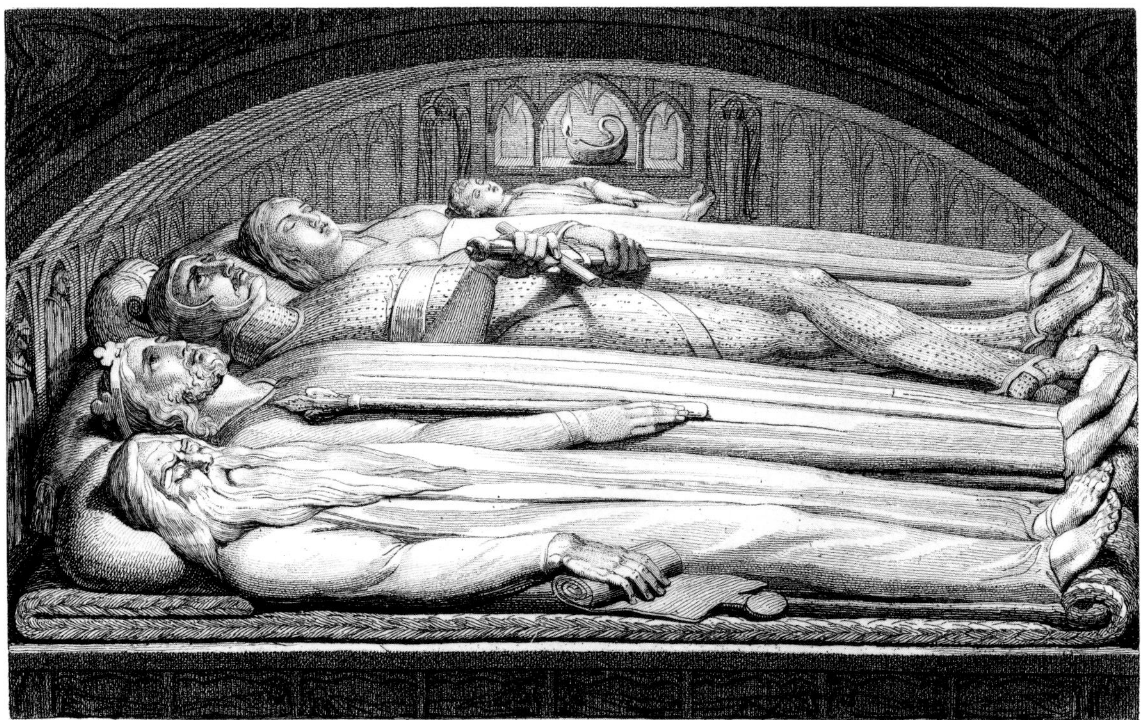

44 e *The Counsellor, King, Warrior, Mother, and Child*

44 f *The Strong Wicked Man Dying*

44 g *The Soul Hovering Over the Body*

facility with engraving in the manner of Francesco Bartolozzi (also an Italian émigré), England's leading print craftsman in the crayon and stipple manner. When he arrived in London in 1790 he quickly came to Bartolozzi's attention, and was taken into the older master's house as 'pupil' and collaborator. Probably benefiting from Bartolozzi's contacts, Schiavonetti soon became a popular, prolific and commercially successful reproductive printmaker in his own right, engraving numerous widely-circulated prints after oils by Angelica Kauffmann and Francis Wheatley in particular (fig. 19).

Blake's *Notebook* verses reveal a curiously ambivalent attitude towards Schiavonetti. His comments after 1810 that 'poor Schiavonetti died of the Cromek' (N 62) and references to 'poor Schiavonetti, whom they to death bothered' (N 22), alternate with a brutally succinct jibe at 'Assassinetti' (N 22). Most of his open hostility was directed against Cromek. None the less, we can surmise that Blake would have reacted negatively to Schiavonetti's status as a popular engraver respected by the art establishment, whose financial success sorely aroused his jealousy. During the years that artists were receiving commissions to work for Josiah Boydell's *Shakespeare Gallery* (1786–1802), for example, Blake was asked to engrave only one copper-plate. Schiavonetti was given six Shakespeare commissions by Boydell, and paid £315 each for at least two of them. At roughly the same time Blake was writing to George Cumberland that 'as to Engraving, in which art I cannot reproach myself with any neglect, yet I am laid by in a corner as if I did not Exist'.[66] Cumberland's thinly veiled attack on Boydell in his *Thoughts on Outline* may have been prompted in part by pique over Blake's exclusion from the project in favour of fashionable engravers such as Schiavonetti.[67]

Judging from their respective *oeuvres*, Schiavonetti's formal training in engraving appears to have been akin to that of Blake, though perhaps with less of an antiquarian emphasis in his formative years. We should bear in mind that Blake was likewise highly proficient at pure stipple engraving; the two men also often employed remarkably similar admixtures of worm-line etching, swelling engraved lines, and selective stippling in their reproductive prints. Moreover, Schiavonetti clearly identified himself closely with Blake's designs, to judge from his comments on the *Last Judgement* plate: 'As to what degree of plaisure I have found in Engraving it you may easily conseive it from the accuracy of the outline, the truth of the light and shadow, and the magical way in which the effect of [h]armony is contrived in the drawing'.[68] Blake's objections to Cromek's choice of Schiavonetti could therefore

44 h *The Descent of Man into the Vale of Death*

44 i *The Last Judgement*

44 j *The Soul Exploring the Recesses of the Grave*

44 k *The Good Old Man Dying*

scarcely have been logically based upon misapprehensions concerning Schiavonetti's artistic mannerisms or skills. This is not to deny the validity of Blake's distress over his displacement by Cromek as sole progenitor of the Blair illustrations.

Cromek has been almost universally pilloried as the arch villain in Blake studies. He has been accused of ridiculing Blake's art, damaging his professional reputation, and swindling him out of *The Grave*'s profits. Recent scholarship has partially exonerated the publisher. Dennis Read has logged Cromek's travels throughout England to promote *The Grave*, placing extensive advertisements which would bring in the 578 subscribers listed at the front of the volume. Aileen Ward has praised Cromek's courage in choosing Blake in the first place, and argued that Blake had no proper claim to copyright on his designs under the current terms of the book trade.[69] Cromek, we now know, was still appreciative of Blake's talents in April 1807, referring to his 'wonderful genius' and 'his usual Characteristics—Sublimity, Simplicity, Elegance and Pathos'. And yet barely a month later he could, when moved to anger, insult Blake with the taunt that 'what public reputation you have, the reputation for eccentricity excepted, I have acquired for you'.[70]

Apparently Cromek panicked upon seeing Blake's rugged and unevenly textured *Death's Door* proof, as the swift switch to Schiavonetti between the two issues of the *Prospectus* indicates. Ironically, it seems Cromek may simply have misinterpreted the strict dichotomy which Blake imposed upon the graphic treatment of his original designs and copy-work. The greatest irony lies in the fact that Cromek, had he understood Blake better, might well have been able to persuade him to reproduce his own designs in his more conservative copy manner—which would have been much closer to Schiavonetti's final results. While this still would have been a regrettable artistic compromise from Blake's point of view, further drowning his hopes of gaining the wide audience for his original style that he had failed to reach with the *Songs of Innocence and of Experience* and Prophetic Books, it would not have cut him out of the lengthy course of *The Grave*'s production (January 1806 to July 1808) to such an extent.

While Alexander Gilchrist found Schiavonetti's 'admirable etchings' for *The Grave* 'a graceful translation' produced by 'skilful and conscientious hands . . . and, as most would think, an improvement', modern opinion has condemned Schiavonetti's engravings as serious misinterpretations which are, at best, dull. S. Foster Damon not only criticized Blair's 'shallow verse' but

44 l *Death's Door*

44 m *The Reunion of Soul and Body*

also attacked Schiavonetti as 'an engraver who all now agree was inferior', and thought that his 'sentimental style had enfeebled [Blake's] designs'.[71] Morris Eaves criticized the numerous 'corrections' Schiavonetti supposedly made to Blake's white-line etching of the *Death's Door* design, arguing that 'Blake's stark background would have looked barbaric to him, so he subdued it to the point of inoffensiveness with fine, light hatching', and that while 'in his white-line print Blake has outlined the body of the figure with a single white line', this 'peculiar effect . . . would have looked simply crude to Schiavonetti, who did the opposite, blending the outline with the shading of the muscles'.[72] Eaves ignores the fact that it is extremely doubtful whether Schiavonetti ever saw the white-line *Death's Door*, and that he is far more likely to have engraved after a separate pencil sketch or water-colour provided by Blake under the terms of his agreement with Cromek. Even Essick and Paley felt that while 'Schiavonetti's plates are skilful and thoroughly professional renditions . . . they substitute competence for genius and partially mask the intense conception of the artist beneath the engraver's conventional patterns of cross-hatching, dot and flick lines, and stipple shading'.[73] In recent years Andrew Wilton alone has stood up in defence of Schiavonetti's beautiful engravings, arguing that their elegance and grace truthfully reflect Blake's intentions for the volume.[74]

Few of Blake's finished designs for Blair's *Grave* are known to have survived, and it is difficult to extrapolate from the known sketches and fragmentary drawings the true nature of the models from which Schiavonetti finally worked.[75] Several of the *Grave* designs quote from Blake's earlier projects, which may reflect his need to produce such a substantial body of work in a short period of time. *The Skeleton Re-Animated* (cat. 44 b) redeploys a motif used to great effect in the *Night Thoughts* commission; the stooped elder of *Death's Door* (cat. 44 l) had appeared in the illuminated books *America* and *The Gates of Paradise* (both 1793); while *The Counsellor, King, Warrior, Mother, and Child* (cat. 44 e) looks back to a sketch of *c.* 1780 and, in turn, to the Gothic tomb sculptures the young Blake had copied for James Basire.[76] It is generally accepted that Blake's own positive religious views enter the *Grave* designs, along with his artistic self-quotations. Christ's forgiveness of sins, the resurrection of the soul, and spiritual reunion in the afterlife, rather than Blair's pessimistic sepulchral musings, are the themes which inform Blake's imagery. Unfortunately, awareness of Blake's visual input has led to a regrettable neglect of Blair's own sublime themes and exquisite language.

In the 1960s S. Foster Damon, taking the situation to extremes, dismissed Blair's poem as 'an ill-proportioned, fashionably vulgar product of the Graveyard School' which Blake 'despised', and argued for the complete independence of the designs—for 'by omitting Blair's unnecessary text and rearranging the pictures, we have another of Blake's Prophetic Books'.[77] Thomas Helmstadter has convincingly shown, however, that all of Blake's designs take their conceptual origins from Blair's text and complement it well on a purely illustrative level, Blake's more positive reading of Blair notwithstanding.[78]

The Grave saw five separate editions during Blake's lifetime. In 1808 Cromek supervised a folio printing on large sheets of laid paper inscribed 'Proof' on the title-page, and a quarto issue on smaller sheets of wove paper, with the title-page marked 'Subscribers' Copy'. The National Gallery of Victoria's *Grave* is from this 1808 quarto issue, but with the 'Subscribers' inscription trimmed off during a later rebinding. It was purchased in 1954 from Gino Nibbi, whose Leonardo Bookshop was a noted source of the modern art reproductions so eagerly sought by Melbourne's radical young artists of the pre-war years.[79] Cromek's widow sold the *Grave* plates to the publisher Rudolph Ackermann in 1812. The following year Ackermann released a second edition in both a folio and a quarto issue with the plates redated 1813. The plates were printed by Ackermann again in 1826, with their titles re-engraved in Spanish to accompany the *Meditaciones Poeticas* of José Joaquin de Mora, a Madrid poet who had fled to London after the French invasion of Spain in 1823.[80] As a result of this broad exposure, Blake's *Grave* designs became his most widely recognized and respected work.[81] Schiavonetti's original copper-plates, subsequently steel-faced, survive in the Lessing J. Rosenwald Collection, Library of Congress, Washington, DC.

Chaucer's Canterbury Pilgrims

In May 1807 Robert Cromek wrote contemptuously to Blake: 'Why did you so *furiously rage* at the success of the little picture of "The Pilgrimage"? Three thousand people have now *seen it and have approved of it*. Believe me, yours is "*the voice of one crying in the wilderness!*" '.[82] The 'little picture' was Thomas Stothard's *Pilgrimage to Canterbury*, an oil painting commissioned by Cromek and exhibited to great public acclaim in 1807. Through this new commission Cromek again proved to be a problematic figure behind Blake's next bid for public attention, his own large engraving of *Chaucer's Canterbury Pilgrims* (cat. 45).

Primary sources for Blake's life agree in their condemnation of Cromek's role in the *Canterbury Pilgrims* saga. According to J. T. Smith, Cromek learned that Blake was planning a Chaucer painting around 1805, at the time of their collaboration on the Blair's *Grave* project. Cromek put the same idea to Thomas Stothard, who quickly finished an oil suitable for engraving before Blake could release his version. Blake's young friend John Linnell elaborated the attack on Cromek's unscrupulousness, claiming that the publisher had initially commissioned the *Canterbury Pilgrims* subject from Blake himself and, after negotiations over remuneration broke down, then turned to Stothard. Linnell exonerated Stothard, however, suggesting that he had been unaware of Blake's original idea for a large Chaucerian frieze when he accepted Cromek's invitation to undertake precisely that type of painting. Indeed, according to Smith's account, Stothard protested that Blake had taken up the Chaucer project after viewing his own *Pilgrimage to Canterbury* painting.[83]

45 *Chaucer's Canterbury Pilgrims*, 1810

Fig. 20 Luigi Schiavonetti and James Heath (after Thomas Stothard), *Pilgrimage to Canterbury*, 1817. Etching and engraving, 26.6 x 92.8 cm. Collection of Robert N. Essick

Aileen Ward, stating forcefully that both Smith's and Linnell's accounts offer us only Blake's word as transmitted to sympathetic friends, has questioned 'why Blake, on seeing Stothard's half-finished painting in 1806, would have failed to mention his own work in progress to his friend, who was surprised and angered on learning later of Blake's rival version'.[84] In Ward's view, the only viable conclusion is to absolve Cromek of blame and accept that Blake probably did suddenly turn to Chaucer as a subject for engraving in rivalry to Stothard's commission. As Blake's personal and financial failures from 1809 onwards pushed him towards increasing depression and paranoia, he whitewashed this appropriation of Stothard's work, and came to believe his own tale of yet another martyrdom at the hands of Cromek.

The fates of Blake's and Stothard's Chaucer designs can be more firmly tracked than their origins. Schiavonetti was commissioned to engrave Stothard's *Pilgrimage to Canterbury* shortly after its successful exhibition in 1807. Left unfinished at Schiavonetti's death in 1810, it was passed on to Francis Eagleheart for completion. Cromek's own death in 1812 ended this arrangement, however. Cromek's widow next engaged Luigi Schiavonetti's brother Niccolo to work on the plate, but he in turn died before progressing very far. The seemingly cursed *Pilgrimage to Canterbury* engraving (fig. 20) was finally completed by James Heath in 1817, a decade after its conception.

Blake's tempera painting of *Chaucer's Canterbury Pilgrims*[85] was probably completed in 1808, and was one of nine temperas included in an exhibition of 'Pictures, Poetical and Historical Inventions . . . for Public Inspection' which Blake opened privately in May 1809 at his brother's house in Soho. The exhibition was accompanied by a comprehensive publication, the *Descriptive Catalogue*, in which Blake analysed and defended his own pictures. The *Canterbury Pilgrims* received thirty-six pages of commentary.[86] In May 1809 there appeared a printed prospectus of *Blake's Chaucer*, which:

> The Designer proposes to Engrave, in a correct and finished Line manner of Engraving, similar to those original Copper Plates of ALBERT DURER, LUCAS, HISBEN, ALDEGRAVE and the old original Engravers . . . whose method, alone, can delineate Character as it is in this Picture, where all the lineaments are distinct.[87]

The execution of the engraving dragged on for another year, the imprint on the earliest state of the plate reading 8 October 1810. Around this time Blake was also drafting in his *Notebook* a lengthy discourse beginning 'Chaucer's Canterbury Pilgrims Being a complete Index of Human Characters as they appear Age after Age', which has come to be known as the *Public Address*. Much of this is a vigorous defence of Blake's deliberately archaizing engraving style, 'the style of Alb. Durer's Histories & the old Engravers', with stern attacks on Cromek in his capacity as

Chaucer's Canterbury Pilgrims (detail)

secretary of the newly formed Chalcographic Society, which Blake considered tainted by 'the artfully propogated opinion that Drawing spoils an Engraver . . . '.[88]

The *Canterbury Pilgrims* engraving did not make Blake's fortune. His 1809 exhibition received little critical notice, and few visitors. The tempera was acquired by his faithful patron Thomas Butts. But although the outlay on materials for the engraving may have been small,[89] the costs to Blake in terms of time and talent, not to mention morale, were considerable. There are at most seven documented sales of the print during his lifetime. Blake continued to work away privately at the *Canterbury Pilgrims* plate until *c.* 1823. However, as Aileen Ward bluntly put it, at his death 'the first three obituaries of Blake failed to mention the *Pilgrims* among his other works; the fourth described it as though it were unknown'.[90]

The *Descriptive Catalogue* set forth Blake's belief that: 'Of Chaucer's characters, as described in his Canterbury Tales, some of the names or titles are altered by time, but the characters themselves for ever remain unaltered, and consequently they are the physiognomies or lineaments of universal life, beyond which Nature never steps. Names alter, things never alter'.[91] His depictions of Chaucer's pilgrims are therefore less individual portraits, than synthetic analyses of universal states of the human condition, symbolizing desires, emotions and diverse philosophical outlooks. In keeping with his stress on the basic human tenets which link the peoples of all ages, he adopted a more archaic and open engraving style, which owes less to Albrecht Dürer than to the medievalizing engraved conceits of his former master James Basire.[92]

The *Canterbury Pilgrims* has attracted a sizeable body of literary criticism and interpretation in recent years. Karl Kiralis has painstakingly correlated Chaucer's account of each character in the *Prologue* with Blake's physical depiction of them in the *Pilgrims* engraving, his analysis of their 'eternal principles' in the *Descriptive Catalogue*, and the parallels one can draw with his own poetic mythology, concluding that 'his thinking is so surprisingly like Chaucer's that the archetypal nature of their thought allows Blake's somewhat unorthodox views to throw a fresh and illuminating light on Chaucer's genius'.[93] Other scholars have pursued tangential paths, analysing minutely Blake's ironic delineation of character, or arguing that his pilgrims are less individuals than symbolic representations of the artist's Orc, Los and Urizen archetypes.[94] Stylistically, Blake's treatment of Chaucer's characters has been considered in the light of his youthful study of medieval sculpture, and in relation to the history of Chaucerian illustration in illuminated manuscripts and early printed books.[95] M. E. Reisner has also argued for a politicized reading of the print, detecting in Blake's Pardoner and Summoner an influence from contemporary caricatures of the rival politicians William Pitt and Charles Fox.[96]

Blake's *Canterbury Pilgrims* plate underwent numerous printings from five different states between 1810 and *c.* 1823. Robert Essick has traced only one impression of the true first state, before much reworking of the fine details; and a mere two impressions of a second state, both delicately hand-tinted with water-colour. In the third state of *c.* 1810–20 the composition has been darkened considerably with additional hatching lines, and contrasts of shading have been strengthened. The Melbourne *Pilgrims* is one of twenty-four known impressions of this, the darkest and most dramatic state of the plate; regrettably, it is in poor condition. A large branching tear extends through the centre of the composition, and water stains and foxing mar it elsewhere. It is a significant asset to the Melbourne collection none the less, as one of but few surviving impressions printed during Blake's lifetime.[97] The copper-plate has survived in its fifth state, and was used for unspecified numbers of restrike impressions by Colnaghi's in the 1880s, and later in the 1940s by the Philadelphia print dealer Charles Sessler. The plate was acquired by the Pittsburgh collector Charles J. Rosenbloom, and bequeathed by him to the Yale University Art Gallery, New Haven, in 1973.[98]

Rees's *Cyclopedia*

In 1799 Blake had written to John Trusler that:

> I have no objection to Engraving after another Artist. Engraving is the profession I was apprenticed to, & should never have attempted to live by anything else, If orders had not come in for my Designs & Paintings, which I have the pleasure to tell you are Increasing Every Day. Thus If I am a Painter it is not to be attributed to Seeking after. But I am contented whether I live by Painting or Engraving.[99]

None the less, Blake's career as a commercial engraver came to a virtual standstill between 1805 and 1814 when reproductive commissions ceased, coinciding disastrously with his falling out with Cromek and the failure of his 1809 exhibition. His major original engraved works of these years, the illuminated poems *Milton* and *Jerusalem*, were not commercially viable.

Blake was in considerable need of support, therefore, when John Flaxman secured him a commission to engrave reproductive designs for Abraham Rees's *The Cyclopedia; or Universal Dictionary of Arts, Sciences, and Literature*. In all Blake engraved seven plates, issued periodically from 1816 to 1819, for three articles which Flaxman contributed to the publication on 'Armour', 'Basso Relievo' and 'Sculpture'. Melbourne possesses a single plate from this group, *Sculpture. Plate I* (cat. 46), which appeared in the *Cyclopedia* in October 1816, shortly after Flaxman's 'Sculpture' article of March 1816. The impression has been slightly trimmed at top and bottom, removing its title and imprint.

Abraham Rees (1743–1825) was trained and worked throughout his life as a Presbyterian minister. He published sermons regularly, and co-edited *A Collection of Hymns and Psalms* in 1795. His lasting claim to distinction, however, stems from his prodigious activities as an encyclopedic editor. In 1786 he had been elected a fellow of the Royal

46 *Sculpture. Plate 1*, 1816

Society for his work on reissuing Ephraim Chambers's two-volume *Cyclopedia* (1728) in an expanded four-volume edition. By the turn of the century he was planning another secular publication which would quite dwarf this project.

Rees's *Cyclopedia* was a monumental encyclopedic work, published in seventy-eight fascicules (plus six separate volumes of plates) from January 1802 to August 1820. On account of its nature as a serial, cumulative publication, the *Cyclopedia's* illustrative plates could accompany the original article, or appear as much as fifteen years before or after it. For example, Blake's *Basso Relievo* engraving, related to Flaxman's 1804 article, did not appear until the September 1819 fascicule; more ironically, Blake's four plates for Flaxman's 'Sculpture' essay, which came out close to the text in 1816–17, superseded two engravings by R. H. Cromek which had been published in fascicule 8 in February 1805, anticipating Flaxman's prose by eleven years.[100]

Blake's friendship with the sculptor John Flaxman dated back to 1779, when the two were apparently introduced by Thomas Stothard.[101] Then working as a designer for Josiah Wedgwood, Flaxman had actively sought to introduce his new friend into his more privileged circles of patronage. It was Flaxman who brought the young journeyman engraver to the salon of Mrs Mathew, and helped the Mathews with the expense of printing Blake's *Poetical Sketches* in 1783. The following year he had contributed to Blake's future fortunes by sending a copy of the *Sketches* to William Hayley, and was busily trying to persuade another patron, John Hawkins, to send Blake to Italy to study. During his own seven years abroad, from 1787 to 1794, he kept in touch with Blake, and on his return to England regularly steered work in his direction. In 1797 he commissioned a set of water-colour illustrations of the poems of Thomas Gray, for which he paid Blake 10 guineas. Blake was employed to engrave a frontispiece for his *Letter to the Committee for Raising the Naval Pillar* (1799), and he talked William Hayley into also using Blake to engrave three plates for Hayley's *Essay on Sculpture* (1800). In the years before his move to Felpham, and particularly after the failure of his *Night Thoughts* venture, Blake was in fair need of all avenues of income. Not surprisingly, his gratitude flowed over into letters 'To my dearest friend, John Flaxman', and to 'a Sublime Archangel, My Friend and Companion from Eternity . . . My Best Friend'.[102]

Flaxman had long been engaged with the neo-classical outline style. While working for Wedgwood in the 1770s he had turned to Greek vases, via the filtered silhouette plates of d'Hancarville's *Collection of Etruscan, Greek and Roman Antiquities from the Cabinet of the Honorable William Hamilton* (1766–67), as a source for the crisply delineated classical compositions that adorned Wedgwood's jasper-ware products. In Italy he perfected the use of outline with a suite of open, fresh line illustrations to *The Iliad of Homer*, which were engraved by Tommaso Piroli for publication in 1793.[103] The emphasis on pure line with no reference to spatial depth or plasticity of form in these engravings, in which Flaxman's studies of Roman bas-relief sculpture and Greek vase-painting fused brilliantly, were to have a strong effect on George Cumberland's *Thoughts on Outline* (despite Cumberland's slightly pedantic criticism of the 'outlines thick and thin alternately' in Piroli's engravings).

Flaxman clearly saw Blake as an ally in his enthusiasm for the classically pure outline. He was fully aware of Blake's meticulous training as an antiquarian engraver under Basire, and appreciated both the *Thoughts on Outline* and more pedestrian antiquarian works such as the four plates of the *Temple of Theseus* which Blake engraved after William Pars for James Stuart and Nicholas Revett's *Antiquities of Athens* (1794). Recommending Blake to Prince Hoare as the best candidate to engrave a recently discovered statue of Ceres for Hoare's *Academic Correspondence, 1803*, he noted specifically that 'as I observed to you he etched & engraved some of the fine Basso Relievos in the 3d Vol of Stuart's Athens in a very masterly manner'.[104] A decade later he was equally straightforward in his dealings with a patron who had sought a Flaxman design for a forthcoming volume:

> If the Revd Doctor should be satisfied with an *outline* of the Monument, such as those published of Homer's Iliad & Odyssey . . . which is now a favourite style of decoration in books, I can make the outline myself . . . the engraving including the Copper plate will cost 6 Guineas if done by Mr Blake the best engraver of outlines.[105]

Blake in turn had frequent occasion to discuss with Flaxman the latter's reverence for Greek and Roman sculpture. On 2 January 1804 the sculptor wrote to William Hayley: 'I have troubled You by Mr Blake with a Short tract written for Dr Rees's Cyclopedia, on Basso Relievo, with one of the prints referred to at the end of the article, the rest are not yet engraven'.[106] Blake had thus been familiar with Rees's publishing project from its inception. A few months later Blake himself informed Hayley that 'there is now in hand a new edition of Flaxman's *Homer*, with additional designs, two of which I am now engraving'.[107] Blake was actually appointed to work on three of the five extra plates Flaxman added to an expanded *Iliad* which appeared in 1805, a commission specially suited to the engraver of *Thoughts on Outline*.

Relations with Flaxman were not entirely smooth, however, and tensions occasionally erupted, with misunderstanding and fault clouding the friendship on both sides. With the major exception of the Gray water-colours, most of the work Flaxman steered in Blake's direction was reproductive in nature. This showed both Flaxman's admiration for the artist's technical excellence, and also some doubt regarding the commercial attractiveness of his originality and creative ambitions. As Flaxman wrote bluntly to Hayley:

> I hope that Blake's residence at Felpham will be a Mutual Comfort to you & him, & I see no reason why he should not make as good a livelihood there as in London, if he engraves & teaches drawing, by which he may gain considerably as also by making neat drawings of

> different kinds but if he places any dependence on painting large pictures, for which he is not qualified, either by habit or study, he will be miserably deceived.[108]

Blake felt this 'typecasting' bitterly, and around 1808 it appears to have prompted a temporary rift between the two friends.[109] The *Public Address* reflected Blake's mounting outrage 'That Engraving as an art is lost in England owing to an artfully propogated opinion that Drawing spoils an Engraver which opinion has been held out to me by such men as Flaxman . . . ' (N 11). He also exploded in his *Notebook* entries at this time with pithy, venomous attacks on Flaxman's own originality and intelligence.[110] The perceived failure of both the *Grave* and *Canterbury Pilgrims* projects no doubt contributed to this breakdown of relations. The memory that Cromek had been Flaxman's 'favourite Engraver' a few years earlier did little to improve the situation.[111]

None the less by 1814 Flaxman was again nurturing Blake's finances. From 1814 to 1817 he secured him a commission to engrave thirty-seven drawings for his own forthcoming *Compositions from the 'Works and Days' and 'Theogony' of Hesiod*, opting for a softer stipple-engraving technique to provide a contrast with the earlier *Homer* outline designs. Though Gilchrist points to Blake's disappointment with the continuing restrictions of reproductive commissions, the artist cannot have resented the £207 he was paid for the *Hesiod* works overall.[112] Flaxman also organized a meeting between Blake and Josiah Wedgwood the younger in 1815, which resulted in Blake's employment to engrave eighteen plates of uniform, outline pottery designs for a Wedgwood company catalogue.[113] Such assistance was immeasurably loyal in these years when George Cumberland found Blake 'still poor still dirty', and Cumberland's son described him as 'durtyer than ever'.[114] Gerald Bentley has calculated that in the lean years of 1814–19 Flaxman's kindness brought the Blakes around £50 a year from these various professional commissions combined.[115]

It is in this context that Flaxman recommended Blake to the firm Longman, publishers of the *Cyclopedia*, for the task of illustrating his articles on 'Basso Relievo' and 'Sculpture'. Blake apparently took to the project with enthusiasm, copying in the British Museum and after plaster casts in the Royal Academy rooms at Somerset House. *Sculpture. Plate I* (cat. 46) groups together a variety of copies after classical bronzes and statues undertaken in 1815. The central figure of Jupiter Olympus is based closely on Pausanius's (2nd century AD) classic account in *The Description of Greece* of this masterpiece by the sculptor Phidias (destroyed in the fire at Constantinople in AD 475), and may have drawn as well on a reconstruction of the statue designed by Flaxman.[116] Blake worked his copies into meticulous preparatory drawings prior to engraving, following the same principle he outlined to Wedgwood at precisely this time: 'It will be more convenient to me to make all the drawings first, before I begin Engraving them, as it will enable me also to regulate a system of working that will be uniform from beginning to end'.[117] Rather than the hard linear style deployed for the Wedgwood catalogue plates, he translated the *Cyclopedia* drawings into the soft, reproductive stipple-engraving mode.

Stipple engraving developed from the 'crayon' manner of printmaking, invented in France in the fifteenth century, which was popularized in England by the work of William Wynne Ryland in the 1760s. The crayon manner employed a roulette—a wheel covered with small spikes—to gouge broken dotted lines on the copper-plate in imitation of the open, powdery lines of chalk drawing. Stipple engraving expanded this dotted-line technique, covering the entire plate with a complex tonal web of dots and small flicks which mimicked the chiaroscuro effects and soft textural transitions of oil painting. Etched lines often initially defined the main parameters of a composition, and etching needles and engraving burins were used over this, in addition to the roulette wheel, to multiply the subtle modulations between shifting patterns of flicks and dots.

Francesco Bartolozzi (1727–1815) became the most famous exponent of stipple engraving at the close of the eighteenth century. After working in Florence and Venice, Bartolozzi first came to England in 1764 to engrave the Guercino drawings held in the Royal Collection. He stayed on to work for Boydell and Angelica Kauffmann, among others, and supervised a flourishing workshop where assistants turned out hundreds of mainly reproductive stipple engravings with the Bartolozzi 'signature'.[118]

Robert Essick noted of the *Cyclopedia* that 'the use of stipple in these reproductive plates can be counted as another instance of Blake's unavoidable subservience to popular tastes when engaged in commercial activities'.[119] As a highly trained commercial apprentice, Blake had been proficient in the stipple manner from his earliest days. In the 1780s he had executed meticulous if dull stipple plates after Stothard, Watteau and George Morland (1763–1804). His two commercial stipple works engraved in 1788 after Morland's moralizing drawings *The Industrious Cottager* and *The Idle Laundress*, provide a dramatic contrast with the technical originality of the *Songs of Innocence*. But his relationship with the medium remained ambivalent. In his *Notebook* he refers mockingly to 'Verse as soft as Bartolloze', and writes that 'I do not condemn Bartolozzi or Woolett / because they did not understand Drawing / but because they did not understand Graving' (N 65, 39). There is a strong measure of irony in the fact that Blake's *Cyclopedia* plates were engraved in the fashionable stipple manner when he would surely have preferred to work with the strongly incised 'bounding' outline which Flaxman had appreciated earlier.

A further irony underscores Blake's changed attitudes to Greek culture, which had drifted far from his claim at the turn of the century that 'the purpose for which I alone live . . . is, in conjunction with such men as my friend Cumberland, to renew the lost Art of the Greeks'.[120] *Milton* (1804–08), by contrast, opens with a dramatic condemnation of classical literature:

> The Stolen and Perverted Writings of Homer & Ovid, of Plato & Cicero, which all Men ought to contemn, are set up by artifice against the

47 *Vala, Hyle and Skofeld* (*c.* 1820), plate 51 from *Jerusalem*, *c.* 1804–15/*c.* 1818–20

Sublime of the Bible . . . Rouze up, O Young Men of the New Age! . . . We do not want either Greek or Roman Models if we are but just & true to our Imaginations, those Worlds of Eternity in which we shall live for ever in Jesus our Lord.[121]

By then Blake had moved to espouse a theory that Greek and Roman sculptures were debased copies, tainted with unnecessary naturalism, of more imaginatively pure Hebraic originals.[122] His copy after the cast of the Laocoön at the Royal Academy, engraved for the *Cyclopedia's Sculpture. Plate III*, was transformed around 1820 into a new and independent original engraving, *The Laocoön as Jehovah with Satan and Adam*. The marginal texts which surround this later print explain the Hellenistic Laocoön sculptural group as a mistaken reading of an Old Testament allegory, a secular perversion typical of the commercially-oriented classical outlook. 'Art Degraded, Imagination Denied, War Governed the Nations' is inscribed on one side of the *Laocoön* plate, an attitude Blake now found embodied in naturalistic Greek sculpture's 'Mathematical Form', which he contrasted with the 'Living Form' of Gothic art.[123] In the reproductive plates he engraved for Abraham Rees's *Cyclopedia*, therefore, we find Blake employed to capture the naturalistic form of Greek sculptures whose Grecian 'truth' he no longer respected, in a stipple manner he found inimical to the 'wirey bounding line' of imaginative artistic expression.

Jerusalem

Blake's fortunes took a sudden turn for the better in 1818, when George Cumberland's son introduced him to the young artist John Linnell (1792–1882). The son of a Bloomsbury frame-maker, John Linnell had been briefly apprenticed to the landscape painter John Varley in his teenage years, before entering the Royal Academy Schools. After leaving the schools in 1811 he established a considerable reputation as a landscape artist in his own right and earned a lucrative living as a fashionable portrait painter. He and Blake immediately became fast friends, their intimacy fostered by shared artistic interests. They toured private art collections together, and visited the British Museum to compare opinions on the sixteenth-century engravings of Albrecht Dürer and Marcantonio Raimondi.[124]

Although he probably appreciated Blake's artistic gifts more than his at times hermetic poetical flights, Linnell's constant financial and moral support encouraged Blake to continue creative self-expression in bleak times. His contributions to the monetary security of the Blake household ranged from fairly mundane commercial work, such as commissioning Blake to lay in the preliminary etched design on the copper-plate of an engraved portrait Linnell would later finish,[125] to active patronage of the artist's original graphic work. A particular enthusiast of the illuminated prophecies, Linnell acquired copies of *Europe*, *America*, *The Marriage of Heaven and Hell*, *Songs of Innocence* and *Songs of Innocence and of Experience* among others. And from 1818 to 1827

Fig. 21 William Blake, *Vala, Hyle and Skofeld*, plate 51 from *Jerusalem*, *c.* 1804–20. White-line etching (posthumous printing), 15.9 x 21.8 cm. Beinecke Rare Books and Manuscript Library, Yale University. Bequest of Charles J. Rosenbloom

Blake executed dozens of drawings, water-colours and engravings at Linnell's specific request.

Jerusalem, the last of Blake's great illuminated books, occupied his imagination for over fifteen years. Begun in 1804, the book had acquired a total of 100 plates by 1818–20, the dates watermarked on the leaves of five of the six surviving copies known to have been printed by Blake (there are also three known posthumous copies). The bulk of the work was completed relatively quickly, for Cumberland jotted in his notebook in 1807 that 'Blake has engd. 60 Plates of a new Prophecy!'.[126] But the printing of such a large volume was slow. In the last year of his life Blake commented wistfully on his *Jerusalem* 'that to print it will cost my time the amount of Twenty Guineas. One I have Finish'd. It contains 100 Plates but it is not likely that I shall get a Customer for it'.[127] Only Copy E (collection Paul Mellon, Virginia) was fully elaborated with water-colours and applied gold. Copy B was also worked up with water-colours, but consists of only the first twenty-five plates of the poem.

Linnell evidently followed the progress of Blake's 'editioning' of the poem closely. In December 1819 his accounts show a payment of 14 shillings for chapter II, and settlement for the balance of the illuminations is recorded for February 1821.[128] Linnell is known to have owned the complete Copy C of *Jerusalem*, printed in black ink with occasional tinted washes added, which may correspond to these accounts. The highly coloured Copy E was still in Blake's hands at the time of his death, and after 1831 passed to Catherine Blake's executor Frederick Tatham (along with the copper-plates which Tatham used to print restrikes). Since Linnell was substantially supporting Blake with the *Job* and Dante commissions in his last years, he may not have been keen to acquire this comparatively expensive volume. However, he either purchased or was given an equally richly worked separate impression of *Jerusalem*'s plate 51 (cat. 47), which stands virtually as an independent and finished water-colour.

The National Gallery of Victoria's *Vala, Hyle and Skofeld* plate, printed in relief in orange ink, was pulled through the press under rather light pressure to allow for subsequent hand colouring. Looking at a *c.* 1831 'Frederick Tatham' restrike of the same page (fig. 21) one can see the complex web of white-line etched and engraved lines with which Blake covered the copper-plate, evoking visually the bondage and oppression of the figures depicted. These linear intricacies are replaced on the Melbourne impression by broad, licking flames washed in with hot, glowing red and yellow pigments, and thick dark clouds of opaquely layered hues. The scattering of gold paint through the upper half of the composition suggests the molten fury of the fires of damnation rather than any opulence of spirit or worldly reward. As Robert Essick noted of late copies of the *Songs of Innocence and of Experience*, 'the impression from the metal plate is little more than a guide for the execution of unique works of drawing and tinting, clearly distinguished from all other versions even though they contain the same underlying print'.[129]

A second separate impression of *Jerusalem*'s plate 51, in the Fitzwilliam Museum, Cambridge, demonstrates Essick's point admirably, and also seems to have been worked up as an independent water-colour. Printed in blue-green ink, it is very finely painted with sombre hues—deep blue, dark grey, lilac over pink (muting both) and dull flaring reds—which differ markedly from the more open and vivid water-colour handling on the Melbourne version. The Cambridge copy, which has the identifying names of 'Vala', 'Hyle' and 'Skofeld' scratched along its base, has been trimmed to the edges of the plate and mounted on stiff card as an independent 'drawing'. The framing lines painted around the Melbourne impression, and the page number '51' inscribed outside the composition, indicate that the sheet once was intended for a complete copy of *Jerusalem* and was subsequently coloured as a 'presentation' piece.

Jerusalem narrates the struggles of Albion (man) and his female emanation Jerusalem, their fall, and final redemption through Christ. Vala, shown crowned on plate 51, is the fallen Jerusalem overcome with anguish and languishing in the fiery depths of Ulro (Blake's kingdom of absolute despair). The names of her naked acolytes are cyphers for the 'enemies' uppermost in Blake's mind when he began the poem around 1804: Hyle, the overbearing and obtuse William Hayley; and Skofeld, the soldier John Scolfield, who had charged Blake with sedition in 1803.

Thornton's *Virgil*

In September 1818 John Linnell introduced Blake to his friend and family physician Dr Robert John Thornton (1768?–1837). An enthusiastic author of botanical tracts in his spare time, Thornton's most sumptuous publication had been his profusely illustrated *Temple of Flora* which appeared in parts from 1798 to 1807. He was surely impressed by the ebulliently floral *Songs of Innocence* plates and this, coupled with Linnell's recommendations, may have persuaded him to approach Blake with a new commercial proposition. In 1812 Thornton had published his *School Virgil: whereby Boys will acquire Ideas as well as Words; Masters be saved the necessity of any explanation; and the Latin Language obtained in the shortest time*. A second edition of Thornton's *Virgil* came out in 1819, and by September 1820 Blake was at work on the third edition, which Thornton envisaged as being lavishly illustrated for the better instruction of its young readers. To sweeten the palates of the schoolboys assigned to study the Latin verse of the Roman poet Virgil (70–19 BC), Thornton also included 'Imitations' of Virgilian poetry by a range of English authors.

The expanded edition was released in two volumes in 1821 as *The Pastorals of Virgil, with a Course of English Reading, Adapted for Schools: in which all the Proper Facilities are given, Enabling Youth to acquire the Latin Language, in the Shortest Period of Time*. Blake's attention was chiefly addressed to illustrating an *Imitation of Eclogue I* by Ambrose Phillips (1675?–1749), whose pastoral poems were written in the first decade of the eighteenth century. The *Eclogues*, ten short poems composed by Virgil between 42 and 37 BC, describe peaceful country scenes and pastoral idylls, though not without occasional political undercurrents. Phillips's *Imitation* picks up Virgil's structural motif of a dialogue between two shepherds, contrasting the cheery reproofs of the older Thenot with the pessimistic complaints of young Colinet, an 'unthankful lad . . . untimely born' whose days are 'all clouded o'er with wo'.

In all Blake was involved with twenty-seven illustrations to Thornton's third edition of *The Pastorals of Virgil*. He engraved seventeen of his own drawings for 'Eclogue I'; but three more of these designs were cut by another, more conservative wood-engraver. Blake also executed six reproductive intaglio engravings on copper after classical statues and coins, and drew a reduced copy after Poussin which was engraved by Byfield.[130] Among the 230 illustrations in the 1821 edition of the *Pastorals*, it is Blake's, grouped together at the front of the first volume, which particularly stand out. For the clearer instruction of the schoolchildren at whom the publication was aimed, Blake's designs followed the dialogue between Thenot and Colinet verse by verse in, on one level, a highly illustrative and literal 'reading' of the poem. They appeared here printed four to a page opposite Phillips's text, above brief typeset captions identifying the speaker of each verse illustrated. Thornton's famous note was printed under the opening image:

> The Illustrations of this English Pastoral are by the famous BLAKE, the illustrator of *Young*'s Night Thoughts and *Blair*'s Grave; who designed and engraved them himself. This is mentioned, as they display less of art than genius, and are much admired by some eminent painters.

Perhaps merely an awkwardly worded enticement for a youthful audience to study the volumes' finest pages, the derogatory intent or otherwise of this 'disclaimer' is still under debate. Proof impressions

48 a–n Thornton's *Virgil* 1820–21
48 a *Thenot Remonstrates with Colinet*

48 c *Thenot Remonstrates with Colinet, Lightfoot in the Distance*

48 b *Thenot Under a Fruit Tree*

48 d *Colinet Departs in Sorrow, A Thunder-Scarred Tree on the Right*

survive of eight of the designs, also printed four to a page, before the compositions were cut down to fit the small dimensions of Thornton's volumes.

As Robert Essick remarked, 'the Virgil illustrations are not the sudden flowering of untutored genius, but the culmination of a long and arduous apprenticeship'.[131] Blake's long experience with relief etching and white-line engraving had certainly trained him to think in terms of handling a relief block, but these processes were necessarily slow and carefully realized. What is extraordinary in the *Virgil* wood-engravings is the roughness of Blake's technique in such a small format—and the freedom, openness and ruggedness of the designs. The engraving tool dances over the wood with complete ease, at times skipping and flicking with light-hearted zest, elsewhere ploughing deep with the dogged determination of darker moods. It has frequently been argued that Blake's elegant pastoral vignettes draw on his idyllic experiences at Felpham, where 'if I should ever build a Palace it would only be My Cottage Enlarged', 'a roller & two harrows lie before my window', and 'the sweet air & the voices of winds, trees & birds, & the odours of the happy ground, makes it a dwelling for immortals'.[132]

But Blake's predilection for engraving away the lines which define form so that they appear white against a dark ground when printed in relief, overlays this pastoral sweetness with a more sombre method. In many of the scenes his insistence on retaining black backgrounds becomes strangely threatening or disturbing. They appear as if bathed in a moonlight which is neither calming nor bestilled, but rather gives the impression that nature is tainted or that the most sublime idyll can be shattered in an instant by forces one is powerless to control. Both Essick and Patterson have seen in Blake's brooding identification with the melancholy shepherd Colinet an echo of his final alienation from the overbearing patronage of Hayley at Felpham. 'Silent representations of social injustice' have also been read into the contrasts drawn between rustic simplicity and elegant urban entertainments in these designs.[133]

Our knowledge of the circumstances surrounding Blake's commission from Thornton derives from nineteenth-century accounts which are at best questionable. In 1843 Henry Cole published the first story of contemporary dissatisfaction with Blake's wood-engravings, claiming that 'When Blake had produced his cuts, which were, however, printed with an *apology*, a shout of derision was raised by the wood-engravers. "This will not do", said they, "we will show what it ought to be"—that is, what the public taste would like'.[134] This version of events, apparently conveyed to Cole by John Linnell, was elaborated in Gilchrist's 1863 *Life of Blake*. Disapproval of Blake's radical white-line technique was here transferred to Thornton himself, who supposedly sided with the *Pastorals*' publishers in condemnation of the designs. Gilchrist related, without documentation, an anecdote describing how Thornton was persuaded over dinner by '[Thomas] Lawrence, James Ward, Linnell, and others' to include the Blake works against his better judgement.

Fig. 22 William Blake, *Illustrations to Thornton's 'Virgil'*, 1820–21. Sheet of proofs of cuts 2–5 printed from one block before trimming. Wood-engravings, 15.3 x 8.7 cm. National Gallery of Art, Washington, DC. Rosenwald Collection

A reluctant Thornton, however, felt obliged to apologize to his readers for this visual inconvenience. Further, since the blocks 'proved in the first instance too wide for the page', they were 'irrespective of the composition, summarily cut down to the requisite size by the publishers'—presumably with Thornton's tacit approval.[135]

In the wake of Gilchrist's account, Thornton has come in for heavy criticism over his alleged maltreatment of Blake. Russell referred to the 'ruthless trimming' of Blake's designs, while Binyon lamented that 'his work had been mutilated', and later decried the manner in which 'the blocks were brutally cut down to fit the book, and villainously presented, four on a small page'.[136] Geoffrey Keynes took this feeling to extremes with imaginative zeal:

> Dr. Thornton was not an imaginative man . . . Unrecognised genius . . . left him unimpressed, and Blake's woodcuts only prompted him to jeer. When they were laid before him he was horrified by such rough and amateurish work, and immediately gave directions that the designs should be recut by a professional wood-engraver . . . Thornton remained uneasy, and felt that he had to apologise for the inclusion of such work in his book.[137]

There is, however, not a single piece of evidence to indicate Thornton's reaction to Blake's wood-engravings.

More balanced views have occasionally emerged. Andrew Wilton has pointed out that Blake's proofs (fig. 22) show that he willingly designed the *Virgil* illustrations for incorporation into the book at four a page, and suggested that, after miscalculating the small format of Thornton's volumes, Blake himself trimmed the blocks. Michael Tolley has gone still further, neatly turning all previous accounts of the *Pastorals* affair on their heads by arguing that 'the third edition of Thornton's Virgil Eclogues was utterly reliant, for its distinctive tone as marking it off from the previous editions, on the Blake factor', and concluding that 'far from being embarrassed by the presence in his book of an artless unskilled worker, Thornton had gone out of his way to promote Blake in his new edition of an already successful school text'.[138]

Wilton's theory leads inevitably to a new issue of whether the final reduced blocks, usually regarded somewhat regretfully by Blake scholars, are in fact just as 'Blakean' as the full-size proof designs. The curiously slanted edges given to some of the smaller compositions could then be seen as a further rusticizing of these ruggedly pastoral blocks by Blake himself, and several of the designs are arguably tighter and more dramatically charged in the smaller format. It remains a mystery why Thornton should have allowed three of Blake's twenty Eclogue designs to be published in the conservative, dry manner of another anonymous engraver if he was so concerned to promote Blake in the *Pastorals* volumes. But Tolley's provocative claims certainly gain support from the fact that Thornton again called on Blake to engrave a *Hiding of Moses* illustration for his 1825 pocket-companion album *Remember Me!*, and even included a commentary on the plate praising 'the imagination and abilities of Mr Blake'.[139] Blake's rantings against 'the Classical Learned' scrawled in the last year of his life on a copy of Thornton's *New Translation of the Lord's Prayer* (1827), are often cited as proof of his emphatic antipathy to this patron.[140] It is unwise, though, to use these hostile scribblings to read back into Blake's mind of six years earlier, and, in any case, his private criticisms tell us nothing of Thornton's feelings towards Blake.

Melbourne possesses an incomplete set of fourteen of the seventeen *Virgil* wood-engravings, which is also clearly a composite group (cat. 48 a–n). Most of these impressions are pulled on the type of thin, white wove paper found in copies of the 1821 book edition. Trimmed to within 1 or 2 mm of the image, they could either have been cut from a dismembered copy of the book or they may be later strikes from the *Virgil* blocks.

The wood-blocks were acquired from Thornton by John Linnell in September 1825 for a mere 2

48 e *Blasted Tree and Blighted Crops*

48 h *Colinet's Fond Desire Strange Lands to Know*

48 f *The Good Shepherd Chases Away the Wolf*

48 i *Colinet Resting at Cambridge by Night*

48 g *Sabrina's Silvery Flood*

48 j *Colinet Mocked by Two Boys*

guineas, or roughly 2 shillings and sixpence per block.[141] While it is not known precisely when Linnell began reissuing proofs from these blocks, his son John Linnell junior did provide a rough account of their subsequent history:

> These blocks after the Publisher had used them, (J. L. bought of him for two guineas) E Calvert printed them for J. L. and self, & c (certain number of imprints of the set) (J. L. jun. & brother printed a few of the blocks, but did not finish the set).[142]

Edward Calvert belonged to the select circle of artists around Linnell who were introduced to Blake in the years 1818–26. John Varley (Linnell's old teacher and the eldest of the group), Samuel Palmer and George Richmond were the other major figures in this coterie, who dubbed themselves 'The Ancients' and Blake 'The Interpreter'. With the death of Fuseli in 1825 and Flaxman the following year, the Ancients' friendship came to fill out Blake's final years with their constant visits to his home and profferings of their own works for his comments and criticism.

The *Virgil* wood-engravings were held in particular reverence by this group of young men, and sets of the prints were owned by at least Linnell, Palmer and Calvert. Evidence of their mystique is furnished by the somewhat exaggerated claim of Palmer's son which accompanies an early proof of the uncut block bearing designs e–h, to the effect that it is 'one of two which were taken by Blake himself at Fountain Court at his own press in my father's presence, and signed at the same time. I possess the companion proof and a letter of my father's describing the transaction'.[143] While Palmer most likely did not see the printing of these early *Virgil* proofs, this testimonial does bear witness to their sacrosanct status among the Ancients. Samuel Palmer himself later recalled them as 'visions of little dells, and nooks, and corners of Paradise; models of the exquisitest pitch of intense poetry'. Edward Calvert was equally in awe, writing to his son: 'Some small woodcuts of Blake are in your possession . . . They are done as if by a child; several of them careless and incorrect, yet there is a spirit in them, humble enough and of force enough to move simple souls to tears'.[144]

An unanswered question is whether Blake personally witnessed or even supervised some restrikes of the *Virgil* prints by the Ancients. He could hardly have remained unaware of Linnell's purchase of the blocks, given the popularity of the series with his young friends. Calvert appears to have given up printmaking around 1831 at the age of thirty-two, and it seems unlikely that he would have undertaken to print from Linnell's blocks after this. Linnell's diary entry of 8 September 1828, noting that Calvert had brought round 'impressions of Blake's woodcuts', need not preclude earlier printing experiments from the blocks under Blake's own eye. Blake and Calvert are known to have experimented with etching techniques together, and Blake is the most probable candidate as instructor behind Calvert's wood-engraving style, which springs forth fully formed with his superb *Ploughman* composition of 1827.[145] A shared printing session using the *Virgil* blocks would have been a fine way for the older artist to demonstrate certain white-line techniques or his particular passion for strong contrasts and deep chiaroscuro in the medium. Calvert himself may subsequently have instructed Linnell in the finer points of printing wood-engravings, for he appears to have later lent his printing press to Linnell.[146]

Five of Melbourne's *Virgil* impressions, which are printed on slightly larger sheets of paper (cat. 48 f, i, k–m), have lower margins sufficiently deep to show that they never bore the letterpress captions of the book edition. These are definitely restrikes, but whether they emanate from Calvert's or Linnell's hand (or, indeed, from Linnell's sons) it is impossible to determine. Little systematic study has yet been undertaken of the paper types used for the various printings of Thornton's *Virgil* blocks, and further clues to elucidate the contributions of Linnell and Calvert may perhaps lie here. Two of the above-mentioned designs (cat. 48 l, m) are printed on a thin, pale cream Oriental laid paper, with a silky sheen, which differs markedly from the thin white wove normally used for both 1821 and post-1821 printings, while *Menalcas' Yearly Wake* (cat. 48 k) is printed on a cream European laid paper. These papers are unusual, but not unique—Robert Essick, for example, also owns a *Virgil* impression, probably from a Linnell printing, on the same silky Oriental paper found in Melbourne.

These variations in paper stock are what one could reasonably expect from a printing history of at least three different post-Blake hands, as are shifts in the intensity and type of ink used on the blocks. The wood-engravings in copies of the original Thornton volumes vary enormously in quality, from pale and patchy under-inked pages to heavy, dark, over-inked impressions. They are printed with a rather grainy ink similar to that used by Blake in *c.* 1820 for proofing the large uncut blocks (also fig. 22). Linnell used a finer ink for his restrikes (British Museum, Tate, Fitzwilliam), and tended to print rather dark but even impressions with little of the white of the paper permeating through the blacks. Most of Melbourne's *Virgil* prints resemble these dark Linnell versions. An exception is *Menalcas' Yearly Wake*, which is somewhat poorly printed in an oily black ink with a slight yellowish tinge. This is most likely a Linnell impression as well; a very similar copy of *Menalcas' Yearly Wake* in the Tate, also on a cream paper, can be traced firmly back to John Linnell or his heirs.[147]

In 1977 the British Museum prepared a limited edition of 135 restrikes on Japanese Hosho paper from each of the seventeen *Virgil* wood-blocks. The project was approached from the viewpoint that 'impressions taken in the nineteenth century did little justice to the beauty of the blocks', and that even proofs printed from electrotype facsimiles of the wood-blocks in 1937 were 'an impressive improvement on the original printing in the book of 1821, and the random prints taken off by Linnell in later years'.[148] While careful inking, printing and choice of paper did produce pristine, clear impressions showing greater definition than their nineteenth-century predecessors, the printers Bain and Chambers failed to capture the rugged vitality and sparkle of Blake's own handiwork.

The best impressions in the 1821 book edition result from a moderate inking of the blocks, which brings out the silvery richness of Blake's white-line technique and allows the paper to breathe through the open, gritty texture of the grainy ink used. This silvery, almost moonlit quality of light, which admittedly softens the definition of form and obscures certain fine details of the wood-engravings, also bathes Blake's early proofs of the uncut blocks, where it is surely intentional. Both William and Catherine Blake were expert printers, experienced hands at relief and intaglio press-work. This strongly suggests that the silvery tonalities and mottled ink of the pre-publication *Virgil* proofs were the precise effects Blake was looking for. They can be compared with earlier experiments with 'wood-cuts on pewter' or white-line metal cuts printed in relief, such as the broadside *Little Tom the Sailor* which the Blakes produced together for William Hayley in 1800. As Essick noted, the uneven and variant inkings of *Little Tom* impressions stem from 'a popular tradition in broadside art where crudities are appropriate', and accord with Blake's own description of these prints for Hayley as 'rough like rough sailors'.[149]

Similarly, if we accept that Blake cut down the *Virgil* blocks himself, and that Thornton's 1821 book edition of the *Pastorals* was intended to showcase Blake's 'genius', then it would seem to follow that Blake also approved the wide and lively printing variations his *Virgil* designs were subject to there. Absolute fidelity to the work on the block may not always be the artist's intention, as can be seen by contrasting the happy idiosyncracy of Blake's own printings of the *Songs of Innocence* plates with accurate but lifeless electrotype restrikes. Freedom from the absolute uniformity and clarity of printing demanded by commercial reproductive engraving surely became as much a part of Blake's statement of liberation in the Thornton wood-engravings as his radical white-line technique itself.

48 k *Menalcas' Yearly Wake*

48 m *With Songs the Jovial Hinds Return from Plow*

48 l *Thenot and Colinet Sup Together*

48 n *Unyoked Heifers Loitering Homeward, Low*

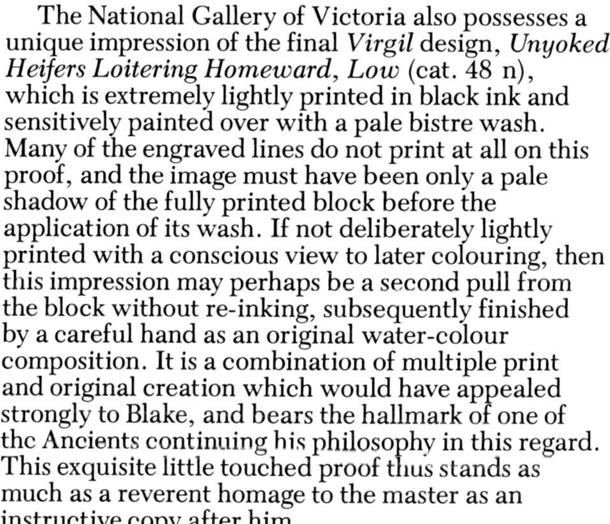

The National Gallery of Victoria also possesses a unique impression of the final *Virgil* design, *Unyoked Heifers Loitering Homeward, Low* (cat. 48 n), which is extremely lightly printed in black ink and sensitively painted over with a pale bistre wash. Many of the engraved lines do not print at all on this proof, and the image must have been only a pale shadow of the fully printed block before the application of its wash. If not deliberately lightly printed with a conscious view to later colouring, then this impression may perhaps be a second pull from the block without re-inking, subsequently finished by a careful hand as an original water-colour composition. It is a combination of multiple print and original creation which would have appealed strongly to Blake, and bears the hallmark of one of the Ancients continuing his philosophy in this regard. This exquisite little touched proof thus stands as much as a reverent homage to the master as an instructive copy after him.

Other examples exist of touched impressions by unspecified hands from the circle of Blake and the Ancients. The complete 'Collins' set of hand-coloured laid India 'Proof' impressions of Blake's twenty-two engravings for *The Book of Job* is close in handling to the 'New Zealand' set of *Job* water-colours which was probably made by John Linnell or his pupil (for one year in 1836–37) Albin Martin. Four more hand-coloured *Job* 'Proof' engravings survive in the Fitzwilliam Museum. All were inked extremely lightly, and so must have been printed in this way specifically to allow for their subsequent colouring, in a manner similar to the Melbourne *Heifers*.[150] In the mid-1970s seven brightly and naturalistically coloured impressions of the *Virgil* wood-engravings appeared in the collection of descendents of John Linnell. Coloured with opaque body colours which obscure the underlying engraved lines, these were possibly painted by John Linnell, or one of his sons or pupils.[151] But they differ markedly from the Melbourne *Heifers* in their heaviness of colour and rather tendentious naturalism. The delicacy of touch in the National Gallery of Victoria's coloured *Virgil* print and the gently melancholic illumination imparted by its soft bistre wash, really only find their counterpart in Blake's own grey wash preparatory drawing for the engraving (Princeton University). Robert Essick's suggestion (letter of 24 February 1989) that Edward Calvert's hand may lie behind this harmonious Blakean composition is extremely appealing.

The Book of Job

Blake's financial troubles were apparently only partially alleviated by the *Virgil* project. In 1821 he and his wife moved to smallish quarters at No. 3 Fountain Court, Strand, and around the same time he was forced to sell his personal print collection to Colnaghi's in order to raise cash. As Samuel Palmer told Gilchrist, 'It put him out very much when Mrs. Blake referred to the financial topic, or found herself constrained to announce, "The money is going, Mr. Blake". "Oh, d— the money!" he would shout, "it's always the money!" '.[152] Recognizing his friend's plight, John Linnell used his influence to lobby the Royal Academy for financial assistance for Blake; in

49 a–v ***The Book of Job*** **1823–26**
49 a *Title-Page*

June 1822 the Academy Council voted a gift of £25 to 'William Blake an able Designer & Engraver laboring under great distress—'.[153]

It was surely in this same spirit that Linnell conceived of the *Job* project, which was to occupy Blake on and off at Linnell's expense for five years. Blake had originally executed a group of water-colour illustrations of *The Book of Job* for Thomas Butts in *c.* 1805–06. Evidently having been taken with these on a visit to Butts, John Linnell proposed in September 1821 that Blake undertake a second series for his own collection. He himself traced a new set of designs from the Butts water-colours, which were then coloured by Blake.

This in turn led to a further plan to commission an engraved series of twenty *Job* designs, for which a contract was drawn up in March 1823, with John Linnell agreeing 'to pay William Blake five Pounds p^r^ Plate or one hundred Pounds for the set part before and the remainder when the Plates are finished, as Mr Blake may require it, besides which J. Linnell agrees to give W. Blake one hundred pounds more out of the Profits of the work as the receipts will admit of it'.[154] Linnell evidently hoped to offset some of the project's costs by raising subscriptions; the names of Flaxman, Thornton and Edward Calvert are among those appearing in Linnell's records of *Job* subscribers between 1823 and 1825. In the end Blake engraved twenty-two plates for his *Illustrations of the Book of Job*, on which he worked throughout these two years. Although dated 8 March 1825 on their imprints, the *Job* engravings were actually published in the early months of 1826.

Blake's *Job* plates were probably initially proofed by Blake and perhaps also Linnell, and early impressions bear Linnell's name as publisher on the imprint. As the project drew nearer to completion Linnell paid the professional printers John Dixon and James Lahee to take over the time-consuming labour of pulling multiple proofs. The final edition, ordered in March 1826, was printed by Lahee and consisted—according to John Linnell's account book—of 150 sets of 'Proof' impressions on laid India paper, 65 sets on French paper and 100 sets on 'Drawing paper'. Of this total edition of 315, Linnell's accounts record advance and post-publication sales of only 20 proof sets and 24 plain sets between 1823 and 1834, most of these to Blake's or his own friends.[155] The plates remained with Linnell, who authorized a further printing of 100 copies on laid India paper by Holdgate Brothers in 1874. There were thus a total of 415 sets of the *Job* engravings printed before 1919, when the trustees of the Linnell estate presented the original copper-plates to the British Museum.

The National Gallery of Victoria's *Job* engravings (cat. 49 a–v) formed one of eighteen sets which survived in the Linnell family collection until its dispersal at auction in 1918. Distinguished by the word 'Proof' engraved outside the lower right edge of each design (scraped or burnished off before later impressions), they are finely and carefully printed, revealing the extraordinary minutiae of Blake's burin work. Blake and Linnell chose laid India paper for the 'Proof' impressions, sets of which were sold at a higher price than the plainer copies on French or drawing paper. Having an exceptionally smooth and ink-receptive surface, and glued to a thicker sheet of Whatman wove paper for support, laid India yielded superb impressions registering even the finest lines and palest tonalities engraved into the copper-plate.[156]

Robert Essick has meticulously analysed Blake's engraving style on the *Job* plates, arguing that his 'enormous concern with illumination in the plates has a clear relationship to the central themes of Job's fall into spiritual darkness and his return to the light of God'.[157] A series of pencil drawings (Fitzwilliam Museum, Cambridge) reduced the water-colour designs traced by Linnell to the size of the final engravings. These were probably then traced for counterproving onto the copper-plates. Broad compositional outlines were next mapped out with tiny dots cut into the plate with a stipple burin or etching needle, and linked by drypoint lines dragged across the surface of the copper with a sharp cutting tool. Deeper engraved furrows simultaneously followed and obliterated the drypoint base of each design. Blake gave a startling prominence to these engraving techniques by eliminating the use of preliminary etching to lay in the initial composition. Even the miniscule curling worm-lines and squiggles which everywhere expand the textural richness of the *Job* world, were engraved directly into the copper with a burin rather than etched through a covering ground. The border designs, which are not found on the earlier water-colour or pencil versions, also appear to have been 'sketched' onto the copper in drypoint and subsequently strengthened with over-engraving.

Ever since Joseph Wicksteed's pioneering study of 1910, Blake scholarship has recognized the artist's distinctly personal interpretation of *The Book of Job*. In the biblical account Satan, having had Job pointed out as a perfect man, taunts God with the suggestion that his piety and love of the Father are due merely to his material wealth; he is therefore allowed by God to test Job's religious loyalty with diverse punishments and torments. Wicksteed maintained that Blake utilized the outward story of the Bible to explore his vision of Job's inward, spiritual life. He made much of a symbolic use of right/spiritual/good and left/material/wrong correspondences in the *Job* designs, which are allegedly manifested through gesture and even the placement of feet in the compositions. Wicksteed's Job is a man deceived into equating moral good with material success, and organized religion with spiritual virtue, errors which he gradually casts out on a troubled voyage towards true understanding of spiritual redemption and the forgiveness of sins.[158]

S. Foster Damon pursued Wicksteed's notion that the whole drama is enacted within Job's soul, elaborating an argument that both the God and Satan of Blake's designs are intended to be read as creations of Job's misdirected mind. For Damon, Blake conceived that only a false God would have allowed Satan to so punish the innocent Job. Job's error lay in giving credence to this false avenging deity. Job's misfortunes are thus 'not punitive but educational' as they 'rouse Job from his complacent submissiveness to tradition, and start him on his search for the true God' who is 'Jesus, the Divine Imagination, and the Forgiveness of Sins: the only God whom Blake recognized'.[159]

Most later scholarship has expanded out from these interpretive stances. Bo Lindberg has analysed extensively Blake's visual sources for the *Job* series and examined the textual base for each engraved plate. From a diametrically opposed perspective Kathleen Raine has attempted to situate Blake's vision of the Job story in the context of the traditions of eighteenth-century hermetic philosophy.[160] David Bindman has looked to the internal coherence of the designs, arguing that 'though in one sense it would be correct to say that Job progresses from the worship of Jehovah to the worship of Christ, in another sense they are one God transformed by Job's perceptions from a vengeful to a merciful one'.[161] Criticism drawing on this typological approach, summed up by Bindman as a belief in Blake's expression of the ability of pre-Christian man to attain to Christian redemption through spiritual awakening and poetic vision, remains in vogue.[162]

49 c *Satan Before the Throne of God*, plate 2

49 b *Job and His Family*, plate 1

49 d *The Destruction of Job's Sons*, plate 3

49 e *The Messenger Tells Job of His Misfortunes*, plate 4

49 f *Satan Going Forth from the Presence of the Lord*, plate 5

49 g *Satan Smiting Job with Boils*, plate 6

49 h *Job's Comforters*, plate 7

49 i *Job's Despair*, plate 8

49 k *Job Rebuked by His Friends*, plate 10

49 j *The Vision of Eliphaz*, plate 9

49 l *Job's Evil Dreams*, plate 11

49 m *The Wrath of Elihu*, plate 12

49 n *The Lord Answering Job Out of the Whirlwind*, plate 13

49 o *The Creation*, plate 14

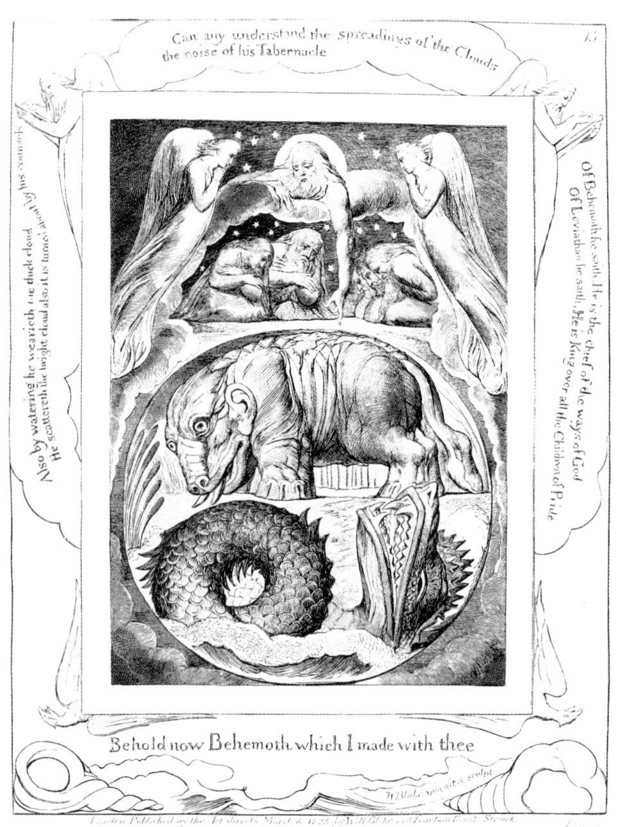

49 p *Behemoth and Leviathan*, plate 15

49 r *The Vision of God*, plate 17

49 q *The Fall of Satan*, plate 16

49 s *Job's Sacrifice*, plate 18

49 t *Job Accepting Charity*, plate 19

49 u *Job and His Daughters*, plate 20

49 v *Job and His Wife Restored to Prosperity*, plate 21

Dante

In March 1827 Blake 'saw Mr Tatham, Senr, . . . [who] sat with me above an hour, & look'd over the Dante; he expressed himself very much pleas'd with the designs as well as the Engravings'.[163] The two had been discussing Blake's last great project, a series of 102 water-colour illustrations of the *Divine Comedy* of Dante Alighieri (1265–1321), for which accompanying engravings were also planned. The series was again commissioned by John Linnell, in 1824 after the *Job* designs were brought to completion (although the *Job* engravings were still being proofed and printed throughout 1825).

Blake had long been familiar with the *Divine Comedy*. His friends Flaxman and Fuseli had both worked on Dante compositions in the 1780s. Perhaps as early as 1800 he annotated a copy of Henry Boyd's 1785 translation of the *Inferno*, which William Hayley had probably given him at Felpham.[164] And in 1806 he wrote bluntly that 'the critic must be a fool who has not read Dante'.[165] After receiving Linnell's commission he returned to serious contemplation of Dante, and apparently worked from both Henry Cary's 1819 translation of the *Divine Comedy* and a sixteenth-century copy of the Italian text with commentaries by Christoforo Landino and Alessandro Vellutello.[166]

Blake, however, was diametrically opposed to Dante's central theme in the *Inferno* of God's punishment of sin. As he scribbled on one of the water-colours undertaken for Linnell, 'Whatever Book is for Vengeance for Sin & whatever Book is Against the Forgiveness of Sins is not of the Father, but of Satan the Accuser & Father of Hell'. Earlier he had expressed the same antipathy to divine punishment on plate 53 of his epic poem *Jerusalem*: 'Listen! Every Religion that Preaches Vengeance for Sin is the Religion of the Enemy & Avenger and not of the Forgiveness of Sin, and their God is Satan, Named by the Divine Name'.[167] These thoughts seem to have been uppermost when Blake turned to engraving his first Dante designs. Of the seven surviving copper-plates he started work on, six deal overtly with Dante's and Virgil's reactions to a succession of witnessed punishments. The fate of the ill-starred lovers Paolo and Francesca (cat. 50 a) provides the most poignant compositional motif in this group, although the cumulative tortures inflicted on the procession of thieves, forgers, embezzlers and traitors in the other plates also reflects more on the Punisher than the punished.

The fact that Blake ignored highly finished Dante water-colours in the first instance and engraved two of the plates, *The Devils Tormenting Ciampolo* and *Dante's Foot Striking Bocca degli Abbati* (cat. 50 b, g), from relatively sketchy designs underscores his negative reaction to Dante's hellfire-and-brimstone text. Roe's fundamental thesis that Blake found 'the entire fabric of Dante's poem' to have been shakily built on the terrible error of belief in divine punishment, still holds true, despite David Fuller's recent argument that 'Interpretation which claims that Blake's illustrations cannot be understood without prior knowledge of his mythology presupposes that as embodiments of meaning in visual terms the illustrations are a failure'.[168]

Blake had pulled only a few working impressions of the Dante plates, on his own rolling press, before his death. Throughout some distasteful wrangles with Catherine Blake and, after her death in 1831, with Frederick Tatham, who claimed her estate, Linnell managed to retain both the group of 104 water-colour drawings and the seven Dante copper-plates. In 1838 he took the plates to the printers Dixon and Ross, and had a total of 120 so-called 'proofs' editioned on a thin India paper laid for strength onto French Colombier paper. These were sold sporadically, sometimes bound in green boards, by Linnell's nephew James Chance among others. This stock had been depleted by 1892, when John Linnell junior supervised the printing of a further fifty copies on 'India on drawing paper' by Holdgate Brothers. The copper-plates remained in the hands of the Linnell trustees until 1937, when they were sold to the American collector Lessing J. Rosenwald. Rosenwald had about twenty-five sets pulled onto a heavy English rag paper in 1955 by an unrecorded printer. At Ruthven Todd's suggestion he also commissioned artist Harry Hoehn to print another twenty-five sets of the Dante engravings (plus some inking proofs) on Japanese paper in 1968. The copper-plates now form part of the Rosenwald Collection in the Library of Congress, Washington, DC.[1]

The National Gallery of Victoria possesses full sets of the two modern restrike editions, both presented to the collection by Lessing J. Rosenwald in recognition of Melbourne's premier holdings of the Dante water-colours. The impressions printed on English paper in 1955 (cat. 50 aI–gI) are dry and unsatisfactory, with areas of the plate appearing to have worn down considerably. This was not actually the case and the problem may have been due to incorrect cleaning of the plates before inking or choice of an unreceptive paper type. After some experimentation in 1968, Harry Hoehn opted for a Japanese Kochi paper made from mulberry fibre, which closely resembled the silky India paper Linnell and Blake had chosen for the 'Proof' impressions of the *Job* series. Hoehn also vigorously cleaned the plates, removing, as he put it, 'mountains of dried ink and powder in the lines'.[170] He editioned the plates meticulously, discarding as many as seventy-five sheets of Kochi from a shipment of 250 to eliminate the slightest imperfection in the paper surface.

The results (cat. 50 aII–gII) are nothing short of superb, as far as posthumous impressions are concerned. As Rosenwald himself remarked in 1968, 'we compared Hoehn's impressions with those that were contemporary with Blake. We came to the conclusion that they were considerably superior to the earlier ones'.[171] Rosenwald was perhaps a little over-effusive in the excitement of discovery, but understandably so. True, the Hoehn prints do not show the velvety drypoint burr which enriches the early working proofs pulled by Blake himself. None the less the 1968 impressions sparkle and glow with a vivacious energy one could hardly have thought possible of restrikes printed almost 150 years after the plates were first 'drawn' on.

The comparison with drawing is apt. Robert Essick has remarked on the extent to which Blake

50 a–g Dante's *Divine Comedy* (engravings) 1826–27
50 a *The Circle of the Lustful. Paolo and Francesca*

50 b *The Circle of the Corrupt Officials. The Devils Tormenting Ciampolo*

50 c *The Circle of the Corrupt Officials. The Devils Mauling Each Other*

used drypoint in sketching the Dante designs onto the copper-plates, by which means he was able to '*draw* directly on the plate, for a drypoint needle is held and pulled through the copper like a pencil'.[172] This freedom of sketching is combined with a subsequent open and fresh network of engraved lines which, even allowing for the unfinished state of the plates, seems a deliberate emulation of the broad manner of fifteenth-century Italian engraving. In November 1823 Blake had proofread the manuscript of George Cumberland's *Essay on the Utility of Collecting the Best Works of the Ancient Engravers of the Italian Schools* (published 1827). Essick has pointed in particular to the prints by Andrea Mantegna in Cumberland's collection as an influence on the crackling, taut lines that score across the Dante plates.

The whole Dante project was plagued by Blake's ill-health. From 1825 to 1827 he spent long periods of time in bed, suffering from inflammation of the gall-bladder, gallstones and piles. His correspondence refers repeatedly to 'a cold in my stomach' or 'a return of the old shivering fit'. In May 1826 he penned the type of letter which must have alarmed the young John Linnell:

> I have had another desperate Shivering Fit; it came on yesterday afternoon after as good a morning as ever I experienced. It began by a gnawing Pain in the Stomach, & soon spread a deathly feel all over the limbs, which brings on the shivering fit . . . It was night when it left me, so I did not get up, but as I was going to rise this morning, the shivering fit attacked me again & the pain, with its accompanying deathly feel.[173]

No doubt, on account of this persistent ill-health, Blake appears to have worked on the Dante copper-plates only intermittently during the last two years of his life. On 7 June 1825 he wrote to Linnell that 'I can draw as well a-Bed as Up, & perhaps better; but I cannot Engrave. I am going on with Dante, & please myself'. On 2 July 1826 he was planning a visit to Linnell at Hampstead, intending to bring 'besides our necessary change of apparel, Only My Book of Drawings from Dante & one Plate shut up in the Book'.[174] In February 1827 he was at last ready to proof four of the plates; and by April he had taken proofs of six of the designs. One final plate, *The Devils Mauling Each Other* (cat. 50 c), can be dated precisely to April–August 1827, for Blake told Linnell that he had only reduced the water-colour design 'ready for the Copper' on 25 April. All of the plates remained unfinished at his death.

William Blake entered the 'Gates of Death' on 12 August 1827. Three days later the eighteen-year-old George Richmond wrote to Samuel Palmer:

> He died on Sunday Night at 6 Oclock in a most glorious manner[.] He said He was going to that Country he had all His life wished to see & expressed Himself Happy hoping for Salvation through Jesus Christ—Just before he died His Countenance became fair—His eyes brighten'd and He burst out in Singing of the things he Saw in Heaven[.]

Elsewhere he recalled that he 'closed the poet's eyes and kissed William Blake in death, as he lay upon his bed, in the enchanted work-room at Fountain Court'. George Richmond had closed Blake's eyes 'to keep the vision in'.[175]

> Engraving is Eternal work . . . I curse & bless Engraving alternately, because it takes so much time & is so untractable, tho' capable of such beauty & perfection.

William Blake[176]

50 d *The Circle of the Thieves. Agnello dei Brunelleschi Attacked by a Six-Footed Serpent*

50 e *The Circle of the Thieves. Buoso dei Donati Attacked by the Serpent*

50 f *The Circle of the Falsifiers. Dante and Virgil Covering Their Noses Because of the Stench*

50 g *The Circle of the Traitors. Dante's Foot Striking Bocca degli Abbati*

Appendix: Young's *Night Thoughts*

While this book was in press the holdings of the National Gallery of Victoria were again enriched by the Felton Bequest, with the acquisition at auction of a magnificently hand-coloured copy of William Blake's engravings for Edward Young's *Night Thoughts*.[177]

In 1795 the bookseller Richard Edwards (1768–1827) commissioned Blake to execute designs illustrating the nine 'Nights' of Edward Young's popular meditative poem *The Complaint, and the Consolation; or, Night Thoughts* (1745). With prodigious energy Blake finished 537 water-colour illustrations of Young's text within two years; these large water-colours, now held in the British Museum Print Room, form virtually a quarter of Blake's surviving *oeuvre*.

The first and only volume of the Edwards–Blake edition of the *Night Thoughts* was published in 1797. It contained the text of four of Young's 'Nights', along with forty-three engraved pages by Blake selected from the initial water-colour designs. The publication was not a success, apparently owing to the economic recession caused by war with France. Plans to publish three more volumes of engravings after the remaining 'Nights' were cancelled at this stage.

Until the appearance of the Melbourne *Night Thoughts* at auction, twenty-three coloured copies of the engravings were believed to exist.[178] It seems likely that some, if not all, of these were hand-tinted after models executed by Blake himself. The Melbourne version is of exceptional quality, and was clearly water-coloured by a highly professional artist as a deluxe presentation piece. The water-coloured engravings have survived extraordinarily well despite nearly two hundred years of handling. Their colours are almost painfully rich, vibrant and sparkling, and leap out of the pages as though the volume was being opened for the first time since its colouration in 1797–98.

The Melbourne *Night Thoughts* is bound between worn brown leather covers, tooled in gold with a restrained classical decoration limited to the border areas. The letters 'London / 1798' have been punched into the base of the spine; presumably, therefore, the water-colour finishing was completed before 1798. At some later stage the tome was broken apart to allow for the insertion of an engraved copy of Phillips's portrait of Blake (see cat. 44 a), an impression on laid India paper taken from the 1808 folio edition of Blair's *Grave*.[179] The crushed and soiled condition of this 'frontispiece' suggests that it was bound into the *Night Thoughts* volume at an early date (possibly in the 1820s), and almost certainly before the book's arrival in Australia.

The National Gallery of Victoria's *Night Thoughts* is highly significant both for being one of a handful of water-coloured copies of the publication, and for its distinguished provenance of William à Beckett—Alfred Felton—Robert and Marion Sticht. The book is inscribed on a front flyleaf 'William à Beckett / from Benjamin Stiner'. Sir William à Beckett (1806–69) arrived in New South Wales with his family in 1837 and was appointed solicitor-general for the colony in 1841. In 1846 à Beckett was transferred to Port Phillip (Melbourne) as resident judge, a post he held until 1852 when he was promoted to first chief justice of the newly established colony of Victoria. William à Beckett was also a prolific if pedestrian poet, contributing verses to the Sydney *Literary News* and the *Port Phillip Herald* under the pseudonym of 'Malwyn'. In 1839 he published *Lectures on the Poets and Poetry of Great Britain*. His ownership of this coloured copy of the *Night Thoughts* is the first documented work of significance by Blake in an Australian collection.[180]

There is strong evidence that the volume remained in Australia after William à Beckett's return to England in 1863. A pencil note in the handwriting of Robert Sticht on one of the front endpapers records that it was 'bt. 1904 (Felton)'. This surely refers to the auction of 'The Magnificent Library of Books, In the Estate of the Late Alfred Felton, Esq.', which took place on 5–6 May 1904 at the chambers of Gemmell, Tuckett and Company in Collins Street, Melbourne.[181] A sticker from 'Angus and Robertson, Sydney', pasted to the tome's inside front cover, suggests that the volume passed through these booksellers between its recorded ownership by à Beckett and, later, Felton. Alfred Felton (1831–1904) spent the last twenty years of his life in bachelor rooms at the St Kilda Hotel in Melbourne, which were filled with a varied collection of pictures and books, the *Night Thoughts* included. Profits from the 1904 sale of Felton's library eventually contributed towards the munificent Felton Bequest, which so richly endowed the National Gallery of Victoria's early purchases.

The inside cover of this copy of the *Night Thoughts* bears the bookplate of Robert Carl and Marion Oak Sticht. Robert Sticht (1856–1922), an American by birth, was educated at the Brooklyn Polytechnic Institute and the Royal School of Mines in Clausthal-Zellerfeld, Germany. In 1894 he was appointed to the position of chief metallurgist of the Mount Lyell Mining and Railway Company in Tasmania. He married Marion Staige the following year, and with her avidly pursued the creation of an art and literature collection of truly wide scope. The bulk of Robert and Marion Sticht's collection was acquired by the Felton Bequest after Robert Sticht's death, and presented to the National Gallery of Victoria in 1923.

In a true sense, therefore, this coloured copy of the *Night Thoughts* has come back to its rightful home. Its early presence in Australia parallels the origins of Melbourne itself, where in William à Beckett's hands it must have been considered an object of extraordinary beauty and cultivation among the crude vigour of the growing colony of Victoria. Its remarkable state of preservation attests to the care and reverence it was accorded in the à Beckett family. And its subsequent owners, Alfred Felton and the Stichts, are of course central to the history of the National Gallery of Victoria itself. The *Night Thoughts* will remain one of the great treasures of the Department of Prints and Drawings.

95

By the great edict, the divine decree,
Truth is deposited with man's last hour ;
An honest hour, and faithful to her trust :
Truth, eldest daughter of the Deity ;
Truth, of his council when he made the worlds,
Nor less when he shall judge the worlds he made ;
Though silent long, and sleeping ne'er so sound
Smother'd with errors, and oppress'd with toys ;
That heaven-commission'd hour no sooner calls,
But from her cavern in the soul's abyss,
Like him they fable under Ætna whelm'd,
* The goddess bursts in thunder and in flame ;
Loudly convinces, and severely pains :
Dark demons I discharge, and hydra-stings ;
The keen vibration of bright truth—is hell :
Just definition ! though by schools untaught.
Ye deaf to truth ! peruse this parson'd page,
And trust for once a prophet and a priest ;
" Men may live fools, but fools they cannot die."

51 xliii *Night Thoughts*, page 95

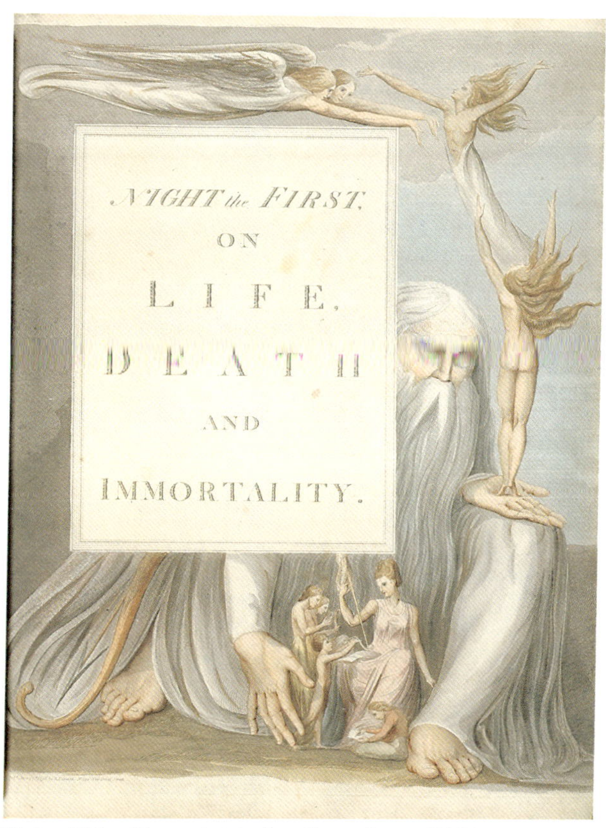

NIGHT the FIRST.
ON
LIFE,
DEATH
AND
IMMORTALITY.

51 i–xliii Young's *Night Thoughts* 1797
51 i *Night the First*, title-page

I

NIGHT THE FIRST.

[illegible]
He, like the world, his ready visit pays
Where fortune smiles; the wretched he forsakes:
* Swift on his downy pinion flies from woe,
And lights on lids unsullied with a tear.
From short, as usual, and disturb'd repose,
I wake: how happy they, who wake no more!
Yet that were vain, if dreams infest the grave.
I wake, emerging from a sea of dreams
Tumultuous; where my wreck'd, desponding thought
From wave to wave of fancied misery,
At random drove, her helm of reason lost:
Though now restored, 'tis only change of pain,
A bitter change! severer for severe:
The day too short for my distress! and night,
Even in the zenith of her dark domain,
Is sunshine, to the colour of my fate.

51 ii ***Night Thoughts*, page 1**

4

An heir of glory! a frail child of dust!
Helpless immortal! insect infinite!
A worm! a God!——I tremble at myself,
And in myself am lost! At home a stranger,
Thought wanders up and down, surprised, aghast,
And wond'ring at her own: how reason reels!
O what a miracle to man is man,
Triumphantly distress'd! what joy, what dread!
Alternately transported, and alarm'd!
What can preserve my life? or what destroy?
An angel's arm can't snatch me from the grave—
Legions of angels can't confine me there.
'Tis past conjecture: all things rise in proof.
While o'er my limbs sleep's soft dominion spread:
* What, though my soul fantastick measures trod
O'er fairy fields; or mourn'd along the gloom
Of pathless woods; or down the craggy steep
Hurl'd headlong, swam with pain the mantled pool;
Or scaled the cliff; or danced on hollow winds,
With antick shapes wild natives of the brain?
Her ceaseless flight, though devious, speaks her nature
Of subtler essence than the trodden clod;
Active, aërial, tow'ring, unconfined,
Unfetter'd with her gross companion's fall.
Even silent night proclaims my soul immortal;
Even silent night proclaims eternal day.
For human weal, Heaven husbands all events;
Dull sleep instructs, nor sport vain dreams in vain.
Why then their loss deplore that are not lost?
Why wanders wretched thought their tombs around,

51 iii ***Night Thoughts*, page 4**

7

How richly were my noontide trances hung
With gorgeous tapestries of pictured joys,
Joy behind joy, in endless perspective!
* Till at Death's toll, whose restless iron tongue
Calls daily for his millions at a meal,
Starting I 'woke, and found myself undone.
Where's now my frenzy's pompous furniture?
The cobweb'd cottage, with its ragged wall
Of mould'ring mud, is royalty to me:
The spider's most attenuated thread,
Is cord, is cable, to man's tender tie
On earthly bliss; it breaks at every breeze.
O ye blest scenes of permanent delight!
Full, above measure! lasting, beyond bound!
A perpetuity of bliss, is bliss.
Could you, so rich in rapture, fear an end,
That ghastly thought would drink up all your joy,
And quite unparadise the realms of light.
Safe are you lodged above these rolling spheres;
The baleful influence of whose giddy dance
Sheds sad vicissitude on all beneath.
Here teems with revolutions every hour,
And rarely for the better; or the best,
More mortal than the common births of fate:
Each moment has its sickle, emulous
Of time's enormous scythe, whose ample sweep
Strikes empires from the root; each moment plays
His little weapon in the narrower sphere
Of sweet domestick comfort, and cuts down
The fairest bloom of sublunary bliss.

51 iv ***Night Thoughts*, page 7**

8

Bliss! sublunary bliss!—proud words, and vain!
Implicit treason to divine decree!
A bold invasion of the rights of heaven!
I clasp'd the phantoms, and I found them air:
O had I weigh'd it ere my fond embrace,
What darts of agony had miss'd my heart!
* Death! great proprietor of all! 'tis thine
To tread out empire, and to quench the stars:
The sun himself by thy permission shines;
And, one day, thou shalt pluck him from his sphere.
Amidst such mighty plunder, why exhaust
Thy partial quiver on a mark so mean?
Why thy peculiar rancour wreak'd on me?
Insatiate archer! could not one suffice?
Thy shaft flew thrice—and thrice my peace was slain;
And thrice, ere thrice yon moon had fill'd her horn.
O Cynthia! why so pale? dost thou lament
Thy wretched neighbour? grieve to see thy wheel
Of ceaseless change outwhirl'd in human life?
How wanes my borrow'd bliss from fortune's smile!
Precarious courtesy! not virtue's sure,
Self-given, solar ray of sound delight.
In every varied posture, place, and hour,
How widow'd every thought of every joy!
Thought, busy thought! too busy for my peace,
Through the dark postern of time long elapsed,
Led softly; by the stillness of the night,
Led like a murderer, and such it proves;
Strays, wretched rover! o'er the pleasing past;
In quest of wretchedness perversely strays;

51 v *Night Thoughts*, page 8

10

What numbers, once in fortune's lap high-fed,
Solicit the cold hand of charity—
To shock us more—solicit it in vain!
Ye silken sons of pleasure! since in pains
You rue more modish visits, visit here,
And breathe from your debauch: give, and reduce
Surfeit's dominion o'er you—but so great
Your impudence, you blush at what is right.
Happy! did sorrow seize on such alone:
Not prudence can defend, or virtue save:
* Disease invades the chastest temperance,
And punishment the guiltless; and alarm,
Through thickest shades pursues the fond of peace.
Man's caution often into danger turns,
And, his guard falling, crushes him to death.
Not happiness itself makes good her name;
Our very wishes give us not our wish:
How distant oft the thing we doat on most,
From that for which we doat, felicity!
The smoothest course of nature has its pains;
And truest friends, through error, wound our rest.
Without misfortune—what calamities!
And what hostilities—without a foe!
Nor are foes wanting to the best on earth:
But endless is the list of human ills,
And sighs might sooner fail, than cause to sigh.
A part how small of the terraqueous globe
Is tenanted by man! the rest a waste;
Rocks, deserts, frozen seas, and burning sands—
Wild haunts of monsters, poisons, stings, and death:

51 vi *Night Thoughts*, page 10

12

But rises in demand for her delay;
She makes a scourge of past prosperity
To sting thee more, and double thy distress.
LORENZO, fortune makes her court to thee;
Thy fond heart dances, while the syren sings:
Dear is thy welfare; think me not unkind,
I would not damp, but to secure thy joys:
Think not that fear is sacred to the storm;
Stand on thy guard against the smiles of fate.
Is heaven tremendous in its frowns? most sure—
And in its favours formidable too:
* Its favours here are trials, not rewards;
A call to duty, not discharge from care;
And should alarm us, full as much as woes;
Awake us to their cause and consequence;
And make us tremble, weigh'd with our desert.
Awe nature's tumults, and chastise her joys,
Lest, while we clasp, we kill them; nay, invert
To worse than simple misery their charms:
Revolted joys, like foes in civil war,
Like bosom friendships to resentment sour'd,
With rage envenom'd rise against our peace.
Beware what earth calls happiness; beware
All joys, but joys that never can expire:
Who builds on less than an immortal base,
Fond as he seems, condemns his joys to death.
Mine died with thee, PHILANDER! thy last sigh
Dissolved the charm; the disenchanted earth
Lost all her lustre: where her glitt'ring towers?
Her golden mountains where?—all darken'd down

51 vii *Night Thoughts*, page 12

13

To naked waste; a dreary vale of tears:
The great magician's dead! thou poor pale piece
Of outcast earth—in darkness! what a change
From yesterday! thy darling hope so near,
Long-labour'd prize, O how ambition flush'd
Thy glowing cheek! ambition, truly great,
Of virtuous praise: death's subtle seed within,
Sly, treacherous miner! working in the dark,
Smiled at thy well-concerted scheme, and beckon'd
The worm to riot on that rose so red,
Unfaded ere it fell—one moment's prey!
Man's foresight is conditionally wise;
LORENZO! wisdom into folly turns
Oft, the first instant its idea fair
To lab'ring thought is born: how dim our eye!
* The present moment terminates our sight;
Clouds, thick as those on doomsday, drown the next;
We penetrate, we prophesy in vain:
Time is dealt out by particles; and each,
Ere mingled with the streaming sands of life,
By fate's inviolable oath is sworn
Deep silence, " where eternity begins."
By nature's law, what may be, may be now;
There's no prerogative in human hours:
In human hearts what bolder thought can rise,
Than man's presumption on to-morrow's dawn?
Where is to-morrow?—in another world!
For numbers this is certain; the reverse
Is sure to none; and yet on this perhaps,
This peradventure—infamous for lies,

51 viii *Night Thoughts*, page 13

15

The thing they can't but purpose, they postpone:
'Tis not in folly, not to scorn a fool;
And scarce in human wisdom to do more:
All promise is poor dilatory man,
And that through every stage: when young, indeed,
In full content we sometimes nobly rest,
Unanxious for ourselves; and only wish,
As duteous sons, our fathers were more wise:
At thirty man suspects himself a fool;
Knows it at forty, and reforms his plan;
At fifty chides his infamous delay,
Pushes his prudent purpose to resolve;
In all the magnanimity of thought
Resolves, and re-resolves; then dies the same.
And why? because he thinks himself immortal:
All men think all men mortal, but themselves;
Themselves;—when some alarming shock of fate
Strikes through their wounded hearts the sudden dread;
But their hearts wounded, like the wounded air,
Soon close; where pass'd the shaft no trace is found.
As from the wing no scar the sky retains;
The parted wave no furrow from the keel;
So dies in human hearts the thought of death:
Even with the tender tear which nature sheds
O'er those we love, we drop it in their grave.
Can I forget PHILANDER? that were strange:
O my full heart!—but should I give it vent,
* The longest night though longer far, would fail,
And the lark listen to my midnight song.

51 ix *Night Thoughts*, page 15

16

The sprightly lark's shrill matin wakes the morn,
Grief's sharpest thorn hard pressing on my breast;
I strive, with wakeful melody, to cheer
The sullen gloom, sweet philomel! like thee,
And call the stars to listen; every star
Is deaf to mine, enamour'd of thy lay:
Yet be not vain; there are, who thine excel,
And charm through distant ages: wrapp'd in shade,
Pris'ner of darkness! to the silent hours,
How often I repeat their rage divine,
To lull my griefs, and steal my heart from woe!
I roll their raptures, but not catch their fire:
Dark, though not blind, like thee, Mæonides!
Or, Milton! thee; ah, could I reach your strain!
Or his, who made Mæonides our own.
Man too he sung—immortal man I sing:
* Oft bursts my song beyond the bounds of life;
What now, but immortality, can please?
O had he press'd his theme, pursued the track,
Which opens out of darkness into day!
O had he mounted on his wing of fire,
Soar'd, where I sink, and sung immortal man!
How had it bless'd mankind, and rescued me!

51 x *Night Thoughts*, page 16

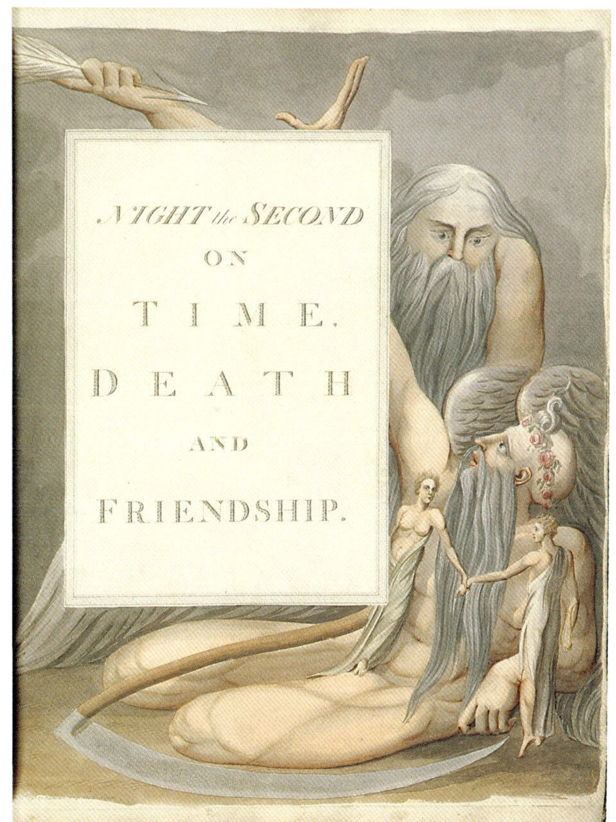

NIGHT the SECOND
ON
TIME,
DEATH
AND
FRIENDSHIP.

51 xi *Night the Second*, title-page

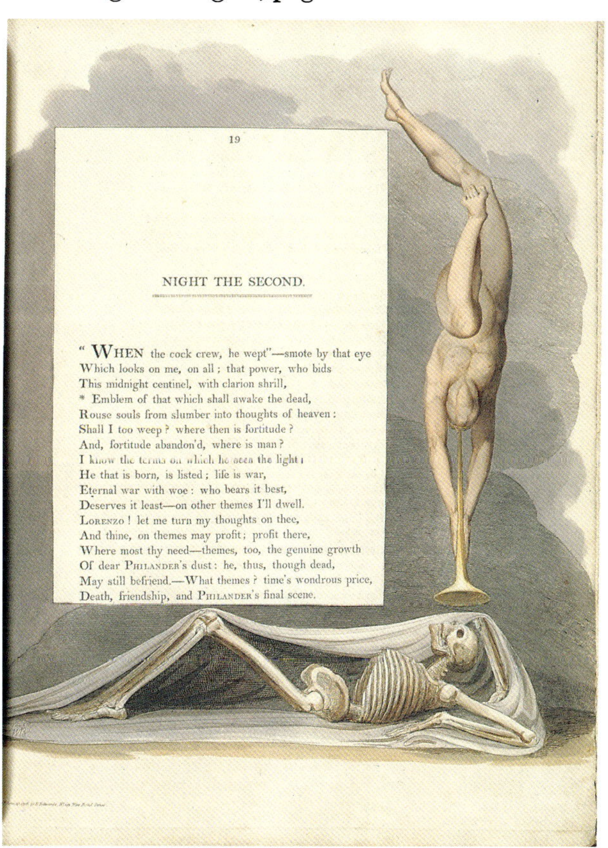

19

NIGHT THE SECOND.

"WHEN the cock crew, he wept"—smote by that eye
Which looks on me, on all; that power, who bids
This midnight centinel, with clarion shrill,
* Emblem of that which shall awake the dead,
Rouse souls from slumber into thoughts of heaven:
Shall I too weep? where then is fortitude?
And, fortitude abandon'd, where is man?
I know the terms on which he sees the light;
He that is born, is listed; life is war,
Eternal war with woe: who bears it best,
Deserves it least—on other themes I'll dwell.
LORENZO! let me turn my thoughts on thee,
And thine, on themes may profit; profit there,
Where most thy need—themes, too, the genuine growth
Of dear PHILANDER's dust: he, thus, though dead,
May still befriend.—What themes? time's wondrous price,
Death, friendship, and PHILANDER's final scene.

51 xii *Night Thoughts*, page 19

24

To man's false opticks, from his folly false,
* Time, in advance, behind him hides his wings,
And seems to creep decrepit with his age:
Behold him, when past by; what then is seen,
But his broad pinions swifter than the winds?
And all mankind, in contradiction strong,
Rueful—aghast—cry out on his career.
Leave to thy foes these errors, and these ills;
To nature just, their cause and cure explore.
Not short Heaven's bounty, boundless our expence;
No niggard nature; men are prodigals:
We waste, not use our time; we breathe, not live:
Time wasted is existence, used is life:
And bare existence, man, to live ordain'd,
Wrings and oppresses with enormous weight:
And why? since time was given for use, not waste,
Enjoin'd to fly; with tempest, tide, and stars
To keep his speed, nor ever wait for man:
Time's use was doom'd a pleasure; waste, a pain;
That man might feel his error, if unseen;
And, feeling, fly to labour for his cure;
Not, blund'ring, split on idleness for ease.
Life's cares are comforts, such by Heaven design'd;
He that has none, must make them, or be wretched:
Cares are employments; and without employ
The soul is on the rack; the rack of rest,
To souls most adverse; action all their joy.
Here, then, the riddle mark'd above, unfolds;
Then time turns torment, when man turns a fool:
We rave, we wrestle with great nature's plan;

51 xiv *Night Thoughts*, page 24

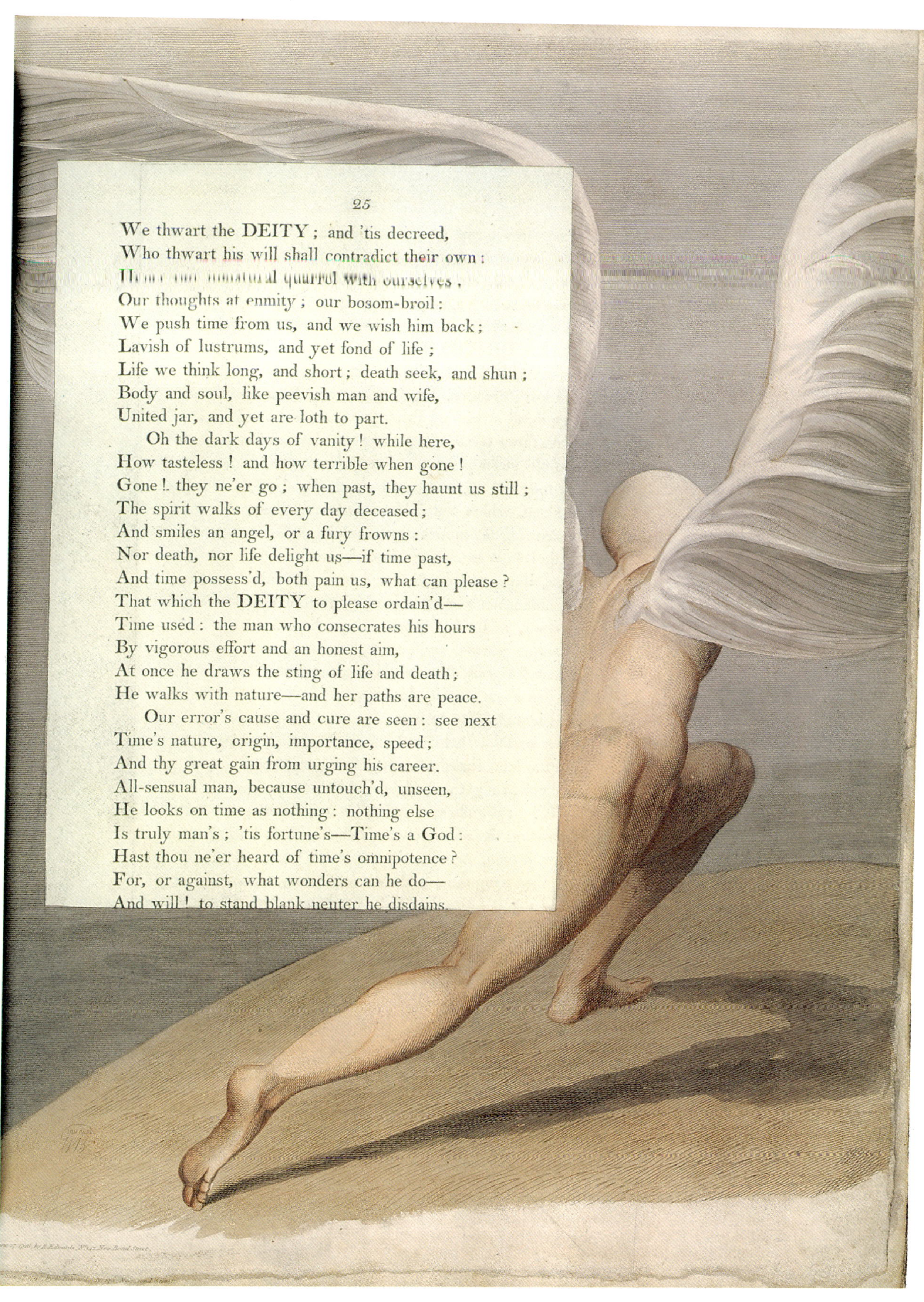

25

We thwart the DEITY ; and 'tis decreed,
Who thwart his will shall contradict their own :
[illegible] quarrel with ourselves ;
Our thoughts at enmity ; our bosom-broil :
We push time from us, and we wish him back ;
Lavish of lustrums, and yet fond of life ;
Life we think long, and short ; death seek, and shun ;
Body and soul, like peevish man and wife,
United jar, and yet are loth to part.
Oh the dark days of vanity ! while here,
How tasteless ! and how terrible when gone !
Gone ! they ne'er go ; when past, they haunt us still ;
The spirit walks of every day deceased ;
And smiles an angel, or a fury frowns :
Nor death, nor life delight us—if time past,
And time possess'd, both pain us, what can please ?
That which the DEITY to please ordain'd—
Time used : the man who consecrates his hours
By vigorous effort and an honest aim,
At once he draws the sting of life and death ;
He walks with nature—and her paths are peace.
Our error's cause and cure are seen : see next
Time's nature, origin, importance, speed ;
And thy great gain from urging his career.
All-sensual man, because untouch'd, unseen,
He looks on time as nothing : nothing else
Is truly man's ; 'tis fortune's—Time's a God :
Hast thou ne'er heard of time's omnipotence ?
For, or against, what wonders can he do—
And will ! to stand blank neuter he disdains.

51 xv *Night Thoughts*, page 25

23

Pregnant with all eternity can give ;
Pregnant with all that makes archangels smile :
Who murders time, he crushes in the birth
A power ethereal, only not adored.
Ah ! how unjust to nature and himself,
Is thoughtless, thankless, inconsistent man !
Like children babbling nonsense in their sports,
* We censure nature for a span too short ;
That span too short, we tax as tedious too ;
Torture invention, all expedients tire,
To lash the ling'ring moments into speed,
And whirl us, happy riddance ! from ourselves.
Art, brainless art ! our furious charioteer,
For nature's voice unstifled would recall,
Drives headlong tow'rds the precipice of death—
Death, most our dread ; death thus more dreadful made
O what a riddle of absurdity !
Leisure is pain ; take off our chariot-wheels,
How heavily we drag the load of life !
Blest leisure is our curse ; like that of Cain,
It makes us wander ; wander earth around
To fly that tyrant, thought. As Atlas groan'd
The world beneath, we groan beneath an hour :
We cry for mercy to the next amusement ;
The next amusement mortgages our fields—
Slight inconvenience ! prisons hardly frown—
From hateful time if prisons set us free ;
Yet when death kindly tenders us relief,
We call him cruel ; years to moments shrink,
Ages to years : the telescope is turn'd,

51 xiii *Night Thoughts*, page 23

31

Heart-buried in the rubbish of the world—
The world, that gulph of souls, immortal souls,
Souls elevate, angelic, wing'd with fire
To reach the distant skies, and triumph there
On thrones, which shall not mourn their masters changèd,
Though we from earth ; ethereal, they that fell.
Such veneration due, O man ! to man.
Who venerate themselves, the world despise.
For what, gay friend, is this escutcheon'd world,
Which hangs out death in one eternal night ?
A night, that glooms us in the noon-tide ray,
And wraps our thought, at banquets, in the shroud.
Life's little stage is a small eminence,
Inch-high the grave above ; that home of man,
Where dwells the multitude ; we gaze around ;
We read their monuments ; we sigh ; and while
We sigh, we sink ; and are what we deplored ;
Lamenting, or lamented, all our lot !
Is death at distance ? no : he has been on thee ;
And given sure earnest of his final blow.
Those hours, which lately smiled, where are they now ?
Pallid to thought, and ghastly ! drown'd, all drown'd
In that great deep, which nothing disembogues ;
And, dying, they bequeath'd thee small renown :
The rest are on the wing ; how fleet their flight !
Already has the fatal train took fire ;
A moment, and the world 's blown up to thee ;
The sun is darkness, and the stars are dust.
* 'Tis greatly wise to talk with our past hours,
And ask them, what report they bore to heaven ;

51 xviii *Night Thoughts*, page 31

26

Not on those terms was time, heaven's stranger, sent
On his important embassy to man.
Lorenzo ! no : on the long-destined hour,
From everlasting ages growing ripe,
That memorable hour of wondrous birth,
When the DREAD SIRE, on emanation bent,
And big with nature, rising in his might,
Call'd forth creation, for then time was born,
By godhead streaming through a thousand worlds ;
Not on those terms, from the great days of heaven,
From old eternity's mysterious orb,
Was time cut off, and cast beneath the skies ;
The skies, which watch him in his new abode,
* Measuring his motions by revolving spheres ;
That horologe machinery divine :
Hours, days, and months, and years, his children play,
Like numerous wings, around him, as he flies ;
Or rather, as unequal plumes they shape
His ample pinions, swift as darted flame,
To gain his goal, to reach his ancient rest,
And join anew eternity his sire ;
In his immutability to nest,
When worlds, that count his circles now, unhinged,
Fate the loud signal sounding, headlong rush
To timeless night and chaos, whence they rose.
Why spur the speedy ? why with levities
New-wing thy short, short day's too rapid flight ?
Know'st thou, or what thou dost, or what is done ?
Man flies from time, and time from man, too soon
In sad divorce this double flight must end ;

51 xvi *Night Thoughts*, page 26

27

And then, where are we ? where, Lorenzo, then
Thy sports—thy pomps ?—I grant thee, in a state
Not unambitious ; in the ruffled shroud,
Thy parian tomb's triumphant arch beneath :
Has death his fopperies ? then well may life
Put on her plume, and in her rainbow shine.
Ye well-array'd ! ye lilies of our land !
Ye lilies male ! who neither toil, nor spin,
As sister lilies might ;—if not so wise
As Solomon, more sumptuous to the sight !
Ye delicate ! who nothing can support,
Yourselves most insupportable ! for whom
The winter rose must blow, the sun put on
A brighter beam in Leo, silky-soft
Favonius breathe still softer, or be chid ;
And other worlds send odours, sauce, and song,
And robes, and notions framed in foreign looms !
O ye Lorenzos of our age ! who deem
One moment unamused, a misery
Not made for feeble man ; who call aloud
For every bauble, drivell'd o'er by sense,
For rattles and conceits of every cast,
For change of follies and relays of joy,
To drag your patience through the tedious length
Of a short winter's day—say—sages ; say
Wit's oracles ; say—dreamers of gay dreams ;
How will you weather an eternal night,
Where such expedients fail ?
* O treacherous conscience ! while she seems to sleep
On rose and myrtle, lull'd with syren song ;

51 xvii *Night Thoughts*, page 27

33

Erewhile high-flush'd with insolence and wine?
* Like that, the dial speaks; and points to thee,
LORENZO! loth to break thy banquet up.
" O man, thy kingdom is departing from thee;
" And, while it lasts, is emptier than my shade."
Its silent language such; nor need'st thou call
Thy magi, to decypher what it means:
Know, like the Median, fate is in thy walls:
Dost ask, how? whence? Belshazzar-like, amazed?
Man's make encloses the sure seeds of death;
Life feeds the murderer: ingrate! he thrives
On her own meal, and then his nurse devours.
[illegible] the delusion lies;
That solar shadow, as it measures life,
It life resembles too: life speeds away
From point to point, though seeming to stand still:
The cunning fugitive is swift by stealth,
Too subtle is the movement to be seen;
Yet soon man's hour is up, and we are gone.
Warnings point out our danger; gnomons, time:
As these are useless when the sun is set;
So those, but when more glorious reason shines.
Reason should judge in all; in reason's eye,
That sedentary shadow travels hard:
But such our gravitation to the wrong,
So prone our hearts to whisper what we wish,
'Tis later with the wise, than he's aware;
A Wilmington goes slower than the sun;
And all mankind mistake their time of day;
Even age itself: fresh hopes are hourly sown

51 xix *Night Thoughts*, page 33

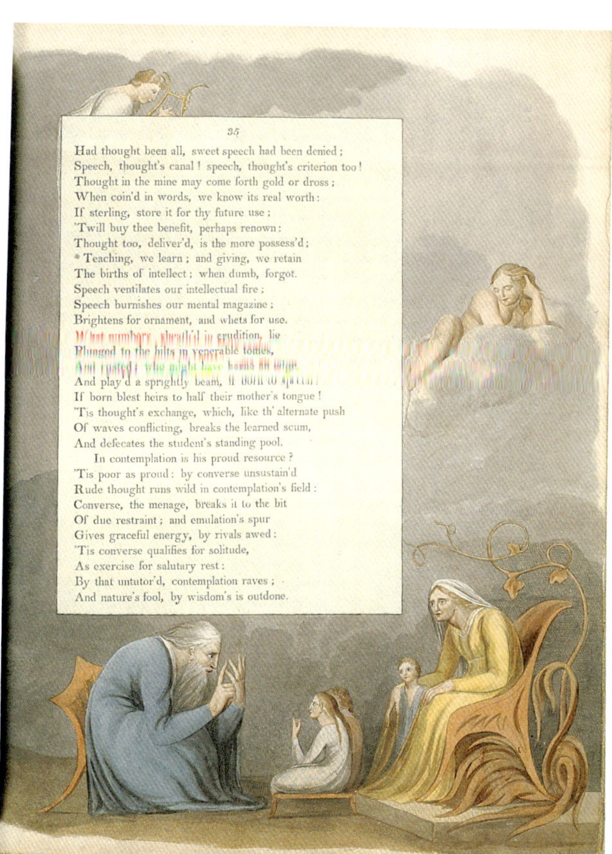

35

Had thought been all, sweet speech had been denied;
Speech, thought's canal! speech, thought's criterion too!
Thought in the mine may come forth gold or dross;
When coin'd in words, we know its real worth:
If sterling, store it for thy future use;
'Twill buy thee benefit, perhaps renown:
Thought too, deliver'd, is the more possess'd;
* Teaching, we learn; and giving, we retain
The births of intellect; when dumb, forgot.
Speech ventilates our intellectual fire;
Speech burnishes our mental magazine;
Brightens for ornament, and whets for use.
What numbers, sheath'd in erudition, lie
Plunged to the hilts in venerable tomes,
[illegible]
And play'd a sprightly beam, if born to speech!
If born blest heirs to half their mother's tongue!
'Tis thought's exchange, which, like th' alternate push
Of waves conflicting, breaks the learned scum,
And defecates the student's standing pool.
In contemplation is his proud resource?
'Tis poor as proud: by converse unsustain'd
Rude thought runs wild in contemplation's field:
Converse, the menage, breaks it to the bit
Of due restraint; and emulation's spur
Gives graceful energy, by rivals awed:
'Tis converse qualifies for solitude,
As exercise for salutary rest:
By that untutor'd, contemplation raves;
And nature's fool, by wisdom's is outdone.

51 xx *Night Thoughts*, page 35

Is virtue kindling at a rival fire,
And, emulously rapid in her race.
O the soft enmity! endearing strife!
This carries friendship to her noon-tide point,
And gives the rivet of eternity.
From friendship, which outlives my former themes,
Glorious surviver of old time, and death!
From friendship thus, that flower of heavenly seed,
The wise extract earth's most hyblean bliss,
Superior wisdom crown'd with smiling joy.
But for whom blossoms this elysian flower?
Abroad they find, who cherish it at home.
LORENZO! pardon what my love extorts,
An honest love, and not afraid to frown.
Though choice of follies fasten on the great,
None clings more obstinate than fancy fond
That sacred friendship is their easy prey;
Caught by the wafture of a golden lure,
Or fascination of a high-born smile.
Their smiles, the great, and the coquet throw out
For other hearts, tenacious of their own;
And we no less of ours, when such the bait.
Ye fortune's cofferers! ye powers of wealth!
You do your rent-rolls most felonious wrong,
By taking our attachment to yourselves:
Can gold gain friendship? impudence of hope!
As well mere man an angel might beget:
* Love, and love only, is the loan for love.
LORENZO! pride repress; nor hope to find
A friend, but what has found a friend in thee.

51 xxi *Night Thoughts*, page 37

40

By mortal hand—it merits a divine:
* Angels should paint it, angels ever there;
There on a post of honour, and of joy.
Dare I presume then? but PHILANDER bids,
And glory tempts, and inclination calls:
Yet am I struck; as struck the soul beneath
Aërial groves' impenetrable gloom;
Or in some mighty ruin's solemn shade;
Or gazing by pale lamps on high-born dust
In vaults; thin courts of poor unflatter'd kings!
Or at the midnight altar's hallow'd flame:
It is religion to proceed: I pause——
And enter, awed, the temple of my theme:
Is it his death-bed? no—it is his shrine:
Behold him, there, just rising to a god.
The chamber, where the good man meets his fate,
Is privileged beyond the common walk
Of virtuous life, quite in the verge of heaven.
Fly, ye profane! if not, draw near with awe,
Receive the blessing, and adore the chance
That threw in this Bethesda your disease;
If unrestored by this, despair your cure:
For here resistless demonstration dwells;
A death-bed 's a detector of the heart;
Here tired dissimulation drops her mask,
Through life's grimace that mistress of the scene!
Here real and apparent are the same—
You see the man; you see his hold on heaven;
If sound his virtue, as PHILANDER's sound.
Heaven waits not the last moment; owns her friends

51 xxii *Night Thoughts*, page 40

70

Caught at a court; purged off by purer air,
And simpler diet; gifts of rural life!
    Blest be that hand divine, which gently laid
My heart at rest, beneath this humble shed.
The world 's a stately bark, on dangerous seas
With pleasure seen, but boarded at our peril:
Here, on a single plank thrown safe ashore,
I hear the tumult of the distant throng,
As that of seas remote, or dying storms;
And meditate on scenes more silent still;
Pursue my theme, and fight the fear of death.
Here, like a shepherd gazing from his hut,
Touching his reed or leaning on his staff,
Eager ambition's fiery chase I see;
I see the circling hunt of noisy men
Burst law's inclosure, leap the mounds of right,
Pursuing and pursued, each other's prey;
As wolves, for rapine; as the fox, for wiles;
* Till death, that mighty hunter, earths them all.
    Why all this toil for triumphs of an hour?
What, though we wade in wealth, or soar in fame,
Earth's highest station ends in, " here he lies!"
And " dust to dust" concludes her noblest song.
If this song live, posterity shall know
One, though in Britain born, with courtiers bred,
Who thought e'en gold might come a day too late;
Nor on his subtle death-bed plann'd his scheme
For future vacancies in church or state;
Some avocation deeming it——to die

51 xxxii *Night Thoughts*, page 70

41

On this side death; and points them out to men:
A lecture silent, but of sovereign power!
To vice, confusion; and to virtue, peace.
    Whatever farce the boastful hero plays,
Virtue alone has majesty in death;
And greater still, the more the tyrant frowns:
PHILANDER! he severely frown'd on thee:
" No warning given—unceremonious fate!
" A sudden rush from life's meridian joys!
" A wrench from all we love—from all we are!
" A restless bed of pain! a plunge opaque
" Beyond conjecture! feeble nature's dread!
" Strong reason's shudder at the dark unknown!
" A sun extinguish'd! a just opening grave!
" And oh! the last—last—what? can words express?
" Thought reach? the last, last—silence of a friend!"
Where are those horrors, that amazement where,
This hideous group of ills, which singly shock?
Demand from man—I thought him man till now.
    Through nature's wreck, through vanquish'd agonies,
Like the stars struggling through this midnight gloom,
What gleams of joy! what more than human peace!
Where, the frail mortal? the poor abject worm?
No, not in death, the mortal to be found.
His conduct is a legacy for all,
Richer than Mammon's for his single heir:
His comforters he comforts; great in ruin,
With unreluctant grandeur gives, not yields
His soul sublime; and closes with his fate.

51 xxiii *Night Thoughts*, page 41

NIGHT
THE
THIRD,
NARCISSA.

51 xxiv *Night the Third*, title-page

46

Or if we wish a fourth, it is a friend——
But friends how mortal! dangerous the desire.
    Take Phœbus to yourselves, ye basking bards!
Inebriate at fair fortune's fountain-head;
And reeling through the wilderness of joy;
Where sense runs savage broke from reason's chain,
And sings false peace, till smother'd by the pall.
My fortune is unlike; unlike my song;
Unlike the DEITY my song invokes.
I to day's soft-eyed sister pay my court,
Endymion's rival! and her aid implore:
Now first implored in succour to the muse.
    Thou who didst lately borrow Cynthia's form,
And modestly forego thine own! O thou
Who didst thyself, at midnight hours, inspire!
Say, why not Cynthia patroness of song?
As thou her crescent, she thy character
Assumes; still more a goddess by the change.
    Are there demurring wits, who dare dispute
This revolution in the world inspired?
Ye train pierian! to the lunar sphere,
In silent hour address your ardent call
For aid immortal—less her brother's right.
She, with the spheres harmonious, nightly leads
The mazy dance, and hears their matchless strain;
A strain for gods, denied to mortal ear.
Transmit it heard, thou silver queen of heaven!
What title or what name endears thee most?
Cynthia! Cyllene! Phœbe!—or dost hear
With higher gust fair P——d of the skies?

51 xxv *Night Thoughts*, page 46

49

And will not the severe excuse a sigh?
Scorn the proud man that is ashamed to weep;
Our tears indulged indeed deserve our shame:
Ye that e'er lost an angel! pity me.
    Soon as the lustre languish'd in her eye,
Dawning a dimmer day on human sight;
And on her cheek, the residence of spring,
Pale omen sat, and scatter'd fears around
On all that saw, and who would cease to gaze
That once had seen? with haste, parental haste
I flew, I snatch'd her from the rigid north,
Her native bed, on which bleak boreas blew,
And bore her nearer to the sun; the sun,
As if the sun could envy, check'd his beam,
Denied his wonted succour, nor with more
Regret beheld her drooping, than the bells
Of lilies! fairest lilies not so fair.
    Queen lilies! and ye painted populace!
Who dwell in fields, and lead ambrosial lives;
In morn and evening dew your beauties bathe,
And drink the sun, which gives your cheeks to glow,
And out-blush, mine excepted, every fair;
You gladlier grew, ambitious of her hand
Which often cropp'd your odours, incense meet
To thought so pure: ye lovely fugitives!
Coeval race with man, for man you smile;
Why not smile at him too? you share indeed
His sudden pass, but not his constant pain.
    So man is made, nought ministers delight
But what his glowing passions can engage;

51 xxvi *Night Thoughts*, page 49

54

Where darkness, brooding o'er unfinish'd fates
With raven wing incumbent, waits the day,
Dread day! that interdicts all future change!
That subterranean world, that land of ruin!
Fit walk, LORENZO, for proud human thought!
There let my thought expatiate; and explore
Balsamic truths, and healing sentiments
Of all most wanted, and most welcome here.
For gay LORENZO's sake, and for thy own
My soul! "The fruits of dying friends survey;
"Expose the vain of life; weigh life and death;
"Give death his eulogy; thy fear subdue;
"And labour that first palm of noble minds—
"A manly scorn of terror from the tomb:"
This harvest reap from thy NARCISSA's grave.
As poets feign'd, from AJAX' streaming blood
Arose, with grief inscribed, a mournful flower;
Let wisdom blossom from my mortal wound.
And first, of dying friends; what fruit from these?
It brings us more than triple aid; an aid
To chase our thoughtlessness, fear, pride, and guilt.
Our dying friends come o'er us like a cloud,
To damp our brainless ardours, and abate
That glare of life which often blinds the wise:
Our dying friends are pioneers, to smooth
Our rugged pass to death: to break those bars
Of terror and abhorrence nature throws
Cross our obstructed way; and thus to make
Welcome as safe our port from every storm:
Each friend by fate snatch'd from us, is a plume

51 xxvii *Night Thoughts*, page 54

55

Pluck'd from the wing of human vanity,
Which makes us stoop from our aërial heights,
And, damp'd with omen of our own decease,
On drooping pinions of ambition lower'd,
Just skim earth's surface, ere we break it up,
O'er putrid earth to scratch a little dust,
And save the world a nuisance: smitten friends
Are angels sent on errands full of love:
For us they languish, and for us they die:
And shall they languish, shall they die in vain?
* Ungrateful, shall we grieve their hovering shades
Which wait the revolution in our hearts?
Shall we disdain their silent soft address,
Their posthumous advice, and pious prayer?
Senseless as herds that graze their hallow'd graves,
Tread under foot their agonies and groans,
Frustrate their anguish, and destroy their deaths?
LORENZO! no; the thought of death indulge;
Give it its wholesome empire—let it reign,
That kind chastiser of thy soul in joy;
Its reign will spread thy glorious conquests far,
And still the tumults of thy ruffled breast:
Auspicious æra! golden days, begin!
The thought of death shall, like a god, inspire.
And why not think on death? is life the theme
Of every thought? and wish of every hour?
And song of every joy? Surprising truth!
The beaten spaniel's fondness not so strange.
To wave the numerous ills that seize on life
As their own property, their lawful prey;

51 xxviii *Night Thoughts*, page 55

57

Still-streaming thoroughfares of dull debauch!
* Trembling each gulp, lest death should snatch the bowl.
Such of our fine ones is the wish refined—
So would they have it: elegant desire!
Why not invite the bellowing stalls and wilds?
But such examples might their riot awe.
Through want of virtue, that is, want of thought,
Though on bright thought they father all their flights,
To what are they reduced? to love and hate
The same vain world; to censure and espouse
This painted shrew of life, who calls them fool
Each moment of each day; to flatter bad
Through dread of worse; to cling to this rude rock,
Barren, to them, of good, and sharp with ills,
And hourly blacken'd with impending storms,
And infamous for wrecks of human hope——
Scared at the gloomy gulph that yawns beneath.
Such are their triumphs! such their pangs of joy!
'Tis time, high time to shift this dismal scene:
This hugg'd, this hideous state what art can cure?
One only, but that one what all may reach,
Virtue—she, wonder-working goddess! charms
That rock to bloom, and tames the painted shrew;
And what will more surprise, LORENZO! gives
To life's sick nauseous iteration, change;
And straitens nature's circle to a line.
Believest thou this, LORENZO? lend an ear,
A patient ear, thou'lt blush to disbelieve.
A languid leaden iteration reigns,
And ever must, o'er those whose joys are joys

51 xxix *Night Thoughts*, page 57

63

To dust when drop proud nature's proudest spheres,
And live entire: death is the crown of life;
Were death denied, poor man would live in vain;
Were death denied, to live would not be life;
Were death denied, even fools would wish to die:
Death wounds to cure: we fall, we rise, we reign!
Spring from our fetters, fasten in the skies
Where blooming Eden withers in our sight.
Death gives us more than was in Eden lost;
* This KING OF TERRORS is the PRINCE OF PEACE.
When shall I die to vanity, pain, death?
When shall I die?—when shall I live for ever?

51 xxx *Night Thoughts*, page 63

51 xxxi *Night the Fourth*, title-page: *The Christian Triumph*

72

* And vapid; sense and reason shew the door,
Call for my bier, and point me to the dust.
O THOU! great arbiter of life and death!
Nature's immortal, immaterial sun!
Whose all-prolific beam late call'd me forth
From darkness—teeming darkness where I lay
The worm's inferior, and in rank beneath
The dust I tread on, high to bear my brow,
To drink the spirit of the golden day,
And triumph in existence! and couldst know
No motive but my bliss! and hast ordain'd
A rise in blessing! with the patriarch's joy,
Thy call I follow to the land unknown:
[illegible]
[illegible]
All weight in this—O let me live to THEE!
Though nature's terrors thus may be repress'd;
Still frowns grim death, guilt points the tyrant's spear:
And whence all human guilt?—from death forgot.
Ah me! too long I set at nought the swarm
Of friendly warnings which around me flew;
And smiled unsmitten: small my cause to smile!
Death's admonitions, like shafts upward shot,
More dreadful by delay; the longer ere
They strike our hearts, the deeper is their wound:
O think how deep, Lorenzo! here it stings;
Who can appease its anguish? how it burns!
What hand the barb'd, envenom'd thought can draw?
What healing hand can pour the balm of peace,
And turn my sight undaunted on the tomb?

51 xxxiii *Night Thoughts*, page 72

75

Not thus, our infidels th' ETERNAL draw,
" A GOD all o'er, consummate, absolute,
" Full orb'd, in his whole round of rays complete;"
They set at odds heaven's jarring attributes,
And with one excellence another wound;
Maim heaven's perfection, break its equal beams,
Bid mercy triumph over—GOD himself,
Undeified by their opprobrious praise:
A GOD all mercy is a GOD unjust.
Ye brainless wits! ye baptized infidels!
Ye worse for mending! wash'd to fouler stains!
The ransom was paid down; the fund of heaven,
Heaven's inexhaustible exhausted fund,
Amazing and amazed, pour'd forth the price
All price beyond; though curious to compute
Archangels fail'd to cast the mighty sum:
Its value vast ungrasp'd by minds create,
For ever hides and glows in the SUPREME.
And was the ransom paid? it was; and paid—
What can exalt the bounty more? for you:
The sun beheld it—no, the shocking scene
Drove back his chariot; midnight veil'd his face,
Not such as this, not such as nature makes;
A midnight nature shudder'd to behold;
A midnight new! a dread eclipse, without
Opposing spheres, from her CREATOR's frown!
Sun! didst thou fly thy MAKER's pain? or start
At that enormous load of human guilt,
Which bow'd his blessed head; o'erwhelm'd his cross;
Made groan the centre; burst earth's marble womb

51 xxxv *Night Thoughts*, page 75

80

What, night eternal—but a frown from thee?
What, heaven's meridian glory—but thy smile?
And shall not praise be thine? not human praise?
While heaven's high host on hallelujahs live?
O may I breathe no longer than I breathe
My soul in praise to HIM who gave my soul
And all her infinite of prospect fair;
Cut through the shades of hell, great love! by THEE,
Oh most adorable, most unadored!
Where shall that praise begin, which ne'er should end?
Where'er I turn, what claim on all applause!
How is night's sable mantle labour'd o'er!
How richly wrought with attributes divine!
What wisdom shines! what love! this midnight pomp,
This gorgeous arch with golden worlds inlaid,
Built with divine ambition, nought to THEE!
For others this profusion: THOU apart,
Above, beyond: oh tell me, mighty mind!
Where art thou? shall I dive into the deep?
Call to the sun, or ask the roaring winds
For their creator? shall I question loud
* The thunder, if in that the ALMIGHTY dwells?
Or holds HE furious storms in streighten'd reins,
And bids fierce whirlwinds wheel his rapid car?
What mean these questions?—trembling I retract;
My prostrate soul adores the present GOD:
Praise I a distant DEITY? HE tunes
My voice, if tuned; the nerve that writes, sustains;
Wrapp'd in his being I resound his praise:
But though past all diffused, without a shore

51 xxxvi *Night Thoughts*, page 80

86

Supporter sole of man above himself ;
Even in this night of frailty, change, and death,
She gives the soul a soul that acts a God.
Religion ! providence ! an after-state !
Here is firm footing—here is solid rock—
This can support us—all is sea besides—
Sinks under us—bestorms, and then devours.
* His hand the good man fastens on the skies,
And bids earth roll, nor feels her idle whirl.
As when a wretch, from thick polluted air,
Darkness and stench, and suffocating damps,
And dungeon-horrors by kind fate discharged,
Climbs some fair eminence, where ether pure
Surrounds him, and elysian prospects rise ;
His heart exults, his spirits cast their load ;
As if new-born he triumphs in the change ;
So joys the soul, when, from inglorious aims
And sordid sweets, from feculence and froth
Of ties terrestrial set at large, she mounts
To reason's region, her own element,
Breathes hopes immortal and affects the skies.
Religion ! thou the soul of happiness ;
And, groaning Calvary, of thee ! there shine
The noblest truths ; there strongest motives sting ;
There sacred violence assaults the soul ;
There nothing but compulsion is forborn.
Can love allure us ? or can terror awe ?
HE weeps !—the falling drop puts out the sun ;
HE sighs !—the sigh earth's deep foundation shakes :
If in his love so terrible, what then

51 xxxvii *Night Thoughts*, page 86

87

His wrath inflamed ? his tenderness on fire ;
Like soft, smooth oil, outblazing other fires ?
Can prayer, can praise avert it ?—THOU ! my all,
My theme, my inspiration, and my crown !
My strength in age, my rise in low estate !
My soul's ambition, pleasure, wealth !—my world !
My light in darkness, and my life in death !
My boast through time ! bliss through eternity—
Eternity, too short to speak thy praise !
Or fathom thy profound of love to man—
To man of men the meanest, even to me !
My sacrifice ! my GOD ! what things are these !
What then art THOU ? by what name shall I call THEE ?
Knew I the name devout archangels use,
Devout archangels should the name enjoy
By me unrivall'd ; thousands more sublime,
None half so dear as that, which, though unspoke
Still glows at heart : O how omnipotence
* Is lost in love ! thou great PHILANTHROPIST !
Father of angels ! but the friend of man !
Like Jacob, fondest of the younger born !
THOU ! who didst save him, snatch the smoking brand
From out the flames, and quench it in thy blood ;
How art thou pleased by bounty to distress !
To make us groan beneath our gratitude,
Too big for birth ! to favour and confound ;
To challenge, and to distance all return !
Lavish of love, stupendous heights to soar
And leave praise panting in the distant vale !
Thy right too great defrauds THEE of thy due ;

51 xxxviii *Night Thoughts*, page 87

88

And sacrilegious our sublimest song :
But since the naked will obtains thy smile,
Beneath this monument of praise unpaid,
And future life symphonious to my strain,
That noblest hymn to heaven ! for ever lie
Intomb'd my fear of death ! and every fear,
The dread of every evil, but thy frown.
Whom see I yonder, so demurely smile ?
Laughter a labour, and might break their rest.
Ye quietists, in homage to the skies !
Serene ! of soft address ! who mildly make
An unobtrusive tender of your hearts,
Abhorring violence ! who halt indeed,
* But for the blessing wrestle not with heaven !
Think you my song too turbulent ? too warm ?
Are passions then the pagans of the soul ?
Reason alone baptized—alone ordain'd
To touch things sacred ?—oh for warmer still !
Guilt chills my zeal, and age benumbs my powers ;
Oh for an humbler heart, and prouder song !
THOU ! my much-injured theme ! with that soft eye
Which melted o'er doom'd Salem, deign to look
Compassion to the coldness of my breast ;
And pardon to the winter in my strain !
Oh ye cold-hearted, frozen formalists !
On such a theme 'tis impious to be calm ;
Passion is reason, transport temper, here.
Shall heaven, which gave us ardour, and has shewn
Her own for man so strongly, not disdain
What smooth emollients in theology,

51 xxxix *Night Thoughts*, page 88

90

'Tis this makes joy a duty to the wise ;
'Tis impious in a good man to be sad.
Seest thou, LORENZO ! where hangs all our hope ?
Touch'd by the cross we live ;—or more than die :
That touch, which touch'd not angels ; more divine
Than that which touch'd confusion into form
And darkness into glory ; partial touch !
Ineffably pre-eminent regard
Sacred to man ! and sovereign, through the whole
Long golden chain of miracles which hangs
From heaven through all duration, and supports
In one illustrious and amazing plan !
Thy welfare, nature ! and thy GOD's renown !
* That touch, with charm celestial heals the soul
Diseased, drives pain from guilt, lights life in death,
Turns earth to heaven, to heavenly thrones transforms
The ghastly ruins of the mouldering tomb !
Dost ask me when ? when HE who died returns :—
Returns, how changed ! where then the man of woe ?
In glory's terrors all the godhead burns ;
And all his courts, exhausted by the tide
Of deities triumphant in his train,
Leave a stupendous solitude in heaven ;
Replenish'd soon, replenish'd with increase
Of pomp and multitude, a radiant band
Of angels new, of angels from the tomb.
Is this by fancy thrown remote ? and rise
Dark doubts between the promise and event ?
I send thee not to volumes for thy cure,
Read nature ; nature is a friend to truth ;

51 xl *Night Thoughts*, page 90

73

With joy—with grief, that healing hand I see ;
Ah! too conspicuous ! it is fix'd on high !
On high ?—what means my phrensy ? I blaspheme ;
Alas ! how low ! how far beneath the skies—
The skies it form'd ! and now it bleeds for me :
But bleeds the balm I want ?—yet still it bleeds.
* Draw the dire steel ?—ah no !—the dreadful blessing
What heart or can sustain, or dares forego ?
There hangs all human hope ! ! ! that nail supports
The falling universe ! ! ! that gone, we drop !
Horror receives us, and the dismal wish
Creation had been smother'd in her birth :
Darkness his curtain ! and his bed the dust !
When stars and sun are dust beneath his throne :
In heaven itself can such indulgence dwell ?
O what a groan was there ! a groan not his,
HE seized our dreadful right ; the load sustain'd ;
And heaved the mountain from a guilty world :
A thousand worlds so bought were bought too dear.
Sensations new, in angels bosoms rise ;
Suspend their song, and make a pause in bliss.
O for their song to reach my lofty theme !
Inspire me, night ! with all thy tuneful spheres inspire,
Whilst I with seraphs share seraphic themes,
And shew to men the dignity of man ;
Lest I blaspheme my subject with my song.
Shall pagan pages glow celestial flame,
And christian languish ? on our hearts, not heads,
Falls the foul infamy : my heart ! awake;
What can awake thee, unawaked by this ?—

51 xxxiv *Night Thoughts*, page 73

92

Live thou with life; live dearer of the two.
Wear I the blessed cross, by fortune stamp'd
On passive nature before thought was born?
My birth's blind bigot! fired with local zeal!
No; reason rebaptized me when adult;
Weigh'd true and false in her impartial scale;
My heart became the convert of my head;
And made that choice, which once was but my fate.
On argument alone my faith is built:
Reason pursued is faith; and, unpursued
Where proof invites, 'tis reason then no more:
And such our proof, that, or our faith is right,
Or reason lies, and heaven design'd it wrong:
Absolve we this? what then is blasphemy?
Fond as we are, and justly fond of faith,
Reason, we grant, demands our first regard;
The mother honour'd, as the daughter dear.
Reason the root; fair faith is but the flower:
The fading flower shall die; but reason lives
Immortal as her father in the skies.
* When faith is virtue, reason makes it so.
Wrong not the christian; think not reason your's;
'Tis reason our great master holds so dear;
'Tis reason's injured rights his wrath resents;
'Tis reason's voice obey'd, his glories crown;
To give lost reason life, HE pour'd his own:
Believe, and shew the reason of a man;
Believe, and taste the pleasure of a [illegible]
Believe, and look with triumph on the tomb:
Through reason's wounds alone thy faith can die,

51 xli *Night Thoughts*, page 92

93

Which, dying, tenfold terror gives to death,
And dips in venom his twice-mortal sting.
Learn hence what honours, what loud pæans due
To those, who push our antidote aside;
Those boasted friends to reason and to man,
Whose fatal love stabs every joy, and leaves
Death's terror heighten'd gnawing on his heart:
These pompous sons of reason idolized
And vilified at once; of reason dead,
Then deified, as monarchs were of old;
What conduct plants proud laurels on their brow?
While love of truth through all their camp resounds,
They draw pride's curtain o'er the noon-tide ray,
Spike up their inch of reason on the point
Of philosophick wit, call'd argument;
And then, exulting in their taper, cry,
"Behold the sun:" and, Indian-like, adore.
Talk they of morals? O thou bleeding love!
Thou maker of new morals to mankind!
The grand morality is love of THEE.
As wise as Socrates, if such they were,
Nor will they bate of that sublime renown,
As wise as Socrates might justly stand
The definition of a modern fool.
A christian is the highest stile of man:
And is there who the blessed cross wipes off,
As a foul blot from his [illegible]
* If angels tremble, 'tis at such a sight;
The wretch they quit, desponding of their charge,
More struck with grief or wonder, who can tell?

51 xlii *Night Thoughts*, page 93

51 *Night Thoughts*, cover

51 *Night Thoughts*, as bound

Notes

1 The complete catalogue of Blake's *commercial* engravings has been undertaken in recent years by Roger Easson and Robert Essick. Two volumes of their *William Blake: Book Illustrator. A Bibliography and Catalogue of the Commercial Engravings* have so far appeared (The American Blake Foundation, Normal, Ill., 1972 & Memphis, Tenn., 1979), and Professor Essick is now completing a further volume on Blake's commercial engraving. The most comprehensive study of both Blake's reproductive and original printmaking is Robert Essick's *William Blake, Printmaker*, Princeton University Press, Princeton, NJ, 1980.

2 Blake to John Trusler, 23 August 1799; G. Keynes (ed.), *The Letters of William Blake*, Rupert-Hart Davis, London, 1969, p. 31.

3 D. Erdman & D. Moore (eds), *The Notebook of William Blake*, Clarendon Press, Oxford, 1973. (References in the text shown as (N   ) indicate the folio numbers of this facsimile edition.) The *Notebook* was a common-place book in which Blake sketched, and transcribed poems, anecdotes, drafts of projected prospectuses and venomous aphorisms over at least eighteen years from 1793 to 1811. It is now kept in the British Library.

4 Tim McCormick *et al.* recently published the assertion that the *Family of New South Wales* was engraved by William Staddon Blake (*c.* 1748–1822), a minor journeyman engraver also working in London at this time, 'not to be confused with the famous English poet and artist William Blake'; see *First Views of Australia 1788–1825*, David Ell Press, Sydney, 1987, p. 319. This unsustainable statement was offered without any evidence of its veracity or any reference to the standard Blake literature, where it is universally accepted as an authentic work of William Blake. On W. S. Blake, the London writing-engraver who etched the aquatint *View of the Town of Sydney* (1802), see G. Keynes, 'Engravers Called Blake', in his *Blake Studies: Essays on his Life and Work*, Rupert-Hart Davis, London, 1949, pp. 50–5; and G. E. Bentley Jr, *Blake Records*, Clarendon Press, Oxford, 1969, pp. 58, 561.

5 Essick, *William Blake, Printmaker*, p. 38. See also Essick's 'Blake and the Traditions of Reproductive Engraving', in R. Essick (ed.), *The Visionary Hand: Essays for the Study of William Blake's Art and Aesthetics*, Hennessy & Ingalls, Los Angeles, 1973, pp. 493–525. Here Essick argues forcefully that: 'the destructive and limiting nature of this entire artistic–commercial system, extending its net from apprentice to connoisseur, was . . . apparent to Blake. His revolt against this system manifests itself in three imaginative forms: separate plates and book illustrations designed and executed for aesthetic purposes beyond the commercial, relief etching, and prophetic narrative in which the abstracting processes of reproductive engraving become basic metaphors in a myth of creation, fall, and entrapment' (p. 499).

6 R. Rienits & T. Rienits, *Early Artists of Australia*, Angus & Robertson, Sydney, 1963, pp. 18–21, 33–6; A. G. L. Shaw, 'King, Philip Gidley', in D. Pike (ed.), *Australian Dictionary of Biography*, Melbourne University Press, Melbourne, vol. 2, pp. 55–61.

7 See G. E. Bentley Jr, *Blake Books*, Clarendon Press, Oxford, 1977, pp. 584–5.

8 B. Smith, *Place, Taste and Tradition*, Ure Smith, Sydney, 1945, pp. 28–9; *European Vision and the South Pacific*, Clarendon Press, Oxford, 1960, pp. 128–9.

9 The delicate washes of the background setting in King's sketch do not reproduce at all in Essick, *William Blake, Printmaker*, plate 41.

10 D. Erdman, 'Blake's Vision of Slavery', *Journal of the Warburg and Courtauld Institutes*, vol. XV, 1952, pp. 242–52; and *Blake: Prophet Against Empire*, Doubleday, New York, 1969, pp. 226–42. On Blake's friendship with Stedman see Bentley, *Blake Records*, pp. 45, 48–9.

11 G. Keynes (ed.), *Blake, Complete Writings*, Oxford University Press, Oxford, 1969, p. 190.

12 J. T. Smith, *A Book for a Rainy Day* (1845), in Bentley, *Blake Records*, p. 26.

13 For an excellent account of the *Songs*' gestation and development see M. Phillips, 'William Blake's *Songs of Innocence* and *Songs of Experience* from Manuscript Draft to Illuminated Plate', *The Book Collector*, vol. 28, no. 1, Spring 1979, pp. 17–59.

14 Keynes, *Blake, Complete Writings*, p. 62.

15 Cumberland to Richard Cumberland, 3 January 1784; quoted in G. Keynes, 'Some Uncollected Authors XLIV. George Cumberland 1754–1848', *The Book Collector*, vol. 19, no. 1, Spring 1970, p. 33.

16 J. T. Smith, *Nollekens and his Times* (1828), in Bentley, *Blake Records*, p. 460.

17 All of these techniques are excellently described in Essick, *William Blake, Printmaker*, pp. 85–120.

18 R. Todd, 'The Techniques of William Blake's Illuminated Printing', *Print Quarterly*, vol. VI, no. 1, 1948, pp. 53–65; also printed in *The Print Collector's Quarterly*, vol. 29, November 1948, pp. 25–37.

19 J. Wright, 'Toward Recovering Blake's Relief-Etching Process', *Blake Newsletter*, vol. 7, no. 2, Fall 1973, pp. 32–9; and 'Blake's Relief-Etching Method', *Blake Newsletter*, vol. 9, no. 4, Spring 1976, pp. 94–114.

20 R. Essick, *William Blake's Relief Inventions*, Press of the Pegacycle Lady, Los Angeles, 1978, p. 13. Gerald Bentley and Joseph Viscomi both agree with Essick that Blake was proficient at mirror-writing. See G. E. Bentley Jr, 'William Blake's Techniques of Engraving and Printing', *Studies in Bibliography*, vol. 34, 1981, p. 243; J. Viscomi, *The Art of William Blake's Illuminated Prints*, Manchester Etching Workshop, Manchester, 1983, pp. 4–8. Bo Lindberg, however, remained committed to the transfer theory; see 'Review of Robert N. Essick, *William Blake, Printmaker*', *Blake: An Illustrated Quarterly*, vol. 15, no. 3, Winter 1981–82, pp. 140–8. For further debate on Blake's printing methods see J. Viscomi, 'Recreating Blake's Illuminated Prints: The Facsimiles of the Manchester Etching Workshop', *Blake: An Illustrated Quarterly*, vol. 19, no. 1, Summer 1985, pp. 4–23; and Essick's review of the Manchester facsimile publication of the *Songs* in *Blake: An Illustrated Quarterly*, vol. 19, no. 1, Summer 1985, pp. 39–51.

21 The standard summaries of the recorded copies of the *Songs of Innocence* and *Songs of Innocence and of Experience* remain G. Keynes & E. Wolf, *William Blake's Illuminated Books: A Census*, Grolier Club, New York, 1953, pp. 9–18, 50–69; and Bentley, *Blake Books*, pp. 364–432. As further bibliographical research has been undertaken and long untraced copies have resurfaced in the sale rooms, new pieces of information have been added to the puzzle. These various fragments form a complex but coherent mosaic. See in particular T. Connolly, 'A Blakean Maze', *Blake Studies*, vol. 3, no. 1, Fall 1970, pp. 61–8; G. E. Bentley Jr, *The Blake Collection of Mrs. Landon K. Thorne*, Pierpont Morgan Library, New York, 1971, pp. 28–9; J. Grant & M. Johnson, 'Illuminated Books in the Cincinnati Art Museum', *Blake Newsletter*, vol. 7, no. 2, Fall 1973, pp. 40–3; M. Glazer & G. Norvig, 'Blake's Book of Changes: On Viewing Three Copies of the *Songs of Innocence and Experience*', *Blake Studies*, vol. 9, nos 1–2, 1980, pp. 100–21; R. Essick, 'New Information on Blake's Illuminated Books' and 'Songs Copy h', *Blake: An Illustrated Quarterly*, vol. 15, no. 1, pp. 4–13, 59–60; D. Dorrbecker, 'Innocence Lost and Found: An Untraced Copy Traced', *Blake: An Illustrated Quarterly*, vol. 15, no.

3, Winter 1981–82, pp. 125–31; R. Essick, *The Works of William Blake in the Huntington Collections*, The Huntington Library, San Marino, 1985, pp. 146–7, 156–65; R. Essick, 'A Copy of William Blake's "Songs of Innocence and of Experience" ', *Christie's International Magazine*, October–November 1988, pp. 22–3.

22 Viscomi, *Art of Blake's Illuminated Prints*, pp. 15, 20.

23 Bentley, *Blake Books*, p. 384.

24 The literature on Copy X is fragmentary. See *Catalogue of Valuable English Printed Books, Autograph Letters and Historical Documents*, Sotheby & Co., London, 9 November 1964, lot 112; R. Lister, 'A Fragmentary Copy of *Songs of Innocence and of Experience*', *Blake Newsletter*, vol. 6, no. 1, Summer 1972, p. 19; D. Bindman, *William Blake 1757–1827*, Hamburger Kunsthalle & Prestel Verlag, Munich, 1975, pp. 122–4; Bentley, *Blake Books*, p. 412; D. Bindman, *The Complete Graphic Works of William Blake*, Thames & Hudson, London, 1978, p. 469; R. Lister, *Samuel Palmer and 'The Ancients'*, Fitzwilliam Museum, Cambridge, 1984, p. 95; Shaunagh Fitzgerald Ltd, advertisement, *Apollo*, June 1985, p. 120; *Old Master, English and Decorative Prints*, Sotheby's, London, 27 June 1986, lot 746; *Visions of Landscape: Romanticism and the British Landscape from William Blake to Paul Nash*, Garton & Co., London, 3–25 May 1988, lot 1; C. Hartley, 'Songs of Innocence', *Print Quarterly*, vol. VI, no. 1, March 1989, p. 63.

25 'Blake's textures are mostly a function of paper preparation and ink viscosity. He does not seem to have dampened his paper very much before printing. The ink almost always lies on the surface and retains its rough patterns, whereas well-soaked paper usually tends to absorb ink and smooth out reticulations'; Essick, *William Blake, Printmaker*, p. 102.

26 Keynes & Wolf, *Census*, p. 50; D. Erdman, *The Illuminated Blake*, Anchor Press, New York, 1974, pp. 42–96.

27 Craig Hartley was the first to mention this connection in print; see 'Songs of Innocence', p. 63. I am most grateful to him for his help in examining this sheet at Cambridge.

28 D. Bindman, *Catalogue of the Collection in the Fitzwilliam Museum, Cambridge*, W. Heffer, Cambridge, 1970, no. 509; Bentley, *Blake Books*, pp. 430–1.

29 See esp. Phillips, 'Manuscript Draft to Illuminated Plate', pp. 36–7; and N. Shrimpton, 'Hell's Hymnbook: Blake's *Songs of Innocence and of Experience* and their Models', in R. T. Davies & B. G. Beatty (eds), *Literature of the Romantic Period*, Barnes & Noble, New York, 1976, pp. 19–35.

30 A. Boime, 'William Blake's Graphic Imagery and the Industrial Revolution', *Arts Magazine*, vol. 59, no. 10, June 1985, pp. 107–19; J. Warner, 'Blake and English Printed Textiles', *Blake Newsletter*, vol. 6, no. 4, Spring 1973, pp. 84–92; J. Warner, *Blake and the Language of Art*, McGill–Queen's University Press, Kingston, Ont., 1984, pp. 69–84.

31 A. Blunt, 'Blake's Pictorial Imagination', *Journal of the Warburg and Courtauld Institutes*, vol. 6, 1943, pp. 190–212; J. Hagstrom, *William Blake: Poet and Painter*, University of Chicago Press, Chicago, 1964, pp. 30–3.

32 K. Easson, 'Blake and the Art of the Book', in R. Essick & D. Pearce (eds), *Blake in his Time*, Indiana University Press, Bloomington, 1978, pp. 35–52.

33 Keynes & Wolf, *Census*, p. 51; D. Erdman, *Blake: Prophet Against Empire*, Doubleday, New York, 1969, p. 117; N. Frye, *Fearful Symmetry: A Study of William Blake*, Princeton University Press, Princeton, NJ, 1947, p. 237.

34 The literature on the *Songs of Innocence* is vast. Good introductions are provided by M. Paley (ed.), *Twentieth Century Interpretations of Songs of Innocence and of Experience*, Prentice-Hall, New York, 1969; and B. Wilkie, 'Blake's *Innocence and Experience*: An Approach', *Blake Studies*, vol. 6, no. 2, 1974, pp. 119–37. For recent interpretations of some of the Melbourne designs see I. Chayes, 'Little Girls Lost: Problems of a Romantic Archetype', *Bulletin of the New York Public Library*, vol. 67, 1963, pp. 579–92; I. Chayes, 'Blake and Tradition: "The Little Girl Lost" and "The Little Girl Found" ', *Blake Newsletter*, vol. 4, no. 1, Summer 1970, pp. 25–8; M. Tolley, 'Blake's Songs of Spring', in M. Paley & M. Phillips (eds), *William Blake: Essays in Honour of Sir Geoffrey Keynes*, Clarendon Press, Oxford, 1973, pp. 96–128; T. Connolly, 'The Real "Holy Thursday" of William Blake', *Blake Studies*, vol. 6, no. 2, 1974, pp. 179–87; R. Gleckner, 'The Strange Odyssey of Blake's "The Voice of the Ancient Bard" ', *Romanticism Past and Present*, vol. 6, 1982, pp. 1–25; and N. Greco, 'Blake's "The Little Girl Lost": An Initiation into Womanhood', *Colby Library Quarterly*, vol. 19, 1983, pp. 144–54.

35 See G. E. Bentley Jr, *A Bibliography of George Cumberland (1754–1848)*, Garland, New York, 1975; G. Keynes, 'Some Uncollected Authors XLIV', pp. 31–65; and A. Mellor, *Blake's Human Form Divine*, University of California Press, Berkeley, 1974, pp. 112–17.

36 M. Butlin, *The Paintings and Drawings of William Blake*, Yale University Press, London, 1981, nos 174–5, pp. 66–7 (hereafter referred to as Butlin 1981).

37 See 'Blake and the Wedgwoods', in G. Keynes, *Blake Studies: Essays on his Life and Work*, Rupert Hart-Davis, London, 1949 (rev. edn, Clarendon Press, Oxford, 1971). In May 1808 Cumberland recalled in his notebook, 'Got Blake to Engrave for Athens'; Bentley, *Blake Records*, p. 189.

38 William Blake, *A Descriptive Catalogue*, in Keynes, *Blake, Complete Writings*, p. 585.

39 See J. Stemmler, 'Cennino, Cumberland, Blake and Early Painting Techniques', *Blake: An Illustrated Quarterly*, vol. 17, no. 4, Spring 1984, pp. 145–9.

40 G. Cumberland, *An Essay on the Utility of Collecting the Best Works of the Ancient Engravers of the Italian Schools, Accompanied by a Critical Catalogue*, W. Nicol, London, 1827, p. 10. Cumberland lent Blake his manuscript for comment in November 1823; Bentley, *Blake Records*, p. 279.

41 Blake to Cumberland, 6 December 1795; Keynes, *Letters*, p. 26. G. E. Bentley Jr, *Blake Records Supplement*, Clarendon Press, Oxford, 1988, p. 11.

42 Keynes, however, dates these memos to 1807; *Blake, Complete Writings*, pp. 440, 907–8.

43 Cumberland to George Cumberland Jr, 18 June 1824; Bentley, *Blake Records*, p. 287. On the technical aspects of *Thoughts on Outline* see Essick, *William Blake, Printmaker*, pp. 53–4. Essick is careful, while noting the philosophical affinities between the two, to stress that 'it would be wrong to see [Cumberland's] theories as a dominant influence on Blake's actual practice as an engraver' (p. 54). Indeed, the opposite is clearly the case.

44 Bentley, *Blake Books*, pp. 542–4.

45 Keynes & Wolf, *Census*, Copy C. *Catalogue of the Very Choice and Valuable Collection of Drawings and Etchings, By the Great Masters of the different Schools, formed by the late Henry Reveley, Esq.*, Christie & Manson, London, 11 May 1852, lot 345: 'The DAUGHTERS OF ALBION, by Blake. Painted in colours by his own process—rare'. Keynes & Wolf note the signature 'H. I. Reveley' on the flyleaf, and raise the possible connection with Willey Reveley in *Census*, p. 29. On Henry Reveley see F. Lugt, *Les Marques de Collections de Dessins et d'Estampes*, Vereenigde Drukkerijen, Amsterdam, 1921, no. 1356, p. 242.

46 Bentley, *Blake Records*, pp. 44, 189. For Willey Reveley's correspondence with Blake see Keynes, *Letters*, p. 25.

47 At some stage, possibly during the Victorian era, the Melbourne copy of *Thoughts on Outline* suffered a slight mutilation to its eighteenth plate, *Iron Age* (cat. 41 f), as the erect penis of the central satyr was rather crudely

scraped off the sheet. This is sadly ironic in view of Cumberland's plea in *Thoughts on Outline* for a less repressed, more natural attitude towards artistic nudity: 'But one more observation I cannot omit on the decency that reigns among the naked figures of their great Artists, a decency which causes our delicacy to be suspected, when we affect to fig-leaf the sexual distinctions of their innocent nudities; of which it may be truly said, that "*they are naked and not ashamed*". An affectation, which shows a corrupted age like this in double deformity, while the obscene inventions of that great genius, *Hogarth*, are in all hands, and the loose descriptions of *Fielding*, are in every body's library' (p. 44).

48 Boime, 'Blake and the Industrial Revolution', p. 11.

49 Blake to Cumberland, 26 August 1799 and 2 July 1800; Keynes, *Letters*, pp. 32, 37.

50 Blake to James Blake, 30 January 1803; Keynes, *Letters*, pp. 65–6.

51 K. Raine, *Blake and Tradition*, Routledge & Kegan Paul, London, 1968, vol. 1, pp. 180–203; I. Chayes, 'The Presence of Cupid and Psyche', in D. Erdman & J. Grant, *Blake's Visionary Forms Dramatic*, Princeton University Press, Princeton, NJ, 1970, pp. 214–43. For the Cupid and Psyche myth generally in neo-classical and romantic art, see J. Hagstrum, 'Eros and Psyche: Some Versions of Romantic Love and Delicacy', *Critical Inquiry*, vol. 3, Spring 1977, pp. 521–42.

52 A. Gilchrist, *The Life of William Blake*, rev. edn, John Lane, London, 1907, p. 95.

53 Erdman, *Blake: Prophet Against Empire*, pp. 210–11.

54 The design dates back to a sketch of *Tiriel Denouncing his Sons and Daughters* of *c.* 1789; Butlin 1981, no. 199. Michael Tolley still sees a significant relation between *Europe* plate 8 and Blake's earlier *Tiriel*. See M. Tolley, 'Europe: "to those ychained in sleep" ', in Erdman & Grant, *Blake's Visionary Forms Dramatic*, p. 133.

55 For a full account of Blake's colour-printing methods see Essick, *William Blake, Printmaker*, pp. 121–35.

56 W. Mitchell, *Blake's Composite Art: A Study of the Illuminated Poetry*, Princeton University Press, Princeton, NJ, 1978, p. 111.

57 The clearest account of *The First Book of Urizen* is provided by D. Bindman, *Blake as an Artist*, Phaidon, Oxford, 1977, pp. 89–95. In Bindman's view, 'Blake, by telling the story of the creation of Urizen, reveals the true nature of the presiding deity of the world: how he was created by man himself, why he assumes the vengeful form of Jehovah, and in what way he imposes his will upon Fallen humanity' (p. 90). See also R. Simmons, '*Urizen*: The Symmetry of Fear', in Erdman & Grant, *Blake's Visionary Forms Dramatic*, pp. 146–73; W. Mitchell, 'Poetic and Pictorial Imagination in Blake's *The Book of Urizen*', in Essick, *The Visionary Hand*, pp. 337–80; K. Easson & R. Easson, *William Blake: The Book of Urizen*, Random House, New York, 1978.

58 D. Bindman, 'Blake's Theory and Practice of Imitation', in Essick & Pearce, *Blake in his Time*, p. 95.

59 Blake to Dawson Turner, 9 June 1818; Keynes, *Letters*, p. 139. On the *Large Book of Designs* see Keynes & Wolf, *Census*, pp. 88–90; Bentley, *Blake Books*, pp. 269, 365–8; Butlin 1981, no. 262, pp. 141–3.

60 Blake to William Hayley, 27 November 1805; Keynes, *Letters*, p. 120.

61 G. Gilfillan (ed.), *The Poetical Works of Beattie, Blair and Falconer*, James Nichol, Edinburgh, 1854, p. 125.

62 For a full analysis of the literary context and history of *The Grave* see R. Essick & M. Paley, *Robert Blair's 'The Grave' Illustrated by William Blake: A Study with Facsimile*, Scolar Press, London, 1982.

63 For thorough discussion of both issues of the *Prospectus* and their implications see G. E. Bentley Jr, 'The Promotion of Blake's *Grave* Designs', *University of Toronto Quarterly*, vol. XXXI, no. 3, April 1962, pp. 339–53; G. E. Bentley Jr, 'A Unique Prospectus for Blake's *Grave* Designs', *The Princeton University Library Chronicle*, vol. XXXV, no. 3, Spring 1974, pp. 321–4; G. E. Bentley Jr, 'Blake and Cromek: The Wheat and the Tares', *Modern Philology*, vol. 71, no. 4, May 1974, pp. 366–79.

64 On the controversial *Death's Door* white-line etching see R. Essick, *The Separate Plates of William Blake: A Catalogue*, Princeton University Press, Princeton, NJ, 1983, pp. 49–51.

65 Cromek to Blake, May 1807; Keynes, *Letters*, p. 126.

66 Blake to George Cumberland, 26 August 1799; Keynes, *Letters*, p. 32. On Boydell see W. Friedman, *Boydell's Shakespeare Gallery*, Garland, New York, 1976.

67 'Printsellers, and painters too, for an hundred years to come, will be continually assuring us, that we are arrived at the pinnacle of perfection. It promotes their profits, and so far, if taken with large allowance, it does no harm; but it does hurt indeed both to art, to poetry, and the country's ideas, when such authors, as *Shakespeare*, are undertaken to be finally illustrated, by exhibitions of pictures, painted according to the orders, and the ideas of men; who so far from being able to guide this triumphal chariot of the British Apollo, are scarcely worthy to hold the horses' heads: pictures painted on the gallop of rivalship, the spur of necessity, and under the lash of power'; G. Cumberland, *Thoughts on Outline*, London, 1796, p. 6.

68 Schiavonetti to Cromek, 21 July 1807; Bentley, *Blake Records Supplement*, p. 53.

69 D. Read, 'Cromek's Provincial Advertisements for Blake's *Grave*', *Notes and Queries*, vol. 27, no. 1, February 1980, pp. 73–6; A. Ward, 'Canterbury Revisited: The Blake–Cromek Controversy', *Blake: An Illustrated Quarterly*, vol. 22, no. 3, Winter 1988–89, pp. 80–92.

70 Cromek to James Montgomery, April 1807; Bentley, *Blake Records Supplement*, pp. 45–9. Cromek to Blake, May 1807; Keynes, *Letters*, p. 125.

71 Gilchrist, *Life of Blake*, p. 238. S. Foster Damon, *Blake's Grave: A Prophetic Book*, Brown University Press, Providence, RI, 1963, n.p.; and *A Blake Dictionary*, Brown University Press, Providence, RI, 1965, 'Robert Blair' entry.

72 M. Eaves, 'Blake and the Artistic Machine: An Essay in Decorum and Technology', *JMLA*, vol. 92, no. 5, October 1977, pp. 903–15.

73 Essick & Paley, *Robert Blair's 'The Grave'*, p. 53.

74 'Even . . . given the inevitable lessening of impact by the addition of conventional line-engraving, Schiavonetti's plates are, in my opinion, extraordinary in the sensitivity with which they handle Blake's idiosyncratic language. Every one of the twelve illustrations . . . is vigorous, if not moving, and unmistakeably Blakean in almost every detail . . . in general the "elegant" and "fashionable" Italian has grasped and rendered the sense and spirituality of Blake's ideas with an insight for which he deserves greater credit. Nowhere, I believe, can he be accused of having "softened" or "improved" Blake: he persuades us (who know Blake's work much better than his contemporaries did) that the elegance that is undeniably present in the designs is Blake's own'; A. Wilton, 'Review of R. Essick & M. Paley, *Robert Blair's "The Grave"* ', *Blake: An Illustrated Quarterly*, vol. 18, no. 1, Summer 1984, p. 55.

75 See Butlin 1981, nos 609–38. Gerald Bentley has traced the finished *Grave* drawings to the Scottish collector Thomas Sivright, with whose estate they were auctioned in 1835; this is the last record of their whereabouts; G. E. Bentley Jr, 'Thomas Sivright and the Lost Designs for Blair's *Grave*, *Blake: An Illustrated Quarterly*, vol. 19, no. 3, Winter 1985–86, pp. 103–6.

76 See Butlin 1981, nos 131 and 136; and R. Essick & J. La Belle, *Night Thoughts*, Dover, New York, 1975, p. 19.

77 Damon, *Blair's Grave: A Prophetic Book*, n.p.

78 T. Helmstadter, ' "Bright Visions of Eternity": Blake's Designs for Blair's *Grave*', *Blake Studies*, vol. 8, no. 1, pp. 37–64.

79 A. McCulloch, 'Nibbi—A True Pioneer', *Herald*, 26 August 1970; M. Bail, *Ian Fairweather*, Bay Books, Sydney, 1981, pp. 26–7.

80 For the printing history of *The Grave* see R. Essick & M. Paley, 'The Printings of Blake's Designs for Blair's *Grave*', *The Book Collector*, vol. 24, no. 4, pp. 535–52; Bentley, *Blake Books*, pp. 525–34; Essick & Paley, *Robert Blair's 'The Grave'*, pp. 203–22.

81 Their popularity, for example, even led to bowdlerized versions being incorporated into the 1838 pictorial edition of *The Book of Common Prayer*; see G. E. Bentley Jr, 'Echoes of Blake's *Grave* Designs in 1838', *Blake: An Illustrated Quarterly*, vol. 12, no. 3, Winter 1979–80, pp. 207–9. In 1868 Melbourne readers were informed that 'Book collectors may remember a certain edition of *Blair's Grave*, with strange weird illustrations, a portly quarto, as the popular volumes were in those days which fell almost still-born from the press, and which has haunted almost every bookseller's catalogue ever since'; 'Mr Swinburne on William Blake', *Argus*, 2 June 1868, pp. 5–6. I am most grateful to Gerard Hayes for providing this reference.

82 Cromek to Blake, May 1807; Keynes, *Letters*, p. 126.

83 Smith, *Nollekens and his Times*, and John Linnell's notes in the Ivimy Papers; both quoted in Bentley, *Blake Records*, pp. 464–5.

84 A. Ward, 'Canterbury Revisited: The Blake–Cromek Controversy', p. 81.

85 Butlin 1981, no. 653, pp. 475–6.

86 The *Descriptive Catalogue* is reprinted in Keynes, *Blake, Complete Writings*, pp. 563–86.

87 Keynes, *Blake, Complete Writings*, p. 586.

88 The *Public Address* is reprinted in Keynes, *Blake, Complete Writings*, pp. 591–603. See D. Read, 'The Context of Blake's "Public Address": Cromek and The Chalcographic Society', *Philological Quarterly*, vol. 60, 1981, pp. 69–86.

89 R. Todd, 'A Tentative Note on the Economics of The Canterbury Pilgrims', *Blake: An Illustrated Quarterly*, vol. 11, no. 1, Summer 1977, pp. 30–1.

90 Ward, 'Canterbury Revisited', p. 91.

91 Keynes, *Blake, Complete Writings*, p. 567.

92 See Essick, *William Blake, Printmaker*, pp. 188–92.

93 K. Kiralis, 'William Blake as an Intellectual and Spiritual Guide to Chaucer's *Canterbury Pilgrims*', *Blake Studies*, vol. 1, no. 2, Spring 1969, pp. 139–90.

94 W. Stevenson, 'Interpreting Blake's *Canterbury Pilgrims*', *Colby Library Quarterly*, vol. XII, no. 2, June 1977, pp. 115–26; O. Allen, 'Blake's Archetypal Criticism: *The Canterbury Pilgrims*', *Genre*, vol. XI, no. 2, Summer 1978, pp. 173–89.

95 B. Bowden, 'The Artistic and Interpretive Context of Blake's "Canterbury Pilgrims" ', *Blake: An Illustrated Quarterly*, vol. 13, no. 4, Spring 1980, pp. 164–90; C. Pace, 'Blake and Chaucer: Infinite Variety of Character', *Art History*, vol. 3, no. 4, December 1980, pp. 388–409.

96 M. Reisner, 'Effigies of Power: Pitt and Fox as Canterbury Pilgrims', *Eighteenth-Century Studies*, vol. 12, no. 4, Summer 1979, pp. 481–503.

97 For a full discussion of the various states and impressions of the *Canterbury Pilgrims* see Essick, *The Separate Plates of William Blake*, pp. 60–89.

98 R. Essick & M. Young, 'Blake's "Canterbury" Print: The Posthumous Pilgrimage of the Copperplate', *Blake: An Illustrated Quarterly*, vol. 15, no. 2, Fall 1981, pp. 78–82.

99 Blake to Dr Trusler, 23 August 1799; Keynes, *Letters*, p. 31.

100 See Bentley & Nurmi, *A Blake Bibliography*, pp. 145–8; and Bentley, *Blake Books*, pp. 603–5.

101 On the evidence of Smith, *Nollekens and his Times*, in Bentley, *Blake Records*, p. 456.

102 Blake to Flaxman, 12 September 1800 and 21 September 1800; Keynes, *Letters*, pp. 38, 42. For Flaxman's support of Blake's art see D. Irwin, *John Flaxman 1755–1826: Sculptor, Illustrator, Designer*, Studio Vista & Christie's, London, 1979; and G. E. Bentley Jr, 'Blake's Engravings and his Friendship with Flaxman', *Studies in Bibliography*, vol. 12, 1959, pp. 161–88.

103 Gilchrist, *Life of Blake*, p. 113, claimed that Piroli's plates to Flaxman's companion volume *The Odyssey of Homer* were lost on the voyage to England 'and Blake was employed to make engravings in their stead, although Piroli's name still remained on the general title page'. While it is tempting to relate this to Blake's outburst against Flaxman in the *Public Address* of *c.* 1810—'how much of his Homer & Dante he will allow to be mine I do not know, as he went far enough off to Publish them, even to Italy, but the Public will know & Posterity will know' (N 53)—Bentley has effectively discredited Gilchrist's assertion. See Bentley, 'Blake's Engravings and Flaxman', pp. 180–1.

104 Flaxman to Prince Hoare, 25 December 1803; Bentley, *Blake Records*, p. 136.

105 Flaxman to John Bischoff, 19 August 1814; Bentley, *Blake Records*, p. 233.

106 Bentley, *Blake Records*, p. 138.

107 Blake to Hayley, 2 April 1804; Keynes, *Letters*, p. 93.

108 Flaxman to Hayley, 19 August 1800; Bentley, *Blake Records*, p. 72.

109 'Besides at present I have no intercourse with Mr Blake—'; Flaxman to Hayley, 4 May 1808; Bentley, *Blake Records*, p. 190.

110 'To F[laxman] / I mock thee not, tho' I by thee am Mocked. / Thou call'st me Madman, but I call thee Blockhead' (N 26); 'On F[laxman] & S[tothard] / I found them blind: I taught them how to see; / and now they know neither themselves nor me' (N 34).

111 For Flaxman's friendship with Cromek see Bentley, 'Blake's Engravings and Flaxman', pp. 182–3.

112 'Task-work as an engraver, Flaxman, still wishful to serve as of old, obtained him, in 1816, from the Longmans: a kind office Blake did not quite take in good part. He would so far rather have been recommended as a designer! . . . Some touch of natural sorrow Blake might well have felt at having to copy, where he could have invented with far more power and originality'; Gilchrist, *Life of Blake*, pp. 268–9.

113 See 'Blake and the Wedgwoods', in Keynes, *Blake Studies*.

114 George Cumberland's diary, 3 June 1814, and George Cumberland Jr to Cumberland, 21 April 1815; Bentley, *Blake Records*, pp. 232, 235.

115 Bentley, *Blake Records Supplement*, p. 72.

116 See J. Bogan, 'Blake's *Jupiter Olympus* in Rees' *Cyclopedia*', *Blake: An Illustrated Quarterly*, vol. 15, no. 4, Spring 1982, pp. 156–63.

117 Blake to Josiah Wedgwood the younger, 8 September 1815; Keynes, *Letters*, p. 138. Preparatory drawings survive for *Sculpture. Plate I* (Library of Congress, Washington, DC), and of the Laocoön from *Sculpture. Plate III* (private collection, New York); Butlin 1981, nos 678A and 679.

118 On Bartolozzi and stipple engraving see R. Godfrey, *Printmaking in Britain*, Phaidon, Oxford, 1978, pp. 54–6; and D. Alexander & R. Godfrey, *Painters and Engraving: The Reproductive Print from Hogarth to Wilkie*, Yale Center for British Art, New Haven, 1980, pp. 7–8, 39–41.

119 Essick, *William Blake, Printmaker*, p. 193.

120 Blake to Dr Trusler, 16 August 1799; Keynes, *Letters*, p. 27.

121 Keynes, *Blake, Complete Writings*, p. 480. According to Andrew Wilton, '*Milton* was the first of the prophetic books to appear after his three years with Hayley, and seems, in part, to embody a violent reaction against the intense studies of classical art in which Hayley had encouraged him'; A. Wilton, 'Blake and the Antique', *British Museum Yearbook*, vol. 1, 1976, p. 213.

122 'No man can believe that either Homer's Mythology, or Ovid's, were the production of Greece or of Latium; neither will any one believe, that the Greek statues, as they are called, were the invention of the Greek Artists; perhaps the Torso is the only original work remaining; all the rest are evidently copies, though fine ones, from greater works

of the Asiatic Patriarchs. The Greek Muses are daughters of Mnemosyne, or Memory, and not of Inspiration or Imagination, therefore not authors of such sublime conceptions'; William Blake, *A Descriptive Catalogue of Pictures*, London, 1809; Keynes, *Blake, Complete Writings*, pp. 565–6.

123 On the complex issue of Blake's changing opinions of Greek sculpture see M. Paley, ' "Wonderful Originals"—Blake and Ancient Sculpture', in R. Essick & D. Pearce (eds), *Blake in his Time*, Indiana University Press, Bloomington, 1978, pp. 170–97; P. Fisher, 'Blake's Attacks on the Classical Tradition', *Philological Quarterly*, vol. XL, no. 1, January 1961, pp. 1–18; I. Tayler, 'Blake's Laocoön', *Blake Newsletter*, vol. 10, no. 3, Winter 1976–77, pp. 72–81; G. Keynes, *William Blake's Laocoön, A Last Testament*, The William Blake Trust, London, 1976; Essick, *William Blake, Printmaker*, pp. 193–6.

124 For a good summary of Linnell's life and work see K. Crouan, *John Linnell: A Centennial Exhibition*, Cambridge University Press, Cambridge, 1982.

125 See R. Essick, 'Blake, Linnell, & James Upton: An Engraving Brought to Light', *Blake: An Illustrated Quarterly*, vol. 7, no. 4, Spring 1974, pp. 76–9.

126 Bentley, *Blake Records*, p. 187. The most compact summary is given by Bentley: 'It seems likely . . . that the poem records experiences of Blake between 1790 and 1820, that it was written after 1803, that it was etched from 1804 on, sixty plates being completed by 1807, and the last forty over the next twelve or thirteen years, but that it was not printed, except for proofs, before 1818–19, and that no complete copy was ready before 1820'; Bentley, *Blake Books*, p. 229.

127 Blake to George Cumberland, 12 April 1827; Keynes, *Letters*, p. 163.

128 Bentley, *Blake Records Supplement*, p. 187.

129 Essick, *William Blake, Printmaker*, p. 124. For an analysis of Blake's variant printings of *Jerusalem* see S. Carr, 'William Blake's Print-Making Process in *Jerusalem*', *ELH*, vol. 47, 1980, pp. 520–41.

130 John Linnell owned twenty pencil, pen and wash drawings by Blake for the *Virgil* wood-engravings; these have now been dispersed among various collections, and some remain untraced. See Butlin 1981, 769: 1–20. It is possible that John Linnell may have helped with the copy after Poussin. See Bentley, *Blake Books*, p. 629; and *Blake Records Supplement*, p. 104.

131 Essick, *William Blake, Printmaker*, p. 228.

132 Blake to Thomas Butts, 23 September 1800; Keynes, *Letters*, pp. 42–3.

133 A. Patterson, 'Pastoral and Ideology: The Neoclassical *Fête Champêtre*', *Huntington Library Quarterly*, vol. 48, no. 4, Autumn 1985, p. 340. Landscape drawings made by Blake at Felpham are reproduced in Butlin 1981, pp. 479–83.

134 Bentley, *Blake Records*, p. 267.

135 Gilchrist, *Life of Blake*, pp. 289–93.

136 A. Russell, *The Engravings of William Blake*, Grant Richards, London, 1912, p. 100; L. Binyon, 'Blake's Woodcuts', *Burlington Magazine*, vol. XXXVII, no. CCXIII, December 1920, p. 284; L. Binyon, *The Engraved Designs of William Blake*, Ernest Benn, London & Charles Scribner's Sons, New York, p. 80. Mona Wilson also claimed that 'the thwarted publishers avenged themselves' by cutting the blocks down to make 'mutilated' prints; Wilson, *Life of Blake*, p. 317.

137 Keynes, 'Thornton's Virgil', in *Blake Studies*, pp. 160–1.

138 A. Wilton, *The Wood Engravings of William Blake*, British Museum, London, 1977, p. 16–17; M. Tolley, 'Thornton's Blake Edition', *University of Adelaide Library News*, vol. 10, no. 2, 1988, pp. 4–11. Pointing to the marked contrast between Blake's wood-engravings and the other commercial prints included in the volumes, Michael Tolley comments that: 'It is evident that Thornton expected his readers to notice the difference, too, that he had pinned his enterprise on the success or failure of Blake's innovatory works of printing. Indeed, there is every indication that what Thornton wanted in his book was more Blake, not less' (p. 5). Of the famous 'disclaimer', Tolley remarks that 'in one light, what Thornton is asserting is not that Blake's work lacks art but that it shows more genius (even) than it shows art' (p. 5).

139 Bentley, *Blake Records*, p. 296.

140 Keynes, *Blake, Complete Writings*, pp. 786–9, 925–6.

141 Keynes, *Blake Studies*, p. 165. The blocks stayed in the Linnell family until 1938, when they were acquired at auction for the British Museum.

142 Bentley, *Blake Books*, p. 630, citing a manuscript 'List of John Linnell Senior's Letters and Papers' in the Ivimy Papers.

143 D. Bindman, *Catalogue of the Fitzwilliam*, no. 36–1. The proof was bound up with a holograph copy of Blake's manuscript draft of *An Island in the Moon* (*c.* 1784), along with this letter from A. H. Palmer. Palmer's son was clearly mistaken here. The early *Virgil* proofs must have been printed by the end of 1820 at the latest, when Samuel Palmer was only fifteen. Palmer himself expressly stated that 'at my never-to-be-forgotten first interview [with Blake] the copper of the first plate [of the *Job* engravings] was lying on the table where he had been working on it', thus establishing a fairly firm date of 1824 for their initial meeting; Bentley, *Blake Records*, p. 282, citing Gilchrist, *Life of Blake* (1863), p. 297. A. H. Palmer's mistake perhaps arose from his misinterpretation of his father's reminiscences. In September 1864 Samuel Palmer wrote of a sheet with four of the *Virgil* prints on it: 'Mr Blake gave this page to me in Fountain Court: impressions taken there, at his own press, by his own hands, and signed by him under my eyes'; Bentley, *Blake Records*, p. 272, citing A. H. Palmer, *Catalogue of an Exhibition of Drawings, Etchings and Woodcuts by Samuel Palmer* (1926), p. 33. This would suggest that Samuel Palmer witnessed not the printing of the *Virgil* proofs but only the signing of an early proof sheet, autographed as a special gift.

144 Bentley, *Blake Records*, p. 271, citing A. H. Palmer, *The Life and Letters of Samuel Palmer* (1892), pp. 15–16; and [S. Calvert], *A Memoir of Edward Calvert Artist* (1893), p. 19. For Blake's influence on Palmer, Calvert and their circle see G. E. Bentley Jr, 'Blake and the Ancients: A Prophet With Honour Among the Sons of God', *Huntington Library Quarterly*, vol. 46, no. 1, Winter 1983, pp. 1–17; and L. Binyon, 'The Engravings of William Blake and Samuel Calvert', *Print Collectors' Quarterly*, vol. 17, April 1930, pp. 139–53. David Bindman has analysed the manner in which Palmer overlooked the more ominous undertones in Blake's *Virgil* designs, pointing out that 'For Palmer . . . nature provided a way to the apprehension of the Divine; but for a man like Blake, with intellectual roots in the seventeenth and eighteenth centuries, nature was equivocal and tainted by the Fall'; D. Bindman, *Blake as an Artist*, Phaidon, Oxford, 1977, p. 205.

145 Linnell's 1828 diary account is quoted in Bentley, *Blake Records*, p. 369. Calvert's son recalled that Blake and Calvert were experimenting with an etching ground on the night they set Calvert's chimney ablaze at Brixton; Bentley, *Blake Records*, p. 333.

146 R. Lister, *Edward Calvert*, G. Bell, London, 1962, p. 24, quoting an undated letter from Calvert to Linnell: 'You are most welcome to use the Press such as it is—Its great defects are in being too small and being altogether a *make-shift*'. I am assuming here that Calvert lent Linnell a platen press for printing relief works, rather than an intaglio rolling press. An album of separate proofs from the *Virgil* blocks in California is inscribed both as 'printed by John Linnell' and 'printed by the Linnell family'; see Essick, *The Works of William Blake in the Huntington Collections*, no. 51B.

147 Tate Gallery, London, 3866. This is part of a complete set of the *Virgil* engravings presented to the Tate by Herbert Linnell in 1924. The other sixteen prints in this set are rich, dark impressions of the Linnell type also found in the British Museum and the Fitzwilliam Museum, Cambridge; M. Butlin, *A Complete Catalogue of the Works in the Tate Gallery*, Tate Gallery, London, 1971, p. 24.

148 I. Bain & D. Chambers, 'Printing Blake's Engravings for Thornton's *Virgil*', *The Private Library*, vol. 1, no. 4, Winter 1978, pp. 171, 177. An early set of unusually even, dark impressions in a copy of the 1821 volume, inscribed 'Lady Caroline Lamb' is in the Fitzwilliam Museum, Cambridge (ex Keynes Collection); these are all reproduced in Bindman, *The Complete Graphic Works of William Blake*, nos 602–18. The dark, meticulous modern restrikes, printed by Ian Bain and David Chambers, are reproduced in M. Butlin, *William Blake*, Tate Gallery, London, 1978, nos 287–303.

149 Essick, *William Blake, Printmaker*, p. 153. Blake to William Hayley, 26 November 1800; Keynes, *Blake, Complete Writings*, p. 807.

150 As both the 'Collins' and Fitzwilliam coloured engravings are 'Proof' impressions, they must have been printed so lightly during Blake's lifetime, in 1825–26, either on Blake's or Linnell's authorization. Bo Lindberg has argued strongly that both coloured sets are the work of John Linnell, or Linnell assisted by Albin Martin. John Grant had previously thought the 'Collins' prints to be coloured by Blake himself, while Martin Butlin later defended the four Fitzwilliam engravings as Blake's original work; see B. Lindberg, 'The Authenticity of the New Zealand Set and of the Coloured Engravings', in D. Bindman (ed.), *Colour Versions of William Blake's Book of Job Designs from the Circle of John Linnell*, The William Blake Trust, London, 1987, pp. 11–27; J. Grant, 'Blake's "Illustrations of the Book of Job" ', *Times Literary Supplement*, 30 November 1973, p. 1484; M. Butlin, 'Review of D. Bindman (ed.), *Colour Versions of William Blake's Book of Job Designs from the Circle of John Linnell*', *Blake: An Illustrated Quarterly*, vol. 22, no. 3, Winter 1988/89, pp. 105–10.

151 G. Ingli James, 'Blake's Woodcuts, Plain and Coloured', *Times Literary Supplement*, 18 May 1973, p. 564; and 'Blake's Woodcuts Illuminated', *Apollo*, vol. XCIX, no. 145, pp. 194–5.

152 Gilchrist, *Life of William Blake*, p. 331.

153 Bentley, *Blake Records*, p. 276.

154 Contract between Linnell and Blake, 25 March 1823; Bentley, *Blake Records*, p. 277.

155 See E. Wolf, 'The Blake–Linnell Accounts in the Library of Yale University', *The Papers of the Bibliographical Society of America*, vol. 37, no. 1, 1943, pp. 1–22.

156 Linnell had regularly used laid India paper for his portrait engravings. See R. Essick, 'John Linnell, William Blake, and the Printmaker's Craft', *Huntington Library Quarterly*, vol. 46, no. 1, Winter 1983, p. 27.

157 R. Essick, 'Blake's Engravings to the Book of Job: An Essay on their Graphic Form', in D. Bindman (ed.), *William Blake's Illustrations of the Book of Job*, The William Blake Trust, London, 1987.

158 J. Wicksteed, *Blake's Vision of the Book of Job*, Dent, London, 1910 (repr. Haskell, New York, 1971).

159 S. Foster Damon, *Blake's Job*, Brown University Press, Providence, RI, 1966.

160 B. Lindberg, *William Blake's Illustrations to the Book of Job*, Abö Akademi, Abö, Finland, 1973. K. Raine, *The Human Face of God: William Blake and the Book of Job*, Thames & Hudson, London, 1982.

161 D. Bindman, 'The Book of Job Designs from Butts Series to Final Engravings', in Bindman, *William Blake's Illustrations of the Book of Job*.

162 Among later articles see R. Essick, 'Blake's *Job*: Some Unrecorded Proofs and Their Inscriptions', *Blake: An Illustrated Quarterly*, vol. 19, no. 3, Winter 1985–86, pp. 96–102; P. Davis, 'Revelation in Blake's *Job*', *Philological Quarterly*, vol. 65, no. 4, Fall 1986, pp. 451–77; and H. Summerfield, 'Beards, Disputations and Revelry: Observations on Blake's *Job* Engravings with Special Reference to Plates 2 and 3', *Colby Library Quarterly*, vol. 23, 1987, pp. 89–98.

163 Blake to John Linnell, 15 March 1827; Keynes, *Letters*, p. 161.

164 Keynes, *Blake, Complete Writings*, pp. 411–14.

165 Blake to Richard Phillips, June 1806; Keynes, *Letters*, p. 123.

166 Bentley, *Blake Records*, p. 349; and 'Books Owned by Blake', in Bentley & Nurmi, *Blake Bibliography*, nos 550–2.

167 Keynes, *Blake, Complete Writings*, pp. 682, 785.

168 A. Roe, *Blake's Illustrations to the Divine Comedy*, Princeton University Press, Princeton, NJ, 1953, p. 31; D. Fuller, 'Blake and Dante', *Art History*, vol. 11, no. 3, September 1988, p. 354.

169 See Bentley, *Blake Books*, pp. 544–7; R. Todd, 'Blake's Dante Plates', *Book Collecting and Library Monthly*, October 1968, pp. 3–12; G. Keynes, *Blake's Illustrations of Dante*, Trianon Press, London, 1978. There are some discrepancies. Bentley, citing John Linnell Jr's manuscript 'List of John Linnell Senior's Letters and Papers', states that 50 sets of the Dante engravings were reprinted in 1892; Todd and Keynes claim 100 sets were struck at this time. Keynes writes that Rosenwald had 20 sets of restrikes pulled in 1954; while Todd cites a letter from Rosenwald referring to 25 sets printed in 1955. For the dispute between Linnell, Catherine Blake and Tatham over the Dante work see Bentley, *Blake Records*, pp. 403–9 and 414–18.

170 Hoehn to Rosenwald, 25 July 1968; Todd, 'Blake's Dante Plates', p. 5.

171 Rosenwald to Todd, 29 July 1968; Todd, 'Blake's Dante Plates', p. 6.

172 Essick, *William Blake, Printmaker*, p. 251.

173 Blake to John Linnell, 19 May 1826; Keynes, *Letters*, p. 155.

174 Blake to John Linnell, 7 June 1825 and 2 July 1826; Keynes, *Letters*, pp. 152, 156.

175 Bentley, *Blake Records*, pp. 342, 346–7; *Blake Records Supplement*, p. 87.

176 Blake to William Hayley, 12 March 1804; Keynes, *Letters*, p. 90.

177 *Illustrated and Private Press Books*, Sotheby's, London, Thursday, 1 June 1989, lot 208. This appendix offers only a brief introduction to the Melbourne *Night Thoughts*. A full study is being undertaken by Professor Michael Tolley for the 1989 issue of *The Art Bulletin of Victoria*.

178 For a complete study of the coloured and regular versions see J. Grant, E. Rose & M. Tolley, *William Blake's Designs for Edward Young's 'Night Thoughts'*, 2 vols, Clarendon Press, Oxford, 1980.

179 See Essick & Paley, *'The Grave'. A Study with Facsimile*, pp. 191, 204.

180 See E.G. Coppel, 'The First Chief Justice of Victoria', *The Australian Law Journal*, vol. 27, 30 July 1953, pp. 209–22. I thank Stephen Coppell of the Australian National Gallery, Canberra, for providing me with a copy of his grandfather's article.

181 See the auction notice in the *Argus*, Thursday, 5 May 1904, p. 2. I am grateful to Gerard Hayes, whose painstaking researches uncovered this obscure reference. Although the *Argus* advertisement notes 'Catalogues on application', extensive enquiries have failed to recover the catalogue for this sale.

Catalogue 39–51

Blake Prints and Books in the National Gallery of Victoria

Ted Gott

Abbreviations

Bentley	G. E. Bentley Jr. *Blake Books*. Clarendon Press, Oxford, 1977.
Bentley & Nurmi	G. E. Bentley Jr & M. Nurmi. *A Blake Bibliography*. University of Minnesota Press, Minneapolis, 1964.
Bindman	D. Bindman. *The Complete Graphic Works of William Blake*. Thames & Hudson, London, 1978.
Binyon	L. Binyon. *The Engraved Designs of William Blake*. Ernest Benn, London; Charles Scribner's Sons, New York, 1926.
Butlin	M. Butlin. *The Paintings and Drawings of William Blake*. Yale University Press, London, 1981.
Easson & Essick	R. Easson & R. Essick. *William Blake: Book Illustrator. A Bibliography and Catalogue of the Commercial Engravings*. Vol. 1, The American Blake Foundation, Normal, Ill., 1972. Vol. 2, The American Blake Foundation, Memphis, Tenn., 1979.
Erdman	D. Erdman. *The Illuminated Blake*. Oxford University Press, London, 1975.
Essick	R. Essick. *The Separate Plates of William Blake*. Princeton University Press, Princeton, NJ, 1983.
Essick Job	R. Essick. 'Blake's Engravings to the *Book of Job*. Catalogue of States and Printings', in D. Bindman (ed.), *William Blake's Illustrations of the Book of Job*. The William Blake Trust, London, 1987.
Essick & Paley	R. Essick & M. Paley. *Robert Blair's 'The Grave' Illustrated by William Blake: A Study with Facsimile*. Scolar Press, London, 1982.
Keynes	G. Keynes. *A Bibliography of William Blake*. Grolier Club, New York, 1921.
Keynes *Sep. Pl.*	G. Keynes. *Engravings by William Blake: The Separate Plates*. Emery Walker, Dublin, 1956.
Keynes & Wolf	G. Keynes & E. Wolf. *William Blake's Illuminated Books: A Census*. Grolier Club, New York, 1953.
Roe	A. Roe. *Blake's Illustrations to the Divine Comedy*. Princeton University Press, Princeton, NJ, 1953.
Russell	A. Russell. *The Engravings of William Blake*. Grant Richards, London, 1912.

Measurements are given in centimetres; height precedes width.

The position of *inscriptions* is given by the abbreviations u.l. (upper left), l.r. (lower right), u.c. (upper centre), etc.

39 ***Songs of Innocence*** **1789 (coloured before 1794)**

Fourteen relief etchings from a series of thirty-one, printed in relief in green ink; failed areas of text strengthened with wash; designs finished with water-colour
Bentley's Copy X; not in Keynes & Wolf
Plates formerly arranged in Keynes & Wolf order: 6–7, 12, 14, 18–19, 20, 21, 22, 24, 23, 31, 26, 27
Ex collection Raymond Lister
Volume now unbound, leaves separated
Paper: pale cream wove
Sold Sotheby's, London, 9 November 1964, lot 112; Sotheby's London, 27 June 1986, lot 746
Felton Bequest 1988

a ***The Little Girl Lost*** (second plate) and ***The Little Girl Found*** (first plate) Leaf 1 recto

Keynes & Wolf 6, Erdman 35, Bindman 59
Printed in green ink
18.8 x 13.7 cm (sheet), 11 x 7.2 cm (image)
Inscr. u.r. corner of sheet, pencil: 35
P.122a/1988

b ***The Little Girl Found*** (second plate) Leaf 1 verso

Keynes & Wolf 7, Erdman 36, Bindman 60
Printed in green ink, text strengthened with blue wash
18.8 x 13.7 cm (sheet), 10.9 x 6.9 cm (image)
Inscr. u.r. corner of sheet, pencil: 36
P.122a/1988

c ***The Divine Image*** Leaf 2 recto

Keynes & Wolf 12, Erdman 18, Bindman 56
Printed in green ink
18.9 x 13.6 cm (sheet), 11.1 x 7 cm (image)
Inscr. u.r. corner of sheet, pencil: 18
P.122b/1988

d ***Infant Joy*** Leaf 2 verso

Keynes & Wolf 14, Erdman 25, Bindman 44
Printed in green ink
18.9 x 13.6 cm (sheet), 10.6 x 6.8 cm (image)
Inscr. u.r. corner of sheet, pencil: 25
P.122b/1988

e ***A Cradle Song*** (first plate) Leaf 3 recto

Keynes & Wolf 18, Erdman 16, Bindman 63
Printed in green ink, text strengthened with blue wash
18.9 x 13.6 cm (sheet), 11.2 x 7.3 cm (image)
Inscr. u.r. corner of sheet, pencil: 16
P.122c/1988

f ***A Cradle Song*** (second plate) Leaf 3 verso

Keynes & Wolf 19, Erdman 17, Bindman 64
Printed in green ink
18.9 x 13.6 cm (sheet), 10.8 x 6.8 cm (image)
Inscr. u.r. corner of sheet, pencil: 17
P.122c/1988

g ***The Little Boy Lost*** Leaf 4 recto

Keynes & Wolf 20, Erdman 13, Bindman 61
Printed in green ink
18.9 x 13.5 cm (sheet), 11.5 x 7.1 cm (image)
Watermark: E & P
Inscr. u.r. corner of sheet, pencil: 13
P.122d/1988

h ***The Little Boy Found*** Leaf 4 verso

Keynes & Wolf 21, Erdman 14, Bindman 62
Printed in green ink
18.9 x 13.5 cm (sheet), 11.3 x 7.2 cm (image)
Watermark: E & P
Inscr. u.r. corner of sheet, pencil: 14
P.122d/1988

i ***Nurse's Song*** Leaf 5 recto

Keynes & Wolf 22, Erdman 24, Bindman 48
Printed in green ink, text strengthened with blue wash
18.9 x 13.5 cm (sheet), 11.3 x 7.7 cm (image)
Inscr. u.r. corner of sheet, pencil: 24
P.122e/1988

j ***On Another's Sorrow*** Leaf 5 verso

Keynes & Wolf 24, Erdman 27, Bindman 45
Printed in green ink, text strengthened with blue wash
18.9 x 13.5 cm (sheet), 11.2 x 7.1 cm (image)
P.122e/1988

k ***Holy Thursday*** Leaf 6 recto

Keynes & Wolf 23, Erdman 19, Bindman 47
Printed in green ink, text strengthened with blue wash
18.9 x 13.6 cm (sheet), 11.4 x 7.8 cm (image)
Inscr. u.r. corner of sheet, pencil: 19
P.122f/1988

l ***The Voice of the Ancient Bard*** Leaf 6 verso

Keynes & Wolf 31, Erdman 54, Bindman 52
Printed in green ink, text strengthened with blue wash
18.9 x 13.6 cm (sheet), 10.7 x 6.3 cm (image)
Inscr. u.r. corner of sheet, pencil: 54
P.122f/1988

m ***Spring*** (second plate) Leaf 7 recto

Keynes & Wolf 26, Erdman 23, Bindman 66
Printed in green ink
18.9 x 13.6 cm (sheet), 10.3 x 7.8 cm (image)
Inscr. u.r. corner of sheet, pencil: 23
P.122g/1988

n ***The School-Boy*** Leaf 7 verso

Keynes & Wolf 27, Erdman 53, Bindman 46
Printed in green ink
18.9 x 13.6 cm (sheet), 10.8 x 6.7 cm (image)
Inscr. u.r. corner of sheet, pencil: 53
P.122g/1988

40 ***A Family of New South Wales*** **1792**

Blake, after Governor Philip Gidley King
From John Hunter, *An Historical Journal of the Transactions at Port Jackson and Norfolk Island*, London, 1793

Etching and engraving
Bentley & Nurmi 385A, Bentley 476A, Easson & Essick XXXIX 1A
18.9 x 16 cm (image), 24.9 x 20.7 cm (plate mark), 30.5 x 24.1 cm (sheet)
Paper: white wove
Inscr. in plate l.l.: From a Sketch by Governor King; l.c.: A FAMILY OF NEW SOUTH WALES; l.r.: Blake. Sculpt.
Imprint l.c.: Publish'd by J. Stockdale Picadilly, Novr: 15–1792
Purchased 1974 P.8/1974

41 *Thoughts on Outline* 1794–95

Eight etchings/engravings by Blake, after George Cumberland
From George Cumberland, *Thoughts on Outline, Sculpture and the System that Guided the Ancient Artists in Composing Their Figures and Groupes*, London, 1796
Front-end flyleaf inscr. in black ink u.r.: H. I. Reveley
Title-page inscr. in black ink u.r.: from the Author 1833; and stamped with collector's mark of Henry Reveley (1737–98), Lugt 1356
Text sparsely annotated in pencil, by Henry Reveley(?)
Paper: white wove
Watermark: 1794 I TAYLOR
Endpapers watermarked: CHARLES WISE / 1819
Twenty-four engraved plates (8 by Blake, 16 by Cumberland)
OS 30.a–x

a *Psyche Disobeys* Plate 12

Etching and engraving
Russell 85i, Keynes 112i, Bentley & Nurmi 362, Bentley 447.1, Easson & Essick XLVII 1
11.1 x 14 cm (image), 23.4 x 15.6 cm (plate mark)
Paper: stiff white wove
Inscr. in plate u.l.: PSYCHE DISOBEYS; u.r.: 12
Imprint l.c.: From an original Invention by G. Cumberland. Engd. by W Blake : Published as the Act directs November 5 : 1794
OS 30.l

b *Psyche Repents* Plate 13

Etching and engraving
Russell 85ii, Keynes 112ii, Bentley & Nurmi 362, Bentley 447.2, Easson & Essick XLVII 2
11.2 x 14.3 cm (image), 12.1 x 15.7 cm (plate mark)
Paper: stiff white wove
Inscr. in plate u.l.: PSYCHE REPENTS; u.r.: 13
Imprint l.c.: From the original Invention by G: Cumberland. : Engd: by W Blake. Publish'd as the Act directs Novr: 5 : 1794
OS 30.m

c *Venus Councels Cupid* Plate 14

Engraving
Russell 85iii, Keynes 112iii, Bentley & Nurmi 362, Bentley 447.3, Easson & Essick XLVII 3A
14.1 x 11.1 cm (image), 16.1 x 10.7 cm (plate mark)
Paper: stiff white wove
Inscr. in plate u.c.: VENUS COUNCELS CUPID; u.r.: 14
Imprint l.c.: From an original Invention by G Cumberland. Engd by W Blake. Publishd as the Act directs Nov 5 : 1794
OS 30.n

d *The Conjugal Union of Cupid* Plate 15

Engraving
Russell 85iv, Keynes 112iv, Bentley & Nurmi 362, Bentley 447.4, Easson & Essick XLVII 4A
14.9 x 11.3 cm (image), 16.0 x 12.6 cm (plate mark)
Paper: stiff white wove
Inscr. in plate u.c.: THE CONJUGAL UNION OF CUPID; u.r.: 15
Imprint l.c.: From an original Invention by G. Cumberland. Engd by W Blake. Publishd as the Act directs Nov: 5. 1794
OS 30.o

e *Cupid and Psyche* Plate 16

Engraving
Russell 85v, Keynes 112v, Bentley & Nurmi 362, Bentley 447.5, Easson & Essick XLVII 5
15.6 x 21.6 cm (image), 17.1 x 23.4 cm (plate mark)
Paper: stiff white wove
Inscr. in plate c.l.: CUPID & PSYCHE; u.r.: 16
Imprint l.c.: From an original Invention by G. Cumberland. Engd: by W Blake. Publish'd as the Act directs / Novr. 5 : 1794
OS 30.p

f *Iron Age* Plate 18

Engraving
Russell 85vi, Keynes 112vi, Bentley & Nurmi 362, Bentley 447.6, Easson & Essick XLVII 6
13.2 x 23.1 cm (image), 14.6 x 24.4 cm (plate mark)
Paper: stiff white wove
Inscr. in plate u.l.: IRON AGE; u.r.: Then cursed steel & more accursed gold / Gave mischief birth & made that mischief bold. / Ovid. Iron Age; u.r. outside border: 18
Imprint l.c.: From an original Invention by G: Cumberland : Engd: by W Blake. Publishd as the Act directs. Novr 5 : 1794.
OS 30.r

g *Aristophanes' Clouds, Scene I* Plate 19

Engraving
Russell 85vii, Keynes 112vii, Bentley & Nurmi 362, Bentley 447.7, Easson & Essick XLVII 7A
14.3 x 20.5 cm (image), 18.6 x 22.2 cm (plate mark)
Paper: stiff white wove
Inscr. in plate u.c.: ARISTOPHANES CLOUDS. SCENE.I.; u.r.: 19
Imprint l.c.: From an original Invention by G: C: Engd: by W.B: Published. January. 1 : 1795—
OS 30.s

h *Anacreon, Ode LII* Plate 23

Engraving
Russell 85viii, Keynes 112viii, Bentley & Nurmi 362, Bentley 447.8, Easson & Essick XLVII 8A
12.1 x 16.4 cm (image), 14.8 x 20.3 cm (plate mark)
Paper: stiff white wove

Watermark: 1794 / J WHATMAN
Inscr. in plate u.c.: ANACREON. ODE LII; u.r.: 23
Imprint l.c.: From an Original Invention by G: C: Engd: by W.B: Publishd Jany: 1 : 1795
OS 30.w

42 *Arise, O Rintrah!* c. 1794–95

Plate 8 from *Europe: A Prophecy*, 1794
Relief etching, white-line etching and intaglio engraving, printed in relief in blue ink; simultaneous colour-printing (monotype) with opaque pigments; later water-colour, and pen and ink finish
Ex collection John Linnell
Sold Christie's, London, 15 March 1918, lot 178: 'Design for a Prophetic Book, with 12 lines of text at the top, commencing "Arise O Rintrah" . . . engraved and finely coloured by Blake, 4to.'
Keynes 41 (8), Binyon 295, Bentley 33 p. 163, Bindman 175
23.4 x 16.6 cm (image and plate mark), 34.2 x 25.1 cm (sheet)
Paper: buff wove
Felton Bequest 1920 1028/3

43 *Los, Enitharmon and Orc* c. 1795

Plate 21 from *The First Book of Urizen*, 1794
Reissued as part of Copy B of the so-called *Large Book of Designs*
Relief etching, colour-printed (monotype) with opaque pigments; later water-colour, and pen and ink finish
Ex collection John Linnell
Sold Christie's, London, 15 March 1918, lot 177: 'Unpublished Design from the "EUROPE"; of a Man at a Forge, with a Woman and Youth, engraved and coloured by Blake, 4to.'
Keynes 42 (41), Binyon 323, Keynes & Wolf B3, Bentley 38 p. 184, Bindman 317, Butlin 281
16.6 x 10.2 cm (image and plate mark), 31.3 x 25 cm (sheet)
Paper: buff wove
Watermark: WHATMAN / 1794
Felton Bequest 1920 1027/3

44 Blair's *Grave* 1808

Twelve etchings/engravings by Louis Schiavonetti after William Blake, from *The Grave, A Poem. By Robert Blair*, London, 1808
1808 quarto issue (trimmed for binding)
Paper: cream wove
Watermark: J WHATMAN / 1807 and J WHATMAN / 1808
Purchased 1954 3153.a–m/4

a *Portrait of Blake* Frontispiece

First state
Keynes 81i, Essick & Paley A
34.3 x 26.4 cm (sheet)
Paper: white wove
Inscr. in plate l.l.: Painted by T. Phillips R.A.; l.c.: William Blake; l.r.: Engraved by L Schiavonetti V.A.
Imprint l.c.: London, Published by R. H. Cromek, 64, Newman St. May 1st. 1808—
3153.a/4

b *The Skeleton Re-Animated* Title-page

Second state
Russell 40i, Keynes 81ii, Bindman 465, Essick & Paley 1B
34.3 x 26.4 cm (sheet)
Paper: white wove
Inscr. in plate l.l.: Drawn by W. Blake; l.r.: Etched by L. Schiavonetti.
Imprint l.c.: London, Published May 1, 1808, by R. H. Cromek, No. 64, Newman Street.
'Subscribers' Copy' inscription trimmed from l.r. of sheet
3153.b/4

c *The Descent of Christ into the Grave* Facing page 1

Second state
Russell 40ii, Keynes 81iii, Bindman 466, Essick & Paley 2B
23 x 12.4 cm (image), 27.7 cm x 20 cm (plate mark)
Paper: white wove
Inscr. in plate u.r.: P. 1.; l.l.: Drawn by W. Blake.; l.c.: Christ descending into the Grave. / Eternal King! whose potent Arm sustains / The Keys of Hell and Death.; l.r.: Etched by L. Schiavonetti.
Imprint l.c.: London, Published May 1st. 1808, by Cadell & Davies, Strand.
3153.c/4

d *A Family Meeting in Heaven* Facing page 9

Second state
Russell 40iii, Keynes 81iv, Bindman 467, Essick & Paley 3B
23.2 x 13.2 cm (image), 27.6 x 15.5 cm (plate mark)
Paper: white wove
Watermark: J WHATMAN / 1807
Inscr. in plate l.l.: Drawn by W. Blake.; l.c.: The meeting of a Family in Heaven.; l.r.: Etched by L. Schiavonetti.
Imprint l.c.: London, Published May 1st. 1808, by Cadell & Davies, Strand.
3153.d/4

e *The Counsellor, King, Warrior, Mother, and Child* Facing page 11

Second state
Russell 40iv, Keynes 81v, Bindman 468, Essick & Paley 4B
14 x 22.6 cm (image), 21.2 x 26.2 cm (plate mark)
Paper: white wove
Inscr. in plate u.r.: P. 11.; l.l.: Drawn by W. Blake; l.c.: The Counseller, King, Warrior, Mother & Child, in the Tomb.; l.r.: Etched by L. Schiavonetti.
Imprint l.c.: London, Published May 1st. 1808, by Cadell & Davies, Strand.
3153.e/4

f *The Strong Wicked Man Dying* Facing page 12

Second state
Russell 40v, Keynes 81vi, Bindman 469, Essick & Paley 5B

20.6 x 25.9 cm (image), 23.9 x 27.8 cm (plate mark)
Paper: white wove
Watermark: 1808
Inscr. in plate u.r.: P.12.; l.l.: Drawn by W. Blake; l.c.: Death of the Strong Wicked Man / . . . Heard you that groan? / It was his last.; l.r.: Engraved by L. Schiavonetti.
Imprint l.c.: London, Published May 1st. 1808, by Cadell & Davies, Strand.
3153.f/4

g *The Soul Hovering Over the Body* Facing page 16

Second state
Russell 40vi, Keynes 81vii, Bindman 470, Essick & Paley 6B
16 x 22.5 cm (image), 21.2 x 26.4 cm (plate mark)
Paper: white wove
Inscr. in plate u.r.: P.16.; l.l.: Drawn by W. Blake.; l.c.: The Soul hovering over the Body . reluctantly parting with Life. / ——How wishfully she looks / On all she's leaving, now no longer her's!; l.r.: Etched by L. Schiavonetti.
Imprint l.c.: London, Published May 1, 1808, by Cadell & Davies, Strand.
3153.g/4

h *The Descent of Man into the Vale of Death* Facing page 21

Second state
Russell 40vii, Keynes 81viii, Bindman 471, Essick & Paley 7B
23.7 x 13.5 cm (image), 27.5 x 16.8 cm (plate mark)
Paper: white wove
Inscr. in plate u.r.: P.21.; l.l.: Drawn by W. Blake.; l.c.: The descent of Man into the Vale of Death. / . . . 'Tis here all meet!; l.r.: Engraved by L. Schiavonetti.
Imprint l.c.: London Published May 1st. 1808, by Cadell & Davies Strand.
3153.h/4

i *The Last Judgement* Facing page 28

Second state
Russell 40 viii, Keynes 81ix, Bindman 472, Essick & Paley 8B
27.4 x 22.2 cm (image), 31.4 x 25 cm (plate mark)
Paper: white wove
Inscr. in plate u.r.: P.28.; l.l.: Drawn by W. Blake.; l.c.: The Day of Judgement.; l.r.: Etched by L. Schiavonetti.
Imprint l.c.: London, Published May 1st. 1808, by Cadell & Davies, Strand.
3153.i/4

j *The Soul Exploring the Recesses of the Grave* Facing page 29

Second state
Russell 40ix, Keynes 81x, Bindman 473, Essick & Paley 9B
23.2 x 11.8 cm (image), 28.2 x 15.7 cm (plate mark)
Paper: white wove
Inscr. in plate l.l.: Drawn by W. Blake.; l.c.: The Soul exploring the recesses of the Grave.; l.r.: Etched by L. Schiavonetti.
Imprint l.c.: London, Published May 1st. 1808, by Cadell & Davies, Strand.
3153.j/4

k *The Good Old Man Dying* Facing page 30

Second state
Russell 40x, Keynes 81xi, Bindman 474, Essick & Paley 10B
20.2 x 25.8 cm (sheet), 23.6 x 27.2 cm (plate mark)
Paper: white wove
Inscr. in plate u.r.: P 30; l.l.: Drawn by W. Blake.; l.c.: The Death of The Good Old Man. / . . . Sure the last end / Of the good Man is peace! How calm His exit!; l.r.: Engraved by L. Schiavonetti.
Imprint l.c.: London Published May 1st. 1808, by Cadell & Davies, Strand.
3153.k/4

l *Death's Door* Facing page 32

Second state
Russell 40xi, Keynes 81xii, Bindman 475, Essick & Paley 11B
23.9 x 13.8 cm (image), 29.6 x 17.2 cm (plate mark)
Paper: white wove
Inscr. in plate u.r.: P.32.; l.l.: Drawn by W. Blake.; l.c.: Death's Door. / 'Tis but a Night, a long and moonless Night, We make the Grave our Bed, and then are gone!; l.r.: Etched by L. Schiavonetti.
Imprint l.c.: London, Published May 1st. 1808, by Cadell & Davies, Strand.
3153.l/4

m *The Reunion of Soul and Body* Following page

Second state
Russell 40xii, Keynes 81xiii, Bindman 476, Essick & Paley 12B
23.5 x 17.4 cm (image), 29.4 x 23.2 cm (plate mark)
Paper: white wove
Inscr. in plate u.r.: P.32.; l.l.: Drawn by W. Blake.; l.c.: The Reunion of the Soul & the Body.; l.r.: Etched by L. Schiavonetti.
Imprint l.c.: London, Published May 1st. 1808, by Cadell & Davies, Strand.
3153.m/4

45 *Chaucer's Canterbury Pilgrims* 1810

Etching and engraving, third state of five
Russell 24, Binyon 100i, Keynes Sep. Pl, XVIIii, Bindman 477, Essick XVIiii (3T)
30.1 x 93.8 cm (image), 35.2 x 96 cm (plate mark), 36.2 x 96.6 cm (sheet)
Paper: cream wove
Imprint l.c.: CHAUCER'S CANTERBURY PILGRIMS / Painted in Fresco by William Blake & by him Engraved & Published October 8. 1810, at No 28. Corner of Broad Street / Golden Square
Presented by Mr R. Haughton-James, 1967
OS 32

46 *Sculpture. Plate 1* 1816

From Abraham Rees, *The Cyclopedia or Universal Dictionary of Arts, Sciences and Literature*, 39 vols, London, 1802–20; fascicule 67, October 1816
Stipple engraving
Russell 105iv, Keynes 132iv, Bentley & Nurmi 399A.4, Bentley 489.4

25.4 x 20.2 cm (image and sheet)
Paper: white wove
Inscr. in plate l.r.: Blake sc.
Title trimmed off top edge of sheet: SCULPTURE *PLATE I.*
Imprint trimmed off lower edge of sheet: London, Published as the Act directs Feby. 1, 1816, by Longman, Hurst, Rees, Orme, & Brown, Paternoster Row.
Presented by Nicholas Draffin
OS 31

47 *Vala, Hyle and Skofeld* c. 1820

Plate 51 from *Jerusalem c.* 1804–15/*c.* 1818–20
White-line etching and intaglio engraving, printed in relief in orange ink; later water-colour, pen and ink, and liquefied gold finish
Ex collection John Linnell
Sold Christie's, London, 15 March 1918, lot 158: 'The Three Despondent Persons.'
Keynes 49 (51), Binyon 430, Bentley 76 p. 264, Bindman 530, Butlin 579
15.8 x 22.2 cm (image and plate mark), 27.8 x 33.6 cm (sheet)
Paper: white wove
Watermark: 1820
Inscr. in plate l.l.: WB / inv & s
Felton Bequest 1920 1026/3

48 Thornton's *Virgil* 1820–21

Fourteen wood-engravings from a series of seventeen executed to illustrate Ambrose Phillips's 'Imitation of Eclogue 1' in Robert John Thornton, *The Pastorals of Virgil*, 3rd edn, London, 1821
Except where indicated, all impressions are clipped 2–3 mm from the image
Nos 10 f, i, k, l, m, n may be later impressions, taken after Blake's death from the wood-blocks which survived in the collection of John Linnell

a *Thenot Remonstrates with Colinet*

Russell 30ii, Keynes 77ii, Binyon 138ii, Bindman 603, Easson & Essick X 2
3.7 x 7.4 cm (image)
Paper: white wove mounted to new Japan
Inscr. verso, pencil: 2
OS 16

b *Thenot Under a Fruit Tree*

Russell 30iii, Keynes 77iii, Binyon 139ii, Bindman 604, Easson & Essick X 3
3.2 x 7.4 cm (image)
Paper: white wove mounted to new Japan
Inscr. verso, pencil: 3
OS 17

c *Thenot Remonstrates with Colinet, Lightfoot in the Distance*

Russell 30iv, Keynes 77iv, Binyon 140ii, Bindman 605, Easson & Essick X 4
3.2 x 7.3 cm (image)
Paper: white wove mounted to new Japan
OS 18

d *Colinet Departs in Sorrow, A Thunder-Scarred Tree on the Right*

Russell 30v, Keynes 77v, Binyon 141ii, Bindman 606, Easson & Essick X 5
3.6 x 7.4 cm (image)
Paper: white wove mounted to new Japan
Inscr. verso, pencil: 5
OS 19

e *Blasted Tree and Blighted Crops*

Russell 30vi, Keynes 77vi, Binyon 142ii, Bindman 607, Easson & Essick X 6
3.4 x 7.3 cm (image)
Paper: white wove mounted to new Japan
Inscr. verso, pencil: 6
OS 20

f *The Good Shepherd Chases Away the Wolf*

Russell 30vii, Keynes 77vii, Binyon 143ii, Bindman 608, Easson & Essick X 7
3.4 x 7.4 cm (image), 4.1 x 8.1 cm (paper)
Paper: white wove mounted to new Japan
Inscr. verso, pencil: 7
OS 21

g *Sabrina's Silvery Flood*

Russell 30viii, Keynes 77viii, Binyon 144ii, Bindman 609, Easson & Essick X 8
3.2 x 7.3 cm (image)
Paper: white wove mounted to new Japan
Inscr. verso, pencil: 8
OS 22

h *Colinet's Fond Desire Strange Lands to Know*

Russell 30ix, Keynes 77ix, Binyon 145ii, Bindman 610, Easson & Essick X 9
3.5 x 7.4 cm (image)
Paper: white wove mounted to new Japan
Inscr. verso, pencil: 9
OS 23

i *Colinet Resting at Cambridge by Night*

Russell 30xi, Keynes 77xi, Binyon 147, Bindman 612, Easson & Essick X 11
3.2 x 7.3 cm (image), 4.4 x 8.2 cm (sheet)
Paper: white wove mounted to new Japan
Inscr. verso, pencil: 11
OS 24

j *Colinet Mocked by Two Boys*

Russell 30xii, Keynes 77xii, Binyon 148, Bindman 613, Easson & Essick X 12
3.5 x 7.7 cm (image)
Paper: white wove mounted to new Japan
Inscr. verso, pencil: 12
OS 25

k *Menalcas' Yearly Wake*

Russell 30xiii, Keynes 77xiii, Binyon 149, Bindman 614, Easson & Essick X 13
3.5 x 7.4 cm (image), 6.2 x 9.9 cm (sheet)
Paper: cream laid
Inscr. verso, pencil: 13
OS 26

l ***Thenot and Colinet Sup Together***

Russell 30xv, Keynes 77xviii, Binyon 151, Bindman 616, Easson & Essick X 15
3.4 x 7.6 cm (image), 5.7 x 8.8 cm (sheet)
Paper: thin, pale cream Oriental laid
Inscr. verso, pencil: Plate 18   Grade 1
OS 27

m ***With Songs the Jovial Hinds Return from Plow***

Russell 30xvi, Keynes 77xix, Binyon 152, Bindman 617, Easson & Essick X 16
3.5 x 7.6 cm (image), 5.6 x 9.1 cm (sheet)
Paper: thin, pale cream Oriental laid
Inscr. verso, pencil: [. . .]te 19   Grade 1
OS 28

n ***Unyoked Heifers Loitering Homeward, Low***

Wood-engraving and bistre wash
Russell 30xvii, Keynes 77xx, Binyon 153, Bindman 618, Easson & Essick X 17
3.3 x 7.7 cm (image), 4.7 x 9.4 cm (sheet)
Paper: white wove
Inscr. verso, pencil: 20
OS 29

49 Illustrations of *The Book of Job* 1823–26

Twenty-two engravings on copper
'Proof' impressions (title-page not inscribed 'Proof')
Ex collection John Linnell
Sold Christie's, London, 15 March 1918, lot 182: 'Original Proof impressions on India paper, printed on large paper, imperial 4to, original pink boards, with paper label on side—1825 (the label dated March, 1826).'
Felton Bequest 1920   1058.a–v/3

a ***Title-Page***

Russell 33i, Binyon 105ii, Bindman 625, Essick Job A
19 x 14.6 cm (image), 21.2 x 16.3 cm (plate mark), 38.3 x 26.9 cm (sheet)
Paper: India on white wove
Imprint l.c.: London Published as the Act directs March 8 : 1825. by William Blake No 3 Fountain Court Strand
1058.a/3

b ***Job and His Family*** Plate 1

Russell 33ii, Binyon 106ii, Bindman 626, Essick Job 1A
18.2 x 14.9 cm (image), 19.7 x 16.5 cm (plate mark), 38.5 x 26.9 cm (sheet)
Paper: India on white wove
Inscr. in plate l.r.: WBlake inv & sculp
Imprint l.c.: London. Published as the Act directs. March 8 : 1828. by Willm Blake N 3 Fountain Court Strand
1058.b/3

c ***Satan Before the Throne of God*** Plate 2

Russell 33iii, Binyon 107iv, Bindman 627, Essick Job 2A
19.8 x 15.1 cm (image), 21.7 x 17 cm (plate mark), 38.5 x 26.9 cm (sheet)
Paper: India on white wove
Watermark: J WHATMAN / TURKEY MILL / 1825
Inscr. in plate l.l.; WBlake inv & sc
Imprint l.c.: London Pullished as the Act directs March 8 : 1825. by Willm Blake N 3 Fountain Court Strand
1058.c/3

d ***The Destruction of Job's Sons*** Plate 3

Russell 33iv, Binyon 108iii, Bindman 628, Essick Job 3A
19.8 x 15.1 cm (image), 21.9 x 17 cm (plate mark), 38 x 26.9 cm (sheet)
Paper: India on white wove
Inscr. in plate l.r.: WBlake inven: & sculp
Imprint l.c.: London. Published as the Act directs March 8 : 1825 by Willm Blake No 3 Fountain Court Strand
1058.d/3

e ***The Messenger Tells Job of His Misfortunes*** Plate 4

Russell 33v, Binyon 109ii, Bindman 629, Essick Job 4A
19.9 x 15.1 cm (image), 21.8 x 17 cm (plate mark), 38.5 x 27 cm (sheet)
Paper: India on white wove
Inscr. in plate l.r.: WBlake invent & sculp
Imprint l.c.: London. Published as the Act directs March 8 : 1825. by Willm Blake No 3 Fountain Court Strand
1058.e/3

f ***Satan Going Forth from the Presence of the Lord*** Plate 5

Russell 33vi, Binyon 110iii, Bindman 630, Essick Job 5A
19.8 x 15 cm (image), 21.8 x 17 cm (plate mark), 38.3 x 27 cm (sheet)
Paper: India on white wove
Inscr. in plate l.r.: WBlake inventor & sculp
Imprint l.c.: London. Published as the Act directs March 8 : 1825. by Willm Blake No 3 Fountain Court Strand
1058.f/3

g ***Satan Smiting Job with Boils*** Plate 6

Russell 33vii, Binyon 111ii, Bindman 631, Essick Job 6A
19.9 x 15.2 cm (image), 21.8 x 17.1 cm (plate mark), 38.8 x 25.9 cm (sheet)
Paper: India on white wove
Inscr. in plate l.l.: WBlake inv & sc
Imprint l.c.: London. as Act directs Published March 8 : 1825 by William Blake No 3 Fountain Court Strand
1058.g/3

h ***Job's Comforters*** Plate 7

Russell 33viii, Binyon 112ii, Bindman 632, Essick Job 7A
19.7 x 15.1 cm (image), 21.8 x 17 cm (plate mark), 38.4 x 25.8 cm (sheet)
Paper: India on white wove
Inscr. in plate l.r.: WBlake inven & sculpt

Imprint l.c.: London. Published as the Act directs March 8 : 1825 by William Blake N 3 Fountain Court Strand
1058.h/3

i *Job's Despair* Plate 8
Russell 33ix, Binyon 113ii, Bindman 633, Essick Job 8A
19.9 x 15 cm (image), 21.8 x 16.9 cm (plate mark), 38.8 x 25.8 cm (sheet)
Paper: India on white wove
Inscr. in plate l.r.: WBlake inv & sculp
Imprint l.c.: London Pullish'd as the Act directs March 8 : 1825 by Willm Blake No 3 Fountain Court Strand
1058.i/3

j *The Vision of Eliphaz* Plate 9
Russell 33x, Binyon 114iii, Bindman 634, Essick Job 9A
19.8 x 15 cm (image), 21.8 x 17 cm (plate mark), 37.6 x 25.8 cm (sheet)
Paper: India on white wove
Inscr. in plate l.r.: WBlake invenit & sculp
Imprint l.c.: London. Published as the Act directs March 8 : 1825 by William Blake N 3 Fountain Court Strand
1058.j/3

k *Job Rebuked by His Friends* Plate 10
Russell 33xi, Binyon 115iii, Bindman 635, Essick Job 10A
19.7 x 15.1 cm (image), 21.8 x 17.1 cm (plate mark), 38.9 x 25.8 cm (sheet)
Paper: India on white wove
Inscr. in plate l.r.: WBlake invenit & sculp
Imprint l.c.: London. Published as the Act directs March 8 : 1825. by William Blake N 3 Fountain Court Strand
1058.k/3

l *Job's Evil Dreams* Plate 11
Russell 33xii, Binyon 116v, Bindman 636, Essick Job 11A
19.6 x 15 cm (image), 21.6 x 17 cm (plate mark), 38.2 x 25.9 cm (sheet)
Paper: India on white wove
Watermark: J WHATMAN / TURKEY MILL / 1825
Inscr. in plate l.l.: WBlake invenit & sculp
Imprint l.c.: London. Published as the Act directs March 8 : 1825 by Willm Blake No 3 Fountain Court Strand
1058.l/3

m *The Wrath of Elihu* Plate 12
Russell 33xiii, Binyon 117ii, Bindman 637, Essick Job 12A
19.8 x 15 cm (image), 21.8 x 16.8 cm (plate mark), 37.5 x 26 cm (sheet)
Paper: India on white wove
Inscr. in plate l.c.: WBlake invenit & sculpt
Imprint l.c.: London Published as the Act directs March 8 : 1825 by Willm Blake N 3 Fountain Court Strand
1058.m/3

n *The Lord Answering Job Out of the Whirlwind* Plate 13
Russell 33xiv, Binyon 118ii, Bindman 638, Essick Job 13A
19.6 x 15 cm (image), 21.8 x 17 cm (plate mark), 39.5 x 26.1 cm (sheet)
Paper: India on white wove
Watermark: J WHATMAN / TURKEY MILL / 1825
Inscr. in plate l.r.: WBlake invenit & sculp
Imprint l.c.: London Published as the Act directs March 8 : 1825 by William Blake No 3 Fountain Court Strand
1058.n/3

o *The Creation* Plate 14
Russell 33xv, Binyon 119iii, Bindman 639, Essick Job 14A
19.2 x 14.9 cm (image), 20.7 x 16.5 cm (plate mark), 38.3 x 26.1 cm (sheet)
Paper: India on white wove
Inscr. in plate l.l.: WBlake Invenit & Sc
Imprint l.c.: London. Published as the Act directs March 8 : 1825 by Willm Blake N 3 Fountain Court Strand
1058.o/3

p *Behemoth and Leviathan* Plate 15
Russell 33xvi, Binyon 120ii, Bindman 640, Essick Job 15A
19.9 x 15.2 cm (image), 21.8 x 17 cm (plate mark), 38.6 x 26.1 cm (sheet)
Paper: India on white wove
Watermark: J WHATMAN / TURKEY MILL / 1825
Inscr. in plate l.r.: WBlake invenit & sculpt
Imprint l.c.: London Published as the Act directs March 8 : 1825 by Willm Blake N 3 Fountain Court Strand
1058.p/3

q *The Fall of Satan* Plate 16
Russell 33xvii, Binyon 121iii, Bindman 641, Essick Job 16A
18.6 x 15 cm (image), 20.1 x 16.4 cm (plate mark), 39 x 26.2 cm (sheet)
Paper: India on white wove
Inscr. in plate l.r.: WBlake inv & sculp
Imprint l.c.: London. Published as the Act directs March 8 : 1825 by William Blake No 3 Fountain Court Strand
1058.q/3

r *The Vision of God* Plate 17
Russell 33xviii, Binyon 122ii, Bindman 642, Essick Job 17A
19.9 x 15 cm (image), 21.9 x 17 cm (plate mark), 38.8 x 26.2 cm (sheet)
Paper: India on white wove
Inscr. in plate l.c.: WBlake inv & sculp
Imprint l.c.: London Published as the Act directs March 8 : 1825 by William Blake No 3 Fountain Court Strand
1058.r/3

s *Job's Sacrifice* Plate 18

Russell 33xix, Binyon 123iii, Bindman 643, Essick Job 18A
19.7 x 14.8 cm (image), 21.7 x 17.1 cm (plate mark), 39.1 x 26.2 cm (sheet)
Paper: India on white wove
Watermark: J WHATMAN / TURKEY MILL / 1825
Inscr. in plate l.c.: WBlake inv & / sculpt
Imprint l.c.: London Published as the Act directs March 8 : 1825 by Will Blake Nr 3 Fountain Court Strand
1058.s/3

t *Job Accepting Charity* Plate 19

Russell 33xx, Binyon 124iv, Bindman 644, Essick Job 19A
19.6 x 15 cm (image), 21.8 x 17 cm (plate mark), 37.3 x 28.4 cm (sheet)
Paper: India on white wove
Inscr. in plate l.c.: WBlake inv & sculp
Imprint l.c.: London. Published as the Act directs March 8 : 1825 by William Blake N 3 Fountain Court Strand
1058.t/3

u *Job and His Daughters* Plate 20

Russell 33xxi, Binyon 125iv, Bindman 645, Essick Job 20A
20 x 15.1 cm (image), 21.8 x 17 cm (plate mark), 40.4 x 28.8 cm (sheet)
Paper: India on white wove
Inscr. in plate l.r.: WBlake invenit & sc
Imprint l.c.: London. Published as the Act directs March 8 : 1825 by William Blake No 3 Fountain Court Strand
1058.u/3

v *Job and His Wife Restored to Prosperity* Plate 21

Russell 33xxii, Binyon 126iii, Bindman 646, Essick Job 21A
19.5 x 14.8 cm (image), 21.7 x 16.9 cm (plate mark), 39.7 x 26.5 cm (sheet)
Paper: India on white wove
Inscr. in plate l.r.: WBlake inv & sculp
Imprint l.c.: London Published as the Act directs March 8 : 1825 by William Blake Fountain Court Strand
1058.v/3

50 Illustrations to Dante's *Divine Comedy* 1826–27

Seven engravings with drypoint, unfinished
Two sets of restrikes, presented by Lessing J. Rosenwald in 1960 (set I) and 1968 (set II)

a *The Circle of the Lustful. Paolo and Francesca*

Russell 34i, Binyon 127iii, Roe 10E, Bindman 647
24.3 x 33.6 cm (image), 27.8 x 35.2 cm (plate mark)
Inscr. in plate l.r., in reverse: The Whirlwind of Lovers From Dante's Inferno Canto V

I Paper: heavy white wove
Watermark: MADE IN ENGLAND LINEN FIBRE
Inscr. in pencil l.r.: Impression taken from the plate in my / collection in 1955 / Lessing J. Rosenwald / 1/20/60
614.a/5

II Paper: laid Japan (Kochi)
Inscr. in pencil l.r.: A restrike from the copper plate in my collection / August 1968 Lessing J. Rosenwald; and l.r. of sheet: 21/25 Hoehn imp 68
1835/5

b *The Circle of the Corrupt Officials. The Devils Tormenting Ciampolo*

Russell 34ii, Binyon 128ii, Roe 41E, Bindman 648
23.9 x 33.6 cm (image), 27.8 x 35.3 cm (plate mark)

I Paper: heavy white wove
Watermark: MADE IN ENCLAND LINEN FIBRE
Inscr. in pencil l.r.: Impression taken from the plate / in my collection in 1955 / Lessing J. Rosenwald / 1/20/60
614.b/5

II Paper: laid Japan (Kochi)
Inscr. in pencil l.r.: A restrike from the copper plate in my collection / August 1968 Lessing J. Rosenwald; and l.r. of sheet: 21/25 Hoehn imp 68
1836/5

c *The Circle of the Corrupt Officials. The Devils Mauling Each Other*

Russell 34iii, Binyon 129, Roe 42E, Bindman 649
24.2 x 33.1 cm (image), 27.9 x 35.4 cm (plate mark)

I Paper: heavy white wove
Watermark: MADE IN ENGLAND LINEN FIBRE
Inscr. in pencil l.r.: Impression taken from the plate / in my collection in 1955 / Lessing J. Rosenwald / 1/20/60
614.c/5

II Paper: laid Japan (Kochi)
Inscr. in pencil l.r.: A restrike from the copper plate in my collection / August 1968 Lessing J. Rosenwald; and l.r. of sheet: 21/25 Hoehn imp. 68
1837/5

d *The Circle of the Thieves. Agnello dei Brunelleschi Attacked by a Six-Footed Serpent*

Russell 34iv, Binyon 130, Roe 51E, Bindman 650
24.5 x 33.8 cm (image), 27.8 x 35.3 cm (plate mark)

I Paper: heavy white wove
Watermark: UNBLEACHED ARNOLD
Inscr. in pencil l.r.: Impression taken from the plate in / my collection in 1955 / Lessing J. Rosenwald / 1/20/60
614.d/5

II Paper: laid Japan (Kochi)
Inscr. in pencil l.r.: A restrike from the copper plate in my collection / August 1968 Lessing J. Rosenwald; and l.r. of sheet: 21/25 Hoehn imp. 68
1838/5

e *The Circle of the Thieves. Buoso dei Donati Attacked by the Serpent*

Russell 34v, Binyon 131, Roe 53E, Bindman 651
24.2 x 33.7 cm (image), 27.9 x 35.3 cm (plate mark)

I Paper: heavy white wove
Watermark: UNBLEACHED ARNOLD
Inscr. in pencil l.r.: Impression taken from the plate in my / collection in 1955 / Lessing J. Rosenwald / 1/20/60
614.e/5

II Paper: laid Japan (Kochi)
Inscr. in pencil l.r.: A restrike from the copper plate in my collection / August 1968 Lessing J. Rosenwald; and l.r. of sheet: 21/25 Hoehn imp 68
1839/5

f *The Circle of the Falsifiers. Dante and Virgil Covering Their Noses Because of the Stench*

Russell 34vi, Binyon 132ii, Roe 58E, Bindman 652
24.1 x 33.7 cm (image), 27.6 x 35.2 cm (plate mark)

I Paper: heavy white wove
Watermark: MADE IN ENGLAND LINEN FIBRE
Inscr. in pencil l.r.: Impression taken from the plate in / my collection in 1955 / Lessing J. Rosenwald / 1/20/60
614.f/5

II Paper: laid Japan (Kochi)
Inscr. in pencil l.r.: A restrike from the copper plate in my collection / August 1968 Lessing J. Rosenwald; and l.r. of sheet: 21/25 Hoehn imp. 68
1840/5

g *The Circle of the Traitors. Dante's Foot Striking Bocca degli Abbati*

Russell 34vii, Binyon 133, Roe 65E, Bindman 653
23.6 x 33.8 cm (image), 27.5 x 35.2 cm (plate mark)

I Paper: heavy white wove
Watermark: UNBLEACHED ARNOLD
Inscr. in pencil l.r.: Impression taken from the plate / in my collection in 1955 / Lessing J. Rosenwald / 1/20/60
614.g/5

II Paper: laid Japan (Kochi)
Inscr. in pencil l.r.: A restrike from the copper plate in my collection / August 1968 Lessing J. Rosenwald; and l.r. of sheet: 21/25 Hoehn imp 68
1841/5

51 Young's *Night Thoughts* 1797

Forty-three etchings/engravings by Blake, from *The Complaint, and the Consolation; or, Night Thoughts, By Edward Young*, R. Edwards, London, 1797
Engravings water-coloured *c.*1797–98
Front-end flyleaf inscr. in pencil: Bt / 1904 / (Felton)
Front endpaper inscr. in black ink: William à Beckett / from Benjamin Stiner
Paper: white wove
Watermark: 1794 / J WHATMAN
Average sheet size: 41.5 x 31.7 cm
Felton Bequest 1989 P.183i–xliii/

Select Bibliography

Books

Baine, R. & Baine, M. *The Scattered Portions: William Blake's Biological Symbolism*. University of Georgia, Athens, Ga., 1986.

Beer, J. *Blake's Humanism*. Manchester University Press, Manchester, 1968.

——. *Blake's Visionary Universe*. Manchester University Press, Manchester, 1969.

Behrendt, S. *The Moment of Explosion: Blake and the Illustration of Milton*. University of Nebraska Press, Lincoln, 1983.

Bentley, G. E. Jr. *William Blake: Vala or the Four Zoas*. Clarendon Press, Oxford, 1963.

——. *William Blake: Tiriel*. Clarendon Press, Oxford, 1967.

——. *Blake Records*. Clarendon Press, Oxford, 1969.

——. *The Blake Collection of Mrs. Landon K. Thorne*. Pierpont Morgan Library, New York, 1971.

——. *A Bibliography of George Cumberland (1754–1848)*. Garland, London, 1975.

——. *William Blake, The Critical Heritage*. Routledge & Kegan Paul, London, 1975.

——. *Blake Books*. Clarendon Press, Oxford, 1977.

——. *Blake Records Supplement*. Clarendon Press, Oxford, 1988.

Bentley, G. E. Jr (ed.). *William Blake's Writings*. Clarendon Press, Oxford, 1978.

Bentley, G. E. Jr & Nurmi, M. *A Blake Bibliography*. University of Minnesota Press, Minneapolis, 1964.

Bentley, G. E. Jr *et al. Essays on the Blake Followers*. Huntington Library, San Marino, Calif., 1983.

Bindman, D. *William Blake: Catalogue of the Collection in the Fitzwilliam Museum, Cambridge*. W. Heffer, Cambridge, 1970.

——. *William Blake 1757–1827*. Hamburger Kunsthalle & Prestel Verlag, Munich, 1975.

——. *Blake as an Artist*. Phaidon, Oxford, 1977.

——. *The Complete Graphic Works of William Blake*. Thames & Hudson, London, 1978.

——. *William Blake: His Art and Times*. Thames & Hudson, New York, 1982.

Bindman, D. (ed.). *Colour Versions of William Blake's Book of Job Designs from the Circle of John Linnell*. The William Blake Trust, London, 1987.

——. *William Blake's Illustrations of the Book of Job*. The William Blake Trust, London, 1987.

Binyon, L. *The Drawings and Engravings of William Blake*. The Studio, London, 1922.

——. *The Engraved Designs of William Blake*. Ernest Benn, London & Charles Scribner's Sons, New York, 1926.

Binyon, L. & Keynes, G. *Illustrations of the Book of Job by William Blake*. Pierpont Morgan Library, New York, 1935.

Blake, W. *A Descriptive Catalogue of Pictures, Poetical and Historical Inventions, Painted by William Blake, in Water Colours, Being the*

Ancient Method of Fresco Painting Restored. London, 1809.
Blunt, A. *The Art of William Blake*. Oxford University Press, London, 1959.
Boime, A. *Art in an Age of Revolution 1750–1800*. University of Chicago Press, Chicago, 1987.
Bronowski, J. *William Blake, a Man Without a Mask*. Secker & Warburg, London, 1947.
Butlin, M. *The Blake–Varley Sketchbook of 1819*. Heinemann, London, 1969.
——. *William Blake: A Complete Catalogue of the Works in the Tate Gallery*. Tate Gallery, London, 1971.
——. *William Blake*. Tate Gallery, London, 1978.
——. *The Paintings and Drawings of William Blake*. Yale University Press, London, 1981.
——. *Tate Gallery Collections: William Blake 1757–1827*. Tate Gallery, London, 1989.
[Calvert, S.] *A Memoir of Edward Calvert Artist*. Sampson Low, Marston & Co., London, 1893.
Collins Baker, C. H. & Wark, R. R. *Catalogue of William Blake's Drawings and Paintings in the Huntington Library*. Huntington Library, San Marino, 1957.
Cook, E. B. & Wedderburn, A. *The Works of John Ruskin*, vol. XXXVI, George Allen, London, 1909.
Cunningham, A. *Lives of the Most Eminent British Painters, Sculptors and Architects*. John Murray, London, 1830.
Curran, S. & Wittreich, J. *Blake's Sublime Allegory: Essays on the Four Zoas, Milton and Jerusalem*. University of Wisconsin Press, Madison, 1973.
Damon, S. Foster. *William Blake, His Philosophy and Symbols*. Houghton Mifflin, London, 1924.
——. *Blake's Grave: A Prophetic Book*. Brown University Press, Providence, RI, 1963.
——. *A Blake Dictionary*. Brown University Press, Providence, RI, 1965.
——. *Blake's Job*. Brown University Press, Providence, RI, 1966.
Dean, S. *Master Drawings from the Collection of the National Gallery of Victoria*. National Gallery of Victoria, Melbourne, 1986.
Digby, C. *Symbol and Image in William Blake*. Clarendon Press, Oxford, 1957.
Doskow, M. *William Blake's 'Jerusalem': Structure and Meaning in Poetry and Picture*. Fairleigh Dickinson University Press, London, 1982.
Dunbar, P. *William Blake's Illustrations to the Poetry of Milton*. Clarendon Press, Oxford, 1980.
Easson, K. & Easson, R. *William Blake: The Book of Urizen*. Random House, New York, 1978.
Easson, R. & Essick, R. *William Blake: Book Illustrator. A Bibliography and Catalogue of the Commercial Engravings*. Vol. 1, *Plates Designed and Engraved by Blake*. The American Blake Foundation, Normal, Ill., 1972.
——. *William Blake: Book Illustrator. A Bibliography and Catalogue of the Commercial Engravings*. Vol. 2, *Plates Designed or Engraved by Blake 1774–1796*. The American Blake Foundation, Memphis, Tenn., 1979.
Eaves, M. *William Blake's Theory of Art*. Princeton University Press, Princeton, NJ, 1982.
Erdman, D. *The Poetry and Prose of William Blake*. Doubleday, New York, 1965.
——. *Blake: Prophet Against Empire*. Doubleday, New York, 1969.
——. *The Illuminated Blake*. Anchor Press, New York, 1974 (Oxford University Press, London, 1975).
Erdman, D. & Grant, J. *Blake's Visionary Forms Dramatic*. Princeton University Press, Princeton, NJ, 1970.
Erdman, D. & Moore, D. (eds). *The Notebook of William Blake*. Clarendon Press, Oxford, 1973.
Essick, R. *William Blake's Relief Inventions*. Press of the Pegacycle Lady, Los Angeles, 1978.
——. *William Blake, Printmaker*. Princeton University Press, Princeton, NJ, 1980.
——. *The Separate Plates of William Blake*. Princeton University Press, Princeton, NJ, 1983.
——. *The Works of William Blake in the Huntington Collections*. The Huntington Library, San Marino, 1985.
——. *William Blake and His Contemporaries and Followers: Selected Works from the Collection of Robert N. Essick*. Huntington Art Gallery, San Marino, 1987.
Essick, R. (ed.). *The Visionary Hand: Essays for the Study of William Blake's Art and Aesthetics*. Hennessy & Ingalls, Los Angeles, 1973.
Essick, R. & Paley, M. *Robert Blair's 'The Grave' Illustrated by William Blake: A Study with Facsimile*. Scolar Press, London, 1982.
Essick, R. & Pearce, D. (eds). *Blake in his Time*. Indiana University Press, Bloomington, 1978.
Figgis, D. *The Paintings of William Blake*. Ernest Benn, London, 1925.
Frye, N. *Fearful Symmetry: A Study of William Blake*. Princeton University Press, Princeton, NJ, 1947.
Gilchrist, A. *Life of William Blake*. Macmillan, London, 1863 (rev. edns, Macmillan, London, 1880 & John Lane, London, 1907).
Gizzi, C. (ed.). *Blake e Dante*. Gabriele Mazzotta, Milan, 1983.
Grant, J., Rose, E. & Tolley, M. *William Blake's Designs for Edward Young's 'Night Thoughts'*. Clarendon Press, Oxford, 1980.
Hagstrom, J. *William Blake: Poet and Painter*. University of Chicago Press, Chicago, 1964.
Hilton, N. *Literal Imagination: Blake's Vision of Words*. University of California Press, Berkeley, 1983.
Hoagwood, T. *Prophecy and the Philosophy of Mind: Traditions of Blake and Shelley*. University of Alabama Press, Alabama, 1985.
Hoff, U. *Masterpieces of the National Gallery of Victoria*. National Gallery of Victoria, Melbourne, 1949.
——. *William Blake's Illustrations to Dante's Divine Comedy*. National Gallery of Victoria, Melbourne, 1961.
Hoff, U. & Plant, M. *National Gallery of Victoria: Painting, Drawing and Sculpture*. National Gallery of Victoria, Melbourne, 1968.
Keynes, G. *A Bibliography of William Blake*. Grolier Club, New York, 1921.

Keynes, G. *The Pencil Drawings of William Blake*. Nonesuch Press, London, 1927.
——. *The Notebook of William Blake Called the Rossetti Manuscript*. Nonesuch Press, New York, 1935.
——. *Blake Studies: Essays on his Life and Work*. Rupert Hart-Davis, London, 1949 (rev. edn, Clarendon Press, Oxford, 1971).
——. *William Blake's Engravings*. Faber & Faber, Oxford, 1950.
——. *Engravings by William Blake: The Separate Plates*. Emery Walker, Dublin, 1956.
——. *Pencil Drawings by William Blake*. 2nd series. Nonesuch Press, London, 1956.
——. *William Blake's Illustrations to the Bible*. The William Blake Trust, London, 1957.
——. *Bibliotheca Bibliographica*. Trianon Press, London, 1964.
——. *Drawings of William Blake: 92 Pencil Studies*. Dover, New York, 1970.
——. *William Blake's Laocoön, A Last Testament, with Related Works: 'On Homer's Poetry' and 'On Virgil, The Ghost of Abel'*. The William Blake Trust, London, 1976.
——. *Blake's Illustrations of Dante*. Trianon Press, London, 1978.
——. *The Complete Portraiture of William and Catherine Blake*. The William Blake Trust, London, 1979.
Keynes, G. (ed.). *Milton's Poems in English*. Nonesuch Press, London, 1926.
——. *The Letters of William Blake*. Rupert Hart-Davis, London, 1968 (rev. edn, Clarendon Press, Oxford, 1980).
——. *Blake, Complete Writings*. Oxford University Press, Oxford, 1969.
Keynes, G. & Wolf, E. *William Blake's Illuminated Books: A Census*. Grolier Club, New York, 1953.
Klonsky, M. *William Blake: The Seer and his Visions*. Orbis, London, 1977.
——. *Blake's Dante*. Harmony Books, New York, 1980.
Kremen, K. *The Imagination of the Resurrection: The Poetic Continuity of a Religious Motif in Donne, Blake, and Yeats*. Bucknell University Press, Lewisburg, Pa., 1972.
Lindberg, B. *William Blake's Illustrations to the Book of Job*. Abö Akademi, Abö, Finland, 1973.
Lister, R. *The Paintings of William Blake*. Cambridge University Press, Cambridge, 1986.
Mellor, A. *Blake's Human Form Divine*. University of California Press, Berkeley, 1974.
Mitchell, W. *Blake's Composite Art: A Study of the Illuminated Poetry*. Princeton University Press, Princeton, NJ, 1978.
Paley, M. *Energy and the Imagination*. Clarendon Press, Oxford, 1970.
——. *William Blake*. Phaidon, Oxford, 1978.
——. *The Continuing City: William Blake's 'Jerusalem'*. Clarendon Press, Oxford, 1983.
Paley, M. & Phillips, M. (eds). *William Blake: Essays in Honour of Sir Geoffrey Keynes*. Clarendon Press, Oxford, 1973.
Palmer, A. H. *The Life and Letters of Samuel Palmer*. Seeley & Co., London, 1892.
Pointon, M. *Milton and English Art*. Manchester University Press, Manchester, 1970.
Preston, K. *The Blake Collection of W. Graham Robertson, Described by the Collector*. Faber & Faber, London, 1952.
Raine, K. *Blake and Tradition*. 2 vols. Routledge & Kegan Paul, London, 1968.
——. *Blake and Antiquity*. Routledge & Kegan Paul, London, 1979.
——. *The Human Face of God: William Blake and the Book of Job*. Thames & Hudson, London, 1982.
Roe, A. *Blake's Illustrations to the Divine Comedy*. Princeton University Press, Princeton, NJ, 1953.
Rosenbloom, R. *Transformations in Late Eighteenth Century Art*. Princeton University Press, Princeton, NJ, 1967 (rev. edns 1969 & 1974).
Rosenfeld, A. (ed.). *William Blake: Essays for S. Foster Damon*. Brown University Press, Providence, RI, 1969.
Russell, A. *The Engravings of William Blake*. Grant Richards, London, 1912.
Smith, J. T. *Nollekens and his Times*. Henry Colbum, London, 1828.
Sola Pinto, V. de. *The Divine Vision: Studies in the Poetry and Art of William Blake*. Victor Gollancz, London, 1957.
Soupault, P. *William Blake*. John Lane, London, 1928.
Stirling, A. M. W. *The Richmond Papers*. William Heinemann, London, 1926.
Storey, A. T. *The Life of John Linnell*. Richard Bentley, London, 1892.
Swinburne, A. *William Blake*. Chatto & Windus, London, 1868.
Symons, A. *William Blake*. Archibald Campbell, London, 1907.
Taylor, I. *Blake's Illustrations to the Poems of Gray*. Princeton University Press, Princeton, NJ, 1971.
Todd, R. *Tracks in the Snow: Studies in English Science and Art*. Grey Walls Press, London, 1946.
——. *Blake the Artist*. Studio Vista, London, 1971.
Viscomi, J. *The Art of William Blake's Illuminated Prints*. Manchester Etching Workshop, Manchester, 1983.
Wagenknecht, D. *Blake's Night: William Blake and the Idea of Pastoral*. Harvard University Press, Cambridge, 1973.
Warner, J. *Blake and the Language of Art*. McGill–Queen's University Press, Kingston, Ont., 1984.
Wells, W. & Johnston, E. *William Blake's 'Heads of the Poets'*. Manchester City Art Gallery, Manchester, 1969.
Werner, B. *Blake's Visions of the Poetry of Milton*. Bucknell University Press, Lewisburg, Pa., 1986.
Wicksteed, J. *Blake's Vision of the Book of Job*. Rev. & enlarged 2nd edn. Dent, London, 1924 (1910); (1910 edn repr. Haskell, New York, 1971).
——. *William Blake's Jerusalem*. The William Blake Trust, London, 1953.

William Blake in the Art of his Time. University of California, Santa Barbara, 1976 (exh. cat.).
Wilson, M. *The Life of William Blake*. Peter Davies, London, 1927 (rev. edn, Oxford University Press, London, 1971).
Wilton, A. *The Wood Engravings of William Blake*. British Museum, London, 1977.
Wittreich, J. *Angel of Apocalypse: Blake's Idea of Milton*. University of Wisconsin Press, Madison, 1975.
Wittreich, J. (ed.) *Calm of Mind: Tercentenary Essays in Honour of John S. Diekhoff*. Case Western Reserve University Press, Cleveland, Ohio, 1971.
Wolf-Gumpold, K. *William Blake, Painter, Poet, Visionary*. Rudolf Steiner Press, London, 1969.
Wright, A. *Blake's Job: A Commentary*. Clarendon Press, Oxford, 1972.
Wright, T. *The Life of William Blake*. Thomas Wright, Olney, 1929.

Articles

Allen, O. 'Blake's Archetypal Criticism: The Canterbury Pilgrims'. *Genre*, vol. XI, no. 2, Summer 1978, pp. 173–89.
Bain, I. & Chambers, D. 'Printing Blake's Engravings for Thornton's *Virgil*'. *The Private Library*, vol. 1, no. 4, Winter 1978, pp. 171–7.
Bass, E. 'Songs of Innocence and Experience: The Thrust of Design', in D. Erdman & J. Grant (eds), *Blake's Visionary Forms Dramatic*, Princeton University Press, Princeton, NJ, 1970, pp. 196–213.
Bentley, G. E. Jr. 'William Blake as a Private Publisher'. *Bulletin of the New York Public Library*, vol. 61, 1957, pp. 539–60.
——. 'Blake's Engravings and his Friendship with Flaxman'. *Studies in Bibliography*, vol. 12, 1959, pp. 161–88.
——. 'The Promotion of Blake's *Grave* Designs'. *University of Toronto Quarterly*, vol. XXXI, no. 3, April 1962, pp. 339–53.
——. 'The Date of Blake's Pickering Manuscript *or* The Way of a Poet with Paper'. *Studies in Bibliography*, vol. 19, 1966, pp. 232–43.
——. 'William Blake, Samuel Palmer, and George Richmond'. *Blake Studies*, vol. 2, no. 2, Spring 1970, pp. 43–50.
——. 'Blake's *Job* Copperplates'. *The Library: Transactions of the Bibliographical Society*, vol. 26, September 1971, pp. 231–41.
——. 'Blake and Cromek: The Wheat and the Tares'. *Modern Philology*, vol. 71, no. 4, May 1974, pp. 366–79.
——. 'A Unique Prospectus for Blake's *Grave* Designs'. *The Princeton University Library Chronicle*, vol. XXXV, no. 3, Spring 1974, pp.321–4.
——. 'William Blake's Techniques of Engraving and Printing'. *Studies in Bibliography*, vol. 34, 1981, pp. 241–53.
——. 'Blake and the Ancients: A Prophet With Honour Among the Sons of God'. *Huntington Library Quarterly*, vol. 46, no. 1, Winter 1983, pp. 1–17.
——. 'Thomas Sivright and the Lost Designs for Blair's *Grave*'. *Blake: An Illustrated Quarterly*, vol. 19, no. 3, Winter 1985–86, pp. 103–6.
——. 'From Sketch to Text in Blake: The Case of *The Book of Thel*'. *Blake: An Illustrated Quarterly*, vol. 19, no. 4, Spring 1986, pp. 128–41.
Bindman, D. 'Blake's "Gothicised Imagination" and the History of England', in M. Paley & M. Phillips (eds), *William Blake: Essays in Honour of Sir Geoffrey Keynes*, Clarendon Press, Oxford, 1973, pp. 29–49.
——. 'Blake's *Job*'. *Times Literary Supplement*, 29 March 1974, p. 341.
——. 'Blake's Theory and Practice of Imagination', in R. Essick & D. Pearce (eds), *Blake in his Time*, Indiana University Press, Bloomington, 1978, pp. 91–8.
Binyon, L. 'The Engravings of William Blake and Edward Calvert'. *Print Collector's Quarterly*, vol. 7, no. 4, December 1917, pp. 306–32.
——. 'Blake's Woodcuts'. *The Burlington Magazine*, vol. XXXVII, no. CCXIII, December 1920, pp. 284–9.
Blunt, A. 'Blake's "Ancient of Days": The Symbolism of the Compasses'. *Journal of the Warburg and Courtauld Institutes*, vol. 2, 1938, pp. 53–63.
——. 'Blake's Pictorial Imagination'. *Journal of the Warburg and Courtauld Institutes*, vol. 6, 1943, pp. 190–212.
Bogan, J. 'Blake's Jupiter Olympus in Rees' *Cyclopaedia*'. *Blake: An Illustrated Quarterly*, vol. 15, no. 4, Spring 1982, pp. 156–63.
Boime, A. 'William Blake's Graphic Imagery and the Industrial Revolution'. *Arts Magazine*, vol. 59, no. 10, June 1985, pp. 107–19.
Bowden, B. 'The Artistic and Interpretive Context of Blake's Canterbury Pilgrims'. *Blake: An Illustrated Quarterly*, vol. 13, no. 4, Spring 1980, pp. 164–90.
Burke, J. 'The Eidetic and the Borrowed Image: An Interpretation of Blake's Theory and Practice of Art', in F. Philipp & J. Stewart (eds), *In Honour of Daryl Lindsay: Essays and Studies*, Oxford University Press, Melbourne, 1964, pp. 110–27.
Butlin, M. 'The Bicentenary of William Blake'. *Burlington Magazine*, vol. C, no. 2, 1958, pp. 40–4.
——. 'The Evolution of Blake's Large Colour Prints of 1795', in A. Rosenfeld (ed.), *William Blake: Essays for S. Foster Damon*, Brown University Press, Providence, RI, 1969, pp. 109–16.
——. 'William Blake in the Herbert P. Horne Collection'. *Blake Newsletter*, vol. 6, no. 1, 1972–73, pp. 19–21.
——. 'Five Blakes from a 19th-Century Scottish Collection'. *Blake Newsletter*, vol. 7, no. 1, Summer 1973, pp. 5–8.
——. 'Cataloguing William Blake', in R. Essick & D. Pearce (eds), *Blake in his Time*, Indiana University Press, Bloomington, 1978, pp. 77–90.
——. 'A Newly Discovered Watermark and a Visionary's Way with his Dates'. *Blake: An*

Illustrated Quarterly, vol. 15, no. 2, 1981–82, pp. 101–3.
Carr, S. 'William Blake's Print-Making Process in *Jerusalem*'. *ELH*, vol. 47, 1980, pp. 520–41.
Chayes, I. 'Little Girls Lost: Problems of a Romantic Archetype'. *Bulletin of the New York Public Library*, vol. 67, 1963, pp. 579–92.
——. 'Blake and Tradition: "The Little Girl Lost" and "The Little Girl Found" '. *Blake Newsletter*, vol. 4, no. 1, Summer 1970, pp. 25–8.
——. 'The Presence of Cupid and Psyche', in D. Erdman & J. Grant (eds), *Blake's Visionary Forms Dramatic*, Princeton University Press, Princeton, NJ, 1970, pp. 214–43.
——. 'Blake's Ways with Art Sources: Michelangelo's *Last Judgement*'. *Colby Library Quarterly*, vol. 20, 1984, pp. 60–89.
Collins Baker, C. 'The Sources of Blake's Pictorial Expression'. *Huntington Library Quarterly*, vol. IV, no. 3, April 1941, pp. 359–67.
Connolly, T. 'A Blakean Maze'. *Blake Studies*, vol. 3, no. 1, Fall 1970, pp. 61–8.
——. 'The Real "Holy Thursday" of William Blake'. *Blake Studies*, vol. 6, no. 2, 1974, pp. 179–87.
Cox, S. 'Adventures of "A Little Boy Lost": Blake and the Process of Interpretation'. *Criticism*, vol. XXIII, no. 4, Fall 1981, pp. 301–16.
Curtis, F. 'Blake and the Booksellers'. *Blake Studies*, vol. 6, no. 2, 1974, pp. 167–78.
Davis, P. 'Revelation in Blake's *Job*'. *Philological Quarterly*, vol. 65, no. 4, Fall 1986, pp. 451–77.
Dorrbecker, D. 'Innocence Lost and Found: An Untraced Copy Traced'. *Blake: An Illustrated Quarterly*, vol. 15, no. 3, Winter 1981–82, pp. 125–31.
Easson, K. 'Blake and the Art of the Book', in R. Essick & D. Pearce (eds), *Blake in his Time*, Indiana University Press, Bloomington, 1978, pp. 35–52.
Eaves, M. 'Blake and the Artistic Machine: An Essay in Decorum and Technology'. *PMLA*, vol. 92, no. 5, October 1977, pp. 903–27.
Ellis, H. 'Added and Omitted Plates in *The Book of Urizen*'. *Colby Library Quarterly*, vol. 23, 1987, pp. 99–107.
Erdman, D. 'Blake's Vision of Slavery'. *Journal of the Warburg and Courtauld Institutes*, vol. XV, 1952, pp. 242–52.
——. 'The Dating of William Blake's Engravings'. *Philological Quarterly*, vol. 31, 1952, pp. 337–43.
——. 'The Suppressed and Altered Passages in Blake's *Jerusalem*'. *Studies in Bibliography*, vol. 17, 1964, pp. 1–54.
——. 'Redefining the Texts of Blake (Another Temporary Report)'. *Blake: An Illustrated Quarterly*, vol. 17, no. 1, 1983–84, pp. 4–15.
Essick, R. 'Blake's Newton'. *Blake Studies*, vol. 3, no. 2, Spring 1971, pp. 149–62.
——. 'Blake and the Traditions of Reproductive Engraving'. *Blake Studies*, vol. 5, 1972, pp. 59–103.
——. 'Blake, Linnell, & James Upton: An Engraving Brought to Light'. *Blake Newsletter*, vol. 7, no. 4, Spring 1974, pp. 76–9.
——. 'New Information on Blake's Illuminated Books'. *Blake: An Illustrated Quarterly*, vol. 15, no. 1, Summer 1981, pp. 4–13.
——. 'John Linnell, William Blake, and the Printmaker's Craft'. *Huntington Library Quarterly*, vol. 46, no. 1, Winter 1983, pp. 18–32.
——. 'Blake's *Job*: Some Unrecorded Proofs and Their Inscriptions'. *Blake: An Illustrated Quarterly*, vol. 19, no. 3, Winter 1985–86, pp. 96–102.
Essick, R. & Paley, M. 'The Printings of Blake's Designs for Blair's *Grave*'. *The Book Collector*, vol. 24, no. 4, Winter 1975, pp. 535–52.
Essick, R. & Young, M. 'Blake's "Canterbury" Print: The Posthumous Pilgrimage of the Copperplate'. *Blake: An Illustrated Quarterly*, vol. 15, no. 2, Fall 1981, pp. 78–82.
Fawcus, A. 'Blake's Illustrations for the *Book of Job*'. *Times Literary Supplement*, 15 March 1974, pp. 271–2.
Fisher, P. 'Blake and the Druids'. *Journal of English and Germanic Philology*, vol. LVIII, no. 4, October 1959, pp. 589–612.
——. 'Blake's Attacks on the Classical Tradition'. *Philological Quarterly*, vol. 40, no. 1, January 1961, pp. 1–18.
Fuller, D. 'Blake and Dante'. *Art History*, vol. 11, no. 3, September 1988, pp. 349–73.
Gage, J. 'Blake's *Newton*'. *Journal of the Warburg and Courtauld Institutes*, vol. 34, 1971, pp. 372–7.
Gillespie, D. 'A Key to Blake's *Job*: Design XX'. *Colby Library Quarterly*, vol. 19, 1983, pp. 59–68.
Glazer, M. & Norvig, G. 'Blake's Book of Changes: On Viewing Three Copies of the *Songs of Innocence and of Experience*'. *Blake Studies*, vol. 9, nos 1–2, 1980, pp. 100–21.
Gleckner, R. 'The Strange Odyssey of Blake's "The Voice of the Ancient Bard" '. *Romanticism Past and Present*, vol. 6, 1982, pp. 1–25.
Grant, J. 'Two Flowers in the Garden of Experience', in A. Rosenfeld (ed.), *William Blake: Essays for S. Foster Damon*, Brown University Press, Providence, RI, 1969, pp. 333–67.
——. 'Discussing the Arlington Court Picture'. *Blake Newsletter*, vol. 3, no. 4, 1969, pp. 96–115; vol. 4, no. 1, 1970, pp. 12–25.
——. 'The Meaning of Mirth and Her Companions in Blake's Designs for *L'Allegro* and *Il Penseroso*'. *Blake Newsletter*, vol. 4, no. 4, 1970, pp. 117–34; vol. 5, no. 3, 1971, pp. 190–202.
——. 'Addenda and Some Solutions to Tolley's Blake Puzzles'. *Blake Studies*, vol. 3, no. 2, 1970–71, pp. 129–35.
——. 'Blake's "Illustrations of the *Book of Job*" '. *Times Literary Supplement*, 30 November 1973, p. 1484.
——. 'The Fate of Blake's Sun-Flower'. *Blake Studies*, vol. 5, no. 2, 1974, pp. 2–49.
Grant, J. & Johnson, M. 'Illuminated Books in the Cincinnati Art Museum'. *Blake Newsletter*, vol. 7, no. 2, Fall 1973, pp. 40–3.
Greco, N. 'Blake's "The Little Girl Lost": An Initiation into Womanhood'. *Colby Library Quarterly*, vol. 19, 1983, pp. 144–54.

Hagstrum, J. 'Eros and Psyche: Some Versions of Romantic Love and Delicacy'. *Critical Inquiry*, vol. 3, Spring 1977, pp. 521–42.

Helmstadter, T. ' "Bright Visions of Eternity": Blake's Designs for Blair's *Grave*'. *Blake Studies*, vol. 8, no. 1, 1978, pp. 37–64.

Heppner, C. 'Reading Blake's Designs: *Pity* and *Hecate*'. *Bulletin of Research in the Humanities*, vol. LXXXIV, no. 3, 1981, pp. 337–65.

Hoover, S. 'William Blake in the Wilderness: A Closer Look at his Reputation, 1827–1863', in M. Paley & M. Phillips (eds), *William Blake: Essays in Honour of Sir Geoffrey Keynes*, Clarendon Press, Oxford, 1973, pp. 310–48.

Ingli James, G. 'Blake's Woodcuts, Plain and Coloured'. *Times Literary Supplement*, 18 May 1973, p. 564.

——. 'Blake's Woodcuts Illuminated'. *Apollo*, vol. XCIX, no. 145, March 1974, pp. 194–5.

Keynes, G. 'New Blake Documents: History of the Job Engravings'. *Times Literary Supplement*, 9 January 1943, p. 24.

——. 'Some Uncollected Authors XLIV: George Cumberland 1754–1848'. *The Book Collector*, vol. 19, no. 1, Spring 1970, pp. 31–65.

——. Kiralis, K. 'A Possible Revision in Blake's *Jerusalem*'. *Art Bulletin*, vol. 37, 1955, pp. 203–4.

——. 'William Blake as an Intellectual and Spiritual Guide to Chaucer's Canterbury Pilgrims'. *Blake Studies*, vol. 1, no. 2, Spring 1969, pp. 139–90.

Kostelanetz, A. 'Blake's 1795 Colour Prints: An Interpretation', in A. Rosenfeld (ed.), *William Blake: Essays for S. Foster Damon*, Brown University Press, Providence, RI, 1969, pp. 117–30.

Kroeber, K. 'Graphic-Poetic Structuring in Blake's *Urizen*'. *Blake Studies*, vol. 3, no. 1, Fall 1970, pp. 7–18.

La Belle, J. 'Words Graven with an Iron Pen: The Marginal Texts in Blake's *Job*', in R. Essick (ed.), *The Visionary Hand: Essays for the Study of William Blake's Art and Aesthetics*, Hennessy & Ingalls, Los Angeles, 1973, pp. 526–50.

Lister, R. 'A Fragmentary Copy of *Songs of Innocence and of Experience*'. *Blake Newsletter*, vol. 6, no. 1, Summer 1972, p. 19.

——. 'References to Blake in Samuel Palmer's Letters', in M. Paley & M. Phillips (eds), *William Blake: Essays in Honour of Sir Geoffrey Keynes*, Clarendon Press, Oxford, 1973, pp. 305–9.

Maheux, A. 'An Analysis of the Watercolour Technique and Materials of William Blake'. *Blake: An Illustrated Quarterly*, vol. 17, no. 4, Spring 1984, pp. 124–9.

Mitchell, W. 'Blake's Composite Art', in D. Erdman & J. Grant (eds), *Blake's Visionary Forms Dramatic*, Princeton University Press, Princeton, NJ, 1970, pp. 57–81.

——. 'Poetic and Pictorial Imagination in Blake's *Book of Urizen*', in R. Essick (ed.), *The Visionary Hand: Essays for the Study of William Blake's Art and Aesthetics*, Hennessy & Ingalls, Los Angeles, 1973, pp. 337–80.

——. 'Style as Epistemology: Blake and the Movement Toward Abstraction in Romantic Art'. *Studies in Romanticism*, vol. 16, no. 2, Spring 1977, pp. 145–64.

Moelwyn Merchant, M. 'Blake's Shakespeare'. *Apollo*, vol. LXXIX, no. 4, 1964, pp. 318–24.

Nanavutty, P. 'She Shall Be Called Woman', in V. de Sola Pinto, *The Divine Vision: Studies in the Poetry and Art of William Blake*, Victor Gollancz, London, 1957, pp. 183–9.

Nelms, B. 'Text and Design in *Illustrations of the Book of Job*', in D. Erdman & J. Grant (eds), *Blake's Visionary Forms Dramatic*, Princeton University Press, Princeton, NJ, 1970, pp. 336–58.

Pace, C. 'Blake and Chaucer'. *Art History*, vol. 3, no. 4, December 1980, pp. 388–409.

Paley, M. 'William Blake, The Prince of the Hebrews, and the Woman Clothed with the Sun', in M. Paley & M. Phillips (eds), *William Blake: Essays in Honour of Sir Geoffrey Keynes*, Clarendon Press, Oxford, 1973, pp. 260–93.

——. 'The Truchsessian Gallery Revisited'. *Studies in Romanticism*, vol. 16, no. 2, Spring 1977, pp. 165–77.

——. ' "Wonderful Originals"—Blake and Ancient Sculpture', in R. Essick & D. Pearce (eds), *Blake in his Time*, Indiana University Press, Bloomington, 1978, pp. 170–97.

Patterson, A. 'Pastoral and Ideology: The Neoclassical Fête Champêtre'. *Huntington Library Quarterly*, vol. 48, no. 4, Autumn 1985, pp. 321–44.

Peckham, M. 'Blake, Milton, and Edward Burney'. *Princeton University Library Chronicle*, vol. XI, 1950, pp. 107–26.

Phillips, M. 'William Blake's *Songs of Innocence* and *Songs of Experience* from Manuscript Draft to Illuminated Plate'. *The Book Collector*, vol. 28, no. 1, Spring 1979, pp. 17–59.

Read, D. 'The Context of Blake's "Public Address": Cromek and the Chalcographic Society'. *Philological Quarterly*, vol. 60, 1980, pp. 69–86.

——. 'Cromek's Provincial Advertisements for Blake's *Grave*'. *Notes and Queries*, vol. 27, no. 1, February 1980, pp. 73–6.

——. 'A New Blake Engraving: Gilchrist and the Cromek Connection'. *Blake: An Illustrated Quarterly*, vol. 14, no. 2, Fall 1980, pp. 60–4.

Reisner, M. 'Effigies of Power: Pitt and Fox as Canterbury Pilgrims'. *Eighteenth Century Studies*, vol. 12, no. 4, Summer 1979, pp. 481–503.

Roe, A. 'A Drawing of the Last Judgement'. *Huntington Library Quarterly*, vol. XXI, no. 1, November 1957, pp. 37–55.

Rose, E. 'Blake's Illustrations for *Paradise Lost*, *L'Allegro* and *Il Penseroso*: A Thematic Reading'. *Hartford Studies in Literature*, vol. 2, 1970, pp. 40–67.

——. ' "A Most Outrageous Demon": Blake's Case Against Rubens', in R. Essick (ed.), *The*

Visionary Hand: Essays for the Study of William Blake's Art and Aesthetics, Hennessy & Ingalls, Los Angeles, 1973, pp. 311–36.
——. 'Blake and Dürer'. *Colby Library Quarterly*, vol. 16, 1980, pp. 166–76.
Shrimpton, N. 'Hell's Hymnbook: Blake's *Songs of Innocence and of Experience* and their Models', in R. Davis & B. Beatty (eds), *Literature of the Romantic Period 1750–1850*, Barnes & Noble, New York, pp. 19–35.
Simmons, R. '*Urizen*: The Symmetry of Fear', in D. Erdman & J. Grant (eds), *Blake's Visionary Forms Dramatic*, Princeton University Press, Princeton, NJ, 1970, pp. 146–73.
Simpson, D. 'Blake's Pastoral: A Genesis for "The Echoing Green" '. *Blake: An Illustrated Quarterly*, vol. 13, no. 3, Winter 1979–80, pp. 116–38.
Stemmler, J. 'Cennini, Cumberland, Blake and Early Painting Techniques'. *Blake: An Illustrated Quarterly*, vol. 17, no. 4, pp. 145–9.
Stevenson, W. 'Interpreting Blake's Canterbury Pilgrims'. *Colby Library Quarterly*, vol. XII, no. 2, June 1977, pp. 115–26.
Summerfield, G. 'Beards, Disputations and Revelry: Observations on Blake's *Job* Engravings with Special Reference to Plates 2 and 3'. *Colby Library Quarterly*, vol. 23, 1987, pp. 89–98.
Sutherland, J. 'Blake and *Urizen*', in D. Erdman & J. Grant (eds), *Blake's Visionary Forms Dramatic*, Princeton University Press, Princeton, NJ, 1970, pp. 244–62.
Tayler, I. 'Say First! What Mov'd Blake? Blake's *Comus* Designs and *Milton*', in A. Curran & J. Wittreich, *Blake's Sublime Allegory: Essays on the Four Zoas, Milton and Jerusalem*, University of Wisconsin Press, Madison, 1973, pp. 233–58.
——. 'Blake's Laocoön'. *Blake Newsletter*, vol. 10, no. 3, Winter 1976–77, pp. 72–81.
Todd, R. 'The Techniques of William Blake's Illuminated Printing'. *Print Quarterly*, vol. VI, no. 1, 1948, pp. 53–65.
——. 'Blake's Dante Plates'. *Book Collecting & Library Monthly*, October 1968, pp. 3–12.
——. 'A Tentative Note on the Economics of the Canterbury Pilgrims'. *Blake: An Illustrated Quarterly*, vol. 11, no. 1, Summer 1977, pp. 30–1.
Tolley, M. 'Europe: "to those ychain'd in sleep" ', in D. Erdman & J. Grant (eds), *Blake's Visionary Forms Dramatic*, Princeton University Press, Princeton, NJ, 1970, pp. 115–45.
——. 'Blake's Songs of Spring', in M. Paley & M. Phillips (eds), *William Blake: Essays in Honour of Sir Geoffrey Keynes*, Clarendon Press, Oxford, 1973, pp. 96–128.
——. 'Thornton's Blake Edition', *University of Adelaide Library News*, vol. 10, no. 2, 1988, pp. 4–11.
Viscomi, J. 'The Workshop'. *Studies in Romanticism*, vol. 21, no. 3, Fall 1982, pp. 404–9.
——. 'Recreating Blake's Illuminated Prints: The Facsimiles of the Manchester Etching Workshop'. *Blake: An Illustrated Quarterly*, vol. 19, no. 1, Summer 1985, pp. 4–23.
Ward, A. 'Canterbury Revisited: The Blake–Cromek Controversy'. *Blake: An Illustrated Quarterly*, vol. 22, no. 3, Winter 1988–89, pp. 80–92.
Warner, J. 'Blake's Use of Gesture', in D. Erdman & J. Grant (eds), *Blake's Visionary Forms Dramatic*, Princeton University Press, Princeton, NJ, 1970, pp. 174–95.
——. 'Blake and English Printed Textiles'. *Blake Newsletter*, vol. 6, no. 4, Spring 1973, pp. 84–92.
Wilkie, B. 'Blake's Innocence and Experience: An Approach'. *Blake Studies*, vol. 6, no. 2, 1974, pp. 119–37.
Wilton, A. 'Blake and the Antique'. *British Museum Yearbook*, vol. 1, 1976, pp. 187–218.
Wolf, E. 'The Blake–Linnell Accounts in the Library of Yale University'. *The Papers of the Bibliographical Society of America*, vol. 37, no. 1, 1943, pp. 1–22.
Worrall, D. 'Blake's *Jerusalem* and the Visionary History of Britain'. *Studies in Romanticism*, vol. 16, no. 2, Spring 1977, pp. 189–216.
Wright, J. 'Toward Recovering Blake's Relief-Etching Process'. *Blake Newsletter*, vol. 7, no. 2, Fall 1973, pp. 32–9.
——. 'Blake's Relief-Etching Method'. *Blake Newsletter*, vol. 9, no. 4, Spring 1976, pp. 94–114.
Yates, F. 'Transformations of Dante's Ugolino'. *Journal of the Warburg and Courtauld Institutes*, vol. 14, 1951, pp. 92–117.

General Index

Index of Blake Works

Works by William Blake

Works Illustrated by William Blake